POWER TOOLS FOR THE HOME CRAFTSMAN

Power Tools for the Home Craftsman

EDWIN G. HAMILTON

McGRAW-HILL BOOK COMPANY, INC.
NEW YORK TORONTO LONDON

POWER TOOLS FOR THE HOME CRAFTSMAN

Library of Congress Catalog Card Number: 52-6552

PUBLISHED BY THE McGRAW-HILL BOOK COMPANY, INC.

Printed in the United States of America

THE MAPLE PRESS COMPANY, YORK, PA.

PREFACE

Now more than ever recreational hobbies are needed by everyone, and there is no finer or more practical and absorbing hobby than home woodworking.

With the first use of power tools, the work of the craftsman begins to take on new significance, and finer projects begin to develop. Enthusiasm for the work mounts with the craftsman's progress, troubles are forgotten, and a new mental and physical world opens for the fortunate owner of a home workshop.

Today, with modern power tools, the amateur woodworker can build things for himself which he never before dreamed possible.

In a recent test, a joint used in cabinetmaking was built by two different men. One was a skilled craftsman with many years of experience. He used hand tools and carefully shaped and fitted the wood together. The time required was several long hours. The second man, with only a few months' practice in the use of power tools, constructed the same wood joint, with power tools, in less than an hour. Close examination failed to show any material difference in the appearance and strength of the two pieces.

I do not mean to imply that skill or hand tools are not necessary. Nothing could be further from the truth. The conclusions which should be drawn from this experiment are that power tools make it possible to acquire a certain amount of skill quickly and easily and to save many, many hours, while still doing a professional-looking job. Good power tools have accuracy and precision built into them. The adjustments which provide this accuracy and precision are easy to make. Power tools do most of the hard and painstaking work for you. Final fitting, finishing, and handwork will always be necessary, but think how much easier this last part of your woodworking will be after the power tools have done the major share of the work. Think of the satisfaction you will derive from creating fine projects in your own home. Don't let the fact that you have no special skill or training keep you from enjoying woodworking happiness.

EDWIN G. HAMILTON

ACKNOWLEDGMENT

The author and the McGraw-Hill Book Company gratefully acknowledge the courtesy of the following companies in permitting the use of various cuts and illustrations

The Delta Power and Tool Division—Rockwell Manufacturing Company

South Bend Lathe Works

Duro Metal Products Company

Atlas Press Company

Shopsmith—Magna Corporation

CONTENTS

POWER TOOLS FOR THE HOME CRAFTSMAN

Chapter 1. HOW TO PLAN YOUR WORKSHOP

What to Look for in Power Tools

Your experience in buying has taught you long ago that, all things considered, you usually get just what you pay for. That is, the less you spend for a product the less you receive in the form of quality, accuracy, service, and the like. When you pay more you get more—quality costs money, and there is no substitute for quality.

This is true when you buy tools, especially power tools. It stands to reason that you cannot obtain the quality found in machines at reasonable prices, in a line of tools costing only one-half as much.

The difficulty is that the quality you should look for cannot be detected by the naked eye or by casual inspection in the store. All tools are nicely displayed, are attractively painted, and look good, but these are not the features which mean accuracy, convenience, long life, and safety. The features which do provide these advantages are "designed into" and "built into" power tools from the very start.

It will pay you to look into these quality features before you buy. Always buy power tools from a reputable dealer who will back up the products he sells. Another point which should be considered in your purchase of power tools is the line of accessories which can be supplied in order to multiply the usefulness of each power tool. For example, with the use of a few accessories on a drill press it is possible to perform such varied operations as drilling, routing, sanding, mortising, shaping, and grinding. The performance of such accessories really makes the drill press six machines in one.

What Power Tools to Buy First—and Why

The most important question before beginning to purchase power tools is, "What should I buy first?" The only logical answer to this question is another question, "What type of work are you going to do?" The answer to the first question depends entirely on the second. You no doubt know what types of project interest you most and which of these you will begin with. The next step is to figure out what power tools are necessary to construct the projects you have decided upon. The jig saw is the first choice of many craftsmen who start by making novelties, lawn ornaments, etc. The circular-saw-and-jointer combination is the first choice of the craftsman who intends to use the workshop to do built-in cabinetwork or repair jobs around the home. The lathe is the first choice of the craftsman who intends to do many turned projects such as table lamps, wood bowls, etc. Over a period of years there is a definite pattern which will guide the craftsman in buying power tools in the order of their greatest importance to the home workshop.

The basic power tools for the home workshop is the circular saw. With this power tool the craftsman will be able to build much of the interior cabinetwork necessary in order to furnish a complete shop. The ideal way to buy a circular saw is to obtain at the same time a jointer which is mounted on the same machine stand and powered by the same electric motor. This will provide a power-tool combination enabling the craftsman to make the wide variety of wood joints and fittings so necessary in cabinetwork. The circular-saw-and-jointer combination will also enable him to build the woodworking bench which is the heart of any workshop.

The next power tool on the most popular list is the jig saw, or scroll saw. The jig saw is an ingenious mechanical arrangement which converts the turning motion of the motor into the up-and-down motion of the blade. The size of the jig saw is generally expressed in terms of the throat opening, that is, the distance from the blade to the inner edge of the supporting arm. The capacity, or thickness, generally averages 2 inches, which is as heavy as the mechanical structure permits. The first use of the jig saw is in cutting out intricate curves, corners, etc., as in the construction of wall shelves, magazine racks, toys, and novelties.

The drill press is next on the list of tools which you should purchase in order to equip your workshop. This power tool is one of the most versatile machines for the shop. It is really six machines in one, performing such varied operations as drilling, routing, sanding, mortising, shaping, and grinding. Various accessories which are available for this machine make these various jobs possible. The old idea that the drill press is strictly a machine for drilling holes has been disproved long ago.

The next most useful machine for the workshop is the belt or disk sander. Both types are available, and the choice is a matter of individual preference, since both machines perform equally well. Long tedious hours of hand finishing work may be eliminated by the addition of a power sander. Many other operations such as beveling, end dressing, and sanding inside curves can be performed well with the belt sander.

The band saw is the next power machine on the popular list with most home workshop owners. The principal use of the band saw is in cutting curves or variegated designs where inside cutting is not required. The capacity of this machine is greater than that of the jig saw; hence it is usually used for a heavier type of work. Compound band-sawing is an operation requiring cuts from two or more sides of your stock. A good example of this work is the cabriole leg. Multiple sawing, and ornamental work such as post tops, rail ends, and pickets, are a few of the wide variety of jobs accomplished with the band saw. A rip fence allows the cutting of long straight stock and the resawing of heavy lumber.

The main operation of the lathe is wood turning. With its many attachments, however, the lathe finds other uses. The turning of spindles and spirals and oval turnings are familiar to the craftsman. Faceplate turnings for such projects as wood bowls, lamp bases, etc., and metal spinning are common practice. With suitable attachments the lathe may be used for grinding, polishing, buffing, and sanding. A sanding drum or disk may be attached to the headstock for round or flat work. A chuck for drills allows center drilling to be done on the lathe. A few other operations are split turnings, metal turning, tapping, knurling, etc.

The shaper is indispensable for such jobs as tenoning, sash moldings, rabbets, tongue-and-groove joints, pattern shaping, and cabinetwork. Fluting is one of the many operations which the shaper accomplishes with ease. A wide variety of shaper-knife sizes together with a set of the various widths of shaper collars make an almost unlimited number of moldings available to the craftsman.

No shop is complete without the grinder. Various grinding and sharpening operations may be done by attaching grinding wheels to several of your workshop machines. For precision grinding, however, a machine built especially for these operations is the practical answer. The grinder is indispensable for keeping your tools sharp and in perfect cutting form. The tool rest and various sharpening attachments which are available will greatly simplify this job. Aside from drill grinding and plane-iron, wood-chisel, jointer, and shaper-knife grinding, the grinder is useful for buffing and cutoff work.

Other tools which, while not essential, are usually added to a complete workshop include portable saws, hole shooters, (portable drills), flexible-shaft equipment, small hand-grinding and carving sets, duplicate carvers, etc.

How to Lay out the Shop

The layout of your shop will depend largely on the space available, what you are going to make, and how much equipment you are starting out with. The usual procedure is to start out on a small scale and increase the size and scope of your shop as your skill and your projects advance. Some of the finest shops have had their beginning under the basement stairs. A small bench, a nice collection of high-quality hand tools, and perhaps one power-operated machine will give you a start. From the standpoint of economy, this kind of start is ideal, and you will have the means to plunge right into your hobby. From this simple start you will obtain as much satisfaction as one who has the most complete workshop available. You will have the pleasure of planning your own shop, increasing it as the need arises.

Always allow for future expansion of your workshop, no matter how small you start. You have no doubt heard about the fellow who built the beautiful boat in his basement and then had to tear out the wall to get it out. It is not impossible for this to happen. Remember that while the parts of a project may be small, the assembled project itself may be too large to get up the basement stairs, especially if there is a turn or two in the stairway.

The approximate size for a small shop is 7 by 10 feet. The shape of the floor space should approach the square, as this permits the arrangement of tools, bench, materials storage, and cabinets to the best advantage. The saving of steps and convenient working relationships is a first consideration.

An efficient medium-sized shop might be approximately 9 by 12 feet, and a large, completely equipped workshop would require an area of 15 by 20 feet.

There are no hard and fast rules for the actual layout of a home workshop—the objective you are trying to obtain must be constantly kept in mind. What serves well for one shop may be entirely wrong for another, so that good common sense must be used. The actual placement and arrangement of the machines themselves, their relation to other machines, working space around machines, light, power outlets, and other factors must be carefully considered. Information on some of these factors will be given in later chapters.

One method used in actual layout is to make scale outline drawings of each power tool (top view) on heavy paper and then cut them out. Then take a squared piece of graph paper and lay out to

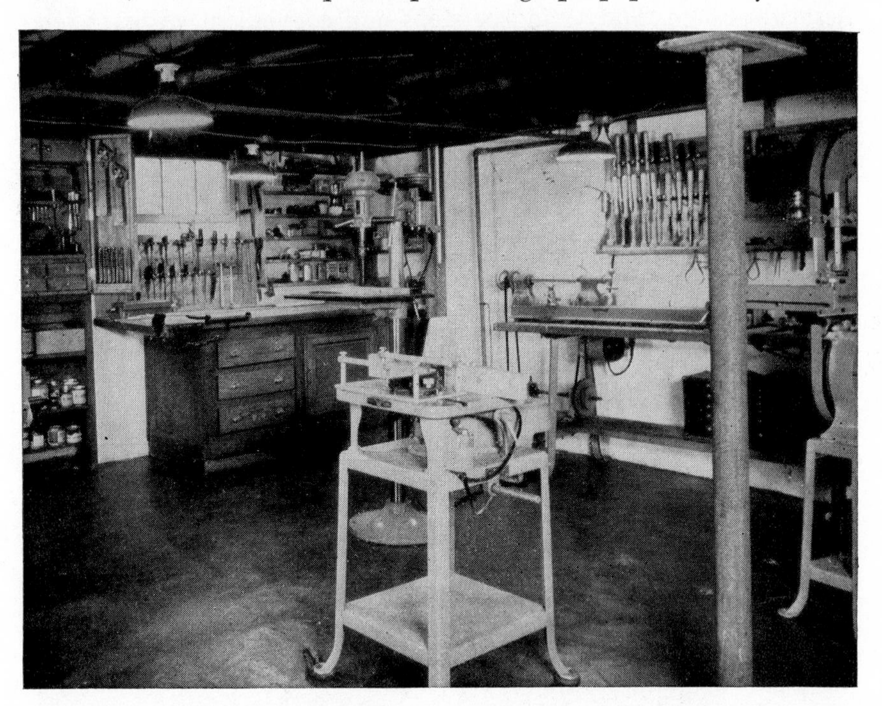

the same scale the floor space which you have available. Mark the placement of windows, doors, etc., and the electrical outlets. Then, with the cutouts, figure the shop arrangement by moving them into typical placement, figuring working area, light, etc.

Another method, though not often used, is to build scale models of the room and the power tools, cabinets, etc., and arrange them in a variety of setups until you arrive at the particular shop layout you desire.

Location in the Home

One of the basic considerations in planning your workshop is its location. You will want your shop to give you the utmost in convenience, dependability, output, and efficiency; in a word, it should be "practical." Experience indicates that the average home workshop is located in the basement. From the practical standpoint this works out very well. The advantages of such a location are many and important.

The first advantage is its proximity to the rest of the house. In many cases this greatly simplifies the problem of heating and availability of other facilities. When you are working in the shop you will be in close contact with the rest of the family. This close contact creates and stimulates family interest. The family often comes down to see what Dad is building in his retreat. This may result in other members of the family taking an active part in craft work. Young boys, especially, become greatly interested in such creative effort, and the possibilities of molding character as well as carrying out fine projects are unlimited. Wives of home workshop owners often take advantage of such opportunities and do fine jobs, especially in jigsaw work. The patience and skill of the lady of the house is often manifest in such activities.

There are, of course, many other places for a good workshop. For example, a workshop is often built onto the house as a wing. Still another solution is the building of a separate and complete unit to suit the owner's needs. The building houses his complete workshop and has the necessary facilities to render it independent. This complete unit may be built separately or connected to the garage. Among the advantages here, besides good light and ventilation are the following: noises will not be transmitted to the house; the workshop is handy for exterior work and repairs; and wide doors can be provided for taking large projects and machinery in and out. Garden furniture and accessories can be made and repaired more easily.

A double garage may be made more practical for a workshop by boarding up one half in order to keep sawdust away from the family car and grease and oil away from woodworking projects.

Other locations, though not ideal, include the back porch, attic, etc. The points for and against such locations may be discussed briefly. The floor must be strong enough, or must be made strong enough, to support with safety the equipment planned for the shop. The noise and vibration transmitted to other parts of the house must be considered and dealt with by sound-deadening methods. The light and ventilation may not offer a problem in such a location; but carrying the materials, finished work, and tools up and down stairs to and from the attic would bear consideration. Still, if this is the only space available, by all means take advantage of it, and work out the details in as practical a manner as possible.

To sum up the location problem, there are certain factors to be considered and planned around.

1. Space available in home, garage, etc.
2. Proximity to rest of house, family, etc.
3. Available facilities, such as electricity, water, heat
4. Amount of floor space available
5. Space available for future expansion
6. Number of natural advantages without additional work and expense

The foregoing list should be considered in general terms only. The different requirements must be weighed against the natural conveniences as they stand, and adjustments can be made as you progress.

The heating system which takes care of the rest of the house, for instance, will for all practical purposes also take care of heat and air circulation for the home workshop. The electrical system usually works in well, with the simple addition of another circuit or two with fuses and switch and another box. Additional information on the electrical system and wiring will be found in a later chapter.

At each step in planning your home workshop, you must look ahead. Plan each step carefully, always striving for your "ideal" shop. You probably will not be able to start with such a shop, but each well-planned step will bring you closer to your goal. Your achievements will be the envy of your friends and will bring unending pleasure to you.

Type of Shop

The next thing to be considered in planning your workshop is the type of shop you wish to have. You must have in your mind a pretty definite idea of what you want to do in your workshop. Is it woodworking or metalworking that you have in mind? Or perhaps, like most fellows, you have a longing to try your hand at both.

With fairly definite ideas along this line you can plan your workshop so that you will obtain the maximum of pleasure and benefit from your efforts. You must buy your tools, plan your workshop, and arrange your machines according to the type of products you wish to make. It is our belief that the average craftsman starts in woodworking and from time to time branches off into plastics, metal, and leather.

Lathe work usually tends to lead the craftsman into working with plastics, and the tendency at some time to spin a few metal trays develops the metalworking end. Some craftsmen go into metalworking as a hobby to the extent of installing forges and small furnaces in their workshops so that metal can be melted for casting purposes.

The metal-turning lathe, metal-cutting band saw, and grinder are standard equipment for the craftsman who intends to do any amount of metalwork. Another requirement is either a heavier type of workbench or a specially built metalworking bench. The latter need not be elaborate. It usually consists of a small bench with heavy hardwood top. It is sometimes built on a heavy beam or several of these timbers placed on end. Usual equipment for such a bench is an anvil and a good metal vise.

Most band saws and scroll saws may be converted for metalwork by simply changing the blades and the operating speeds.

Electrical Wiring

One of your most important problems in planning and laying out the home workshop is correct and adequate electrical wiring. The first step is to check with the electric company in your locality for their requirements. All work must be done according to their service rules and the local electrical codes. Installation of branch circuits that will conform with your electrical code is a simple job and can easily be done by a licensed electrician.

The ideal arrangement for a workshop consists of two branch circuits, independent of each other. One line is used for shop lighting, while the other furnishes outlets for the power tools. There are two reasons for such an arrangement. If a machine is overloaded and blows a fuse, the lighting circuit is unaffected, and you still have light so that you can see to make the necessary repairs or adjustments. The second is to avoid dimming the lights when operating your power tools.

The two lines should be rated as 15-ampere lines. Since you usually run only one machine at a time, the total load on the power line will be no greater than the rated amperage drain shown on the motor. If more machines are operated at the same time, the total current drain should not exceed 15 amperes. Installing fuses of more than 15-ampere size would probably subject your wiring to more current than it can safely carry. If your equipment blows 15-ampere fuses, you need more circuits, *not* heavier fuses.

The installation should be started by attaching two extra leads to bring the current to an extra fuse box. This box is equipped with a breaker switch and should be located high above the floor. The breaker switch should be equipped so that it may be locked in the open position. If it is located near the ceiling, so that you must stand on a small ladder or box to throw the switch, then no unauthorized person can operate any of the machines. This is an excellent safety measure where there are small children who may inadvertently start one of the machines. The switch as described makes such an action impossible.

The two circuits are encased in conduit and fitted with outlets at convenient intervals. An excellent location for the circuit containing machine outlets is around the wall of the shop at bench height. The ceiling light fixtures should be conveniently located for adequate over-all lighting. The fixtures themselves should be of a pull-chain variety with wide reflectors. The pull-chain switches will enable you to economize in efficiently lighting your shop. A master wall switch should be mounted near the door of your workshop.

In some localities the law requires that all wiring below ground level be encased in conduit. In others, BX cable is permissible.

The wire used in the lighting circuit should be no smaller than No. 14, and in the circuit for the power outlets, No. 12 is recommended. The wire which carries the extra circuit to the workshop box should be No. 8 and should be as short as possible.

Light and Ventilation

The problem of light and ventilation in the shop, while very important, need not frighten any home workshop owners. A few simple principles provide solutions to suit any size shop.

When the workshop is on the main floor, the owner may have almost as many windows as he wishes. The shop may be flooded with daylight from all sides, making a bright, cheerful place to work. In a basement shop, the windows are usually too small and too few in number. Small windows may sometimes be replaced with larger ones.

A second method is to illuminate the shop by artificial means only. Always remember that a well-illuminated workshop means better work and more ease of operation. The principal idea is to have enough of the correct lights in the right places. General illumination is taken care of through the regular ceiling fixtures. In addition there should be individual lights at each machine where close work will be done. Many of the power tools such as the jig saw, the band saw, and the drill press have lamp attachments built into them for proper illumination.

The workbench should be well lighted, as much of the project work is carried on there. You may prefer fluorescent lighting, which is easier on the eyes if properly and efficiently installed. This type of fixture is quite inexpensive and in some cases effects a noticeable saving in current. Good places for such fluorescent fixtures would be the workbench and the lathe. The exacting work carried on in both these locations would warrant such installations. Large industrial-type reflectors should be used for both the fluorescent and the regular lights.

See your local electrical-supply dealer and consider his advice on the best types of fixtures, bulbs, etc.

This brings us to the question of ventilation. The problems of light and ventilation are related, and of course if you have plenty of large windows, you should have no trouble in obtaining good ventilation.

When you are doing a lot of sanding, ripping, and lathe work, there will be a certain amount of sawdust. If your shop is well ventilated, this dust is blown outside, leaving the shop clean and free from such nuisances. A good rule to start with is to clean up your sawdust or shavings each time you are finished working in the shop. When you return for your next session, you will find a clean, friendly place in which to work. Such a shop means better projects.

The same problem arises in finishing and staining work, where good ventilation is necessary to dispose of odors and dissipate them in the outside air. One solution, when the shop is in the basement and the windows are small, is to install an exhaust fan to draw out the fumes so that they do not stay bottled up in one section of the house. A small exhaust fan may be assembled from an old electric fan and a piece of thin galvanized metal. The money involved is negligible, and results are excellent.

Another practical method, where the home is equipped with a forced-air heating system, is to have an outlet from the heating pipe into the shop, so that warm fresh air is forced into the shop and the stale air is forced out. This type of heating system is common in many homes and lends itself well to shop ventilation.

What Type of Floor Is Best

You have now decided where your shop is to have its start and what size it is going to be. The next question is the type of floor. The workman often cannot be too fussy about the type of floor he has in his shop. The floor already in your shop location may be perfectly suited for your purpose. If you have a choice, however, the following suggestions will be of help.

Most basements have ordinary concrete floors, which are well suited to home workshops. This floor may be left natural or, for easier cleaning and a neater appearance, may be finished with one of the many concrete finishing paints available from your local dealer.

If you wish to improve a concrete floor, one excellent way is with ordinary rubber matting. Another method is to lay a wood floor over the concrete. The wood flooring may be laid on top of the concrete, or it may be put down as an integral part of the concrete base. In the latter case, the sleepers are set up and the concrete poured around them and then finished as shown in the drawing. Conduit carrying electrical wiring may be put down and numerous floor plugs distributed at convenient places throughout the shop when building a floor of this type. When putting down wood flooring, remember that the wood should be left unpolished for good footing and safety.

Another good floor can be obtained with linoleum blocks purchased at small cost and put down in regular strips or patterns.

If your workshop is to be in the attic or on an upper floor, and the floor is not of sufficient strength, it must be strengthened by cross-bracing. The subflooring and finished flooring are then built up as usual.

If standing for long hours on a concrete floor tires you excessively, a simple solution is to build a platform to be placed in front of your workbench or lathe.

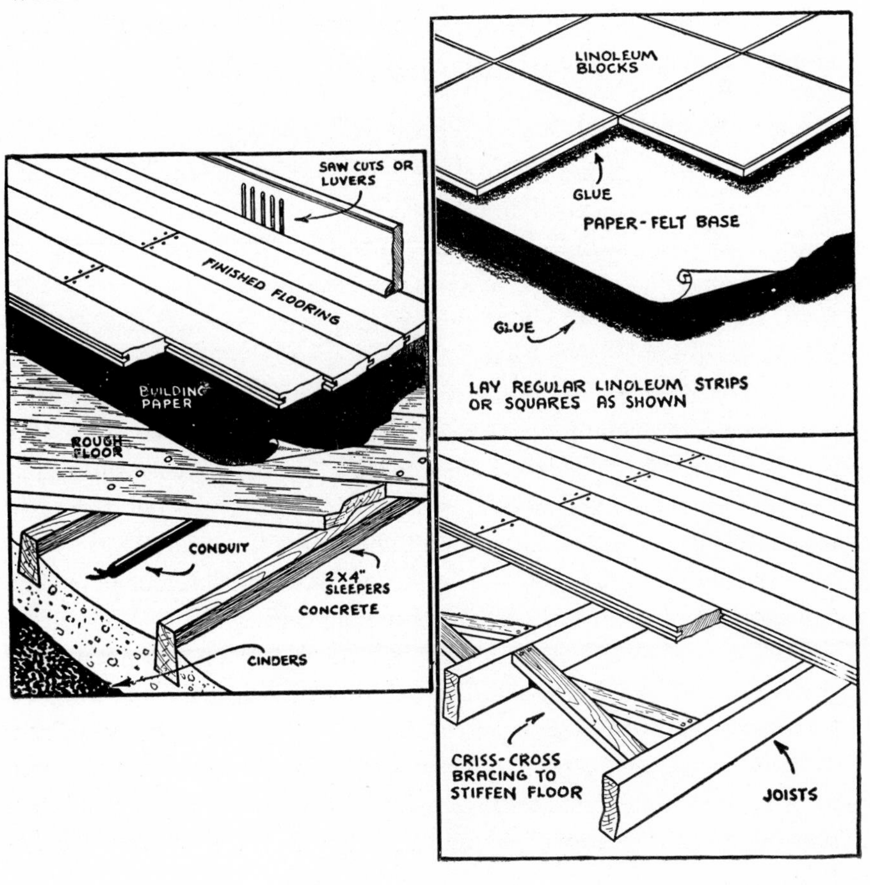

How to Enlarge Your Shop

It is important to allow for expanding your shop. Your start will no doubt be small, both in space and equipment, in comparison with your ultimate goal. If you keep this fact in mind as you proceed with your planning, you will be able to gradually expand your shop as your hobby grows.

Your projects will increase in size and workmanship along with your workshop. Your interest, too, will increase as the projects take shape in your hands. A careful check of each power tool as described in this book will give you information on what it will do and how each operation will fit in with the project you have in mind. Preferences for one machine or another will vary, but with this information and your own ideas you will be able to prepare your own list of machines and enlarge your shop to meet your own needs.

Woodworking Benches

"The workbench is the heart of the home workshop." The bench for your workshop need not be elaborate or expensive. You may build it yourself, as one of your first projects. Two bench designs are shown from which you may choose one to fit your present needs. You may wish to build the first design and later replace it with the heavier and more elaborate bench.

The first bench is of simple construction and may be built with a minimum of tools and equipment. The legs are 2- by 4-inch and the rest of the frame is ¾- by 4-inch stock. Fasten the parts of the bench together with glue and wood screws. Strips of 2- by 2-inch stock are used as shown to fasten the top unit and frame together. All the lumber used should be straight, high-grade, kiln-dried birch or pine. The top should be hardwood such as maple or birch.

The second bench is sturdier and of neater construction. The frame is 2- by 4-inch lumber. The ends are built in panels and joined together with 2- by 4-inch rails as shown. The back is covered by a plywood panel rabbeted in the same manner as the ends. The partitions are screw-fastened in place with half-lap joints at the rail intersections. Drawer, drawer runner, and guides are shown in the detailed drawing on page 16.

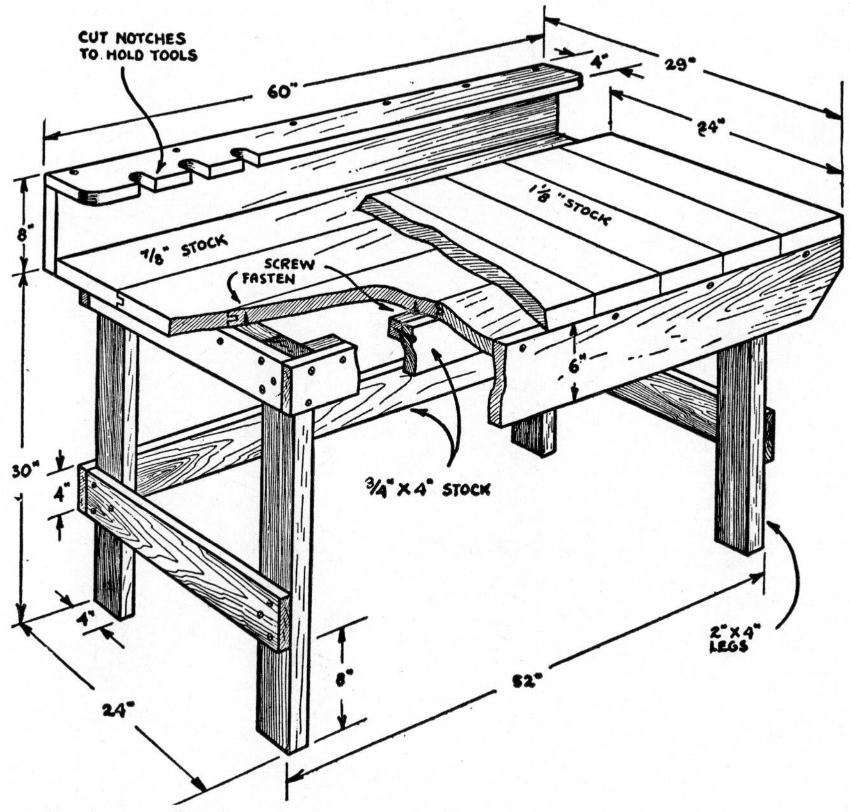

Heating the Shop

This is one problem that should provide no difficulties. There are so many solutions to the heating problem that one is bound to fit your own arrangement.

To start with, let us point out that the proper temperature for your workshop is from 62 to 68°F. The higher temperature is preferable only when small work, requiring little exertion, is being done. You may find when you first come into the shop that it seems rather chilly, but after working only a few minutes, you will be comfortably warm from the exertion.

Some home workshops have small heaters or laundry stoves. The workshop can be heated easily with such a stove. A few handfuls of shavings and a little wood will make a good fire, and if a little coal or coke is added, the workshop will be comfortable in a very short time. This is an excellent method, incidentally, for disposing of small

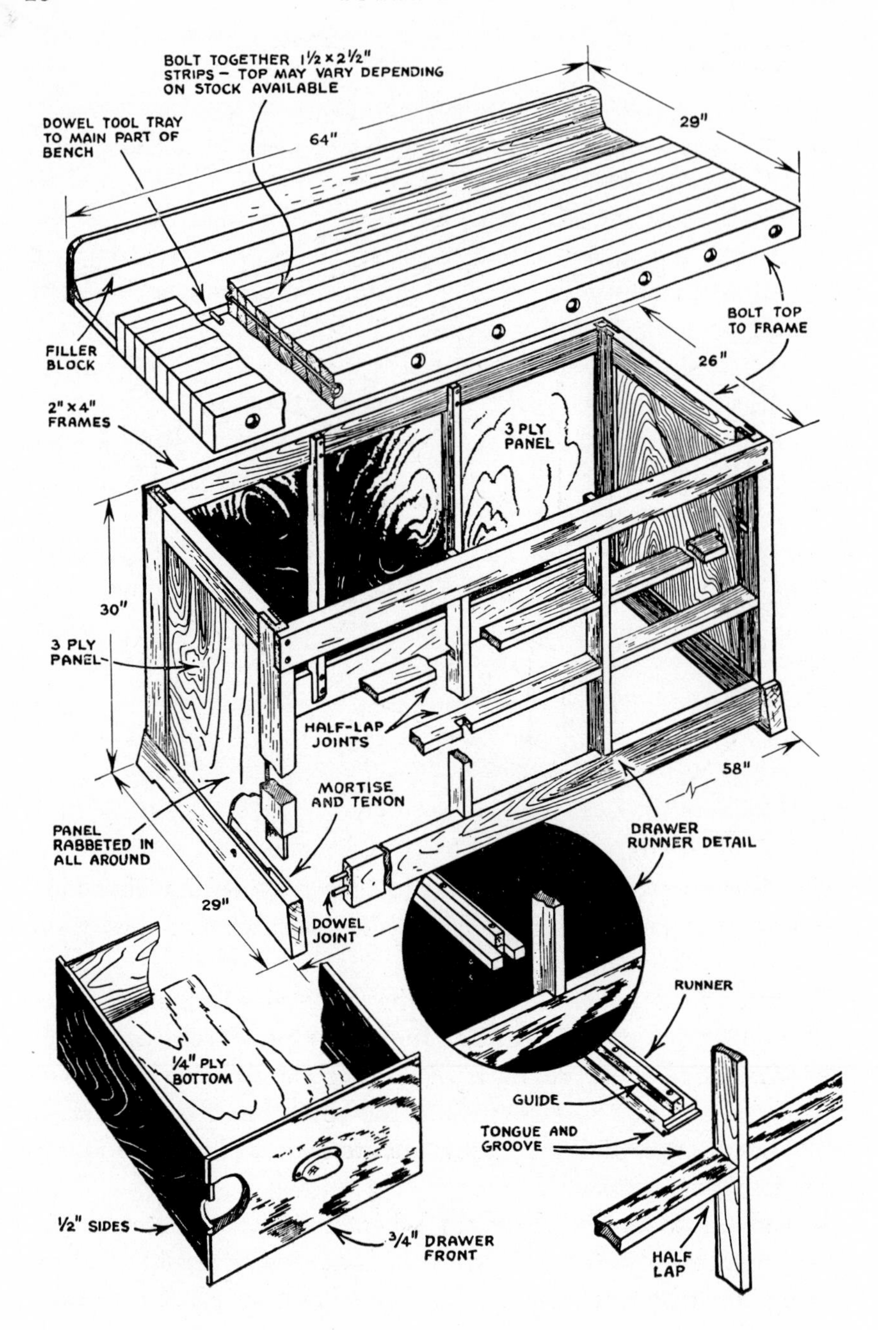
BOLT TOGETHER 1½ x 2½"
STRIPS – TOP MAY VARY DEPENDING
ON STOCK AVAILABLE
DOWEL TOOL TRAY
TO MAIN PART OF
BENCH
64"
29"
FILLER
BLOCK
BOLT TOP
TO FRAME
26"
2" x 4"
FRAMES
3 PLY
PANEL
30"
3 PLY
PANEL
HALF-LAP
JOINTS
58"
MORTISE
AND TENON
PANEL
RABBETED IN
ALL AROUND
DRAWER
RUNNER DETAIL
29"
DOWEL
JOINT
RUNNER
¼" PLY
BOTTOM
GUIDE
TONGUE AND
GROOVE
½" SIDES
¾" DRAWER
FRONT
HALF
LAP

pieces of scrap wood, which would otherwise accumulate around a woodshop.

Some workshop owners install hot-water radiators connected directly with the heating unit for the rest of the home and regulated to give the temperature conditions they prefer.

As explained in the section on ventilating, the workshop may be connected to the warm-air heating system and the shop kept at a regulated temperature. This outlet or extra register should be fitted with a regulator or damper to limit the amount of heat.

If your home is heated with a hot-water boiler and you have a radiator in the basement shop, it is best to have a pump for forced circulation when the radiator is placed lower than the boiler. This will give you efficient, economical heating.

Another efficient heating unit for the home workshop is the circulating oil heater. This type of unit burns economical fuel oil and radiates an abundance of heat for the amount of fuel consumed. The fuel-oil heater is usually attractive in appearance as well as economical to operate.

The addition of a heating unit to your workshop makes it a year-round proposition. All of us find more time in the long winter evenings to pursue our hobbies. Of particular interest during the Christmas season are the many fine toys and gifts which are produced in thousands of home workshops throughout the country. The holiday spirit is increased when you can give your family and friends gifts which you have built in your home workshop.

Dust Collection

Dust collection, as such, is not a necessary procedure in all home workshops. It is much more fun, however, to work in a nice clean shop—work seems to flow more easily, the job turns out better, and it is much pleasanter to have your friends and visitors see a neat shop free from dust.

As previously pointed out, if you have plenty of windows for ventilation there is no problem. The only job is to sweep up the shavings regularly and dispose of them in the usual way.

The machines that produce most dust are the sanders, circular saw, and lathe. Many power sanders are built to be equipped with electrically operated dust collectors, which are highly efficient.

Ingenious shop owners have equipped their shop units with individual dust collectors in a very similar manner by adapting old vacuum cleaners for the purpose. There may be repair shops in your community where used vacuum cleaners can be obtained at small cost. These, while unserviceable for their original domestic purposes without major repairs and replacements, may still be mechanically sound and may easily be fitted to the various units. Individual mechanical dust collectors are the most inexpensive and convenient, because they allow the machines to be moved around when necessary.

The circular saw and jointer present the least difficult problem; a simple bag or bin over the sawdust chute will gather most of the waste, allowing practically all the chips to be collected for disposal.

In many cases the chips and shavings are allowed to fall where they may, to be swept up in the simplest possible way—with broom and dustpan.

On the other hand, some home workshop owners have gone "all out" by installing home shop adaptations of a modern industrial system, in which a single blower handles all the waste from the various machines, carrying it off to a terminal collector. In all such systems the blower is the central unit. The conductor system should be laid out so that pipes to and from the blower will have long, easy curves. For the entire conductor system, 4-inch stovepipe will represent the most convenient material. The efficiency of the system may be increased by providing each branch line with a cutoff or blast gate at some convenient point, thus reducing the power consumption.

There are probably few persons who haven't at some time wondered how these systems work. The answer is that the air and refuse discharged through the inlet near the top of the collector is thrown against the side with a whirling motion. The air from the 4-inch pipes, thus suddenly admitted into a larger area, loses most of its velocity and escapes through an opening in the top. The heavier refuse, no longer supported by the velocity of the air, falls to the discharge opening and into a bin or container provided for it.

A cyclone separator adequate for any home workshop can be built by many craftsmen themselves.

What Motors to Use

Electric motors must be chosen with regard to the type and voltage of current available in your locality. Most house circuits use 110-volt single-phase alternating current. Standard d-c motors of 1,750 rpm are satisfactory for workshops where a direct current is available.

Consult and follow closely the recommendations of the power-tool manufacturers, because they know best which motor should be used for each application to give maximum efficiency at lowest cost.

Light dimming is often evident where a split-phase motor is used. The best motor is the repulsion-induction type, which uses a minimum of current, carries a large overload with safety, and is very reliable. This type of motor starts easily under load, requires little starting current, may be used on either 115- or 230-volt lines, and is capable of standing up under a considerable overload.

A ½-horsepower repulsion-induction motor will often not require so much starting current as a split-phase ¼- or ⅓-horsepower motor and may be operated from a lighting socket. Repulsion-induction motors of more than ½ horsepower are usually connected to a 230-volt power line.

It is better to have a high-quality oversized motor than one which is too small to do the job. Not only does too small a motor make your work difficult, but it is hard on the tools themselves.

All motors were originally built with bronze sleeve bearings, and the cheaper ones still are. They cost less than ball bearings and, besides introducing considerable friction, require frequent lubrication. Some motors with bronze bushings cannot be used vertically and, in numerous cases, cannot be mounted upside down under a bench for driving a lathe or grinder unless some provision is made to prevent oil from dripping out of the bearings. Some makers of plain bronze-bearing motors provide for this inverted application by using proper oil cups.

Many complaints of "low power" are due to the use of very long extension cords of small-diameter wire. To obtain full power, always keep the extension cords short and of No. 12 or No. 14 wire.

Inspect your motors frequently for any signs of wear or hard usage. Make certain of the soundness of your extension cords. Keep the motors bolted down securely to avoid excessive vibration. Check the plugs and terminals at regular intervals to make sure of good contact and the uninterrupted flow of current, and your motor should give long and efficient service.

Choice of Hand Tools

One of the first and most important points in the planning of your workshop is always to buy the best quality tools. The importance of this cannot be overlooked. It is better to have a few really good tools than an entire basement full of inferior-quality tools. To ensure your purchase of the best, go to a good reliable hardware dealer.

Since the home workshop usually starts with a selection of hand tools, the choosing of such a primary list is important. Your reliable hardware dealer will be of great help to you in selecting this list of tools. The assurance of quality will be well worth the extra cost which may be involved. A tool designed and made right will give

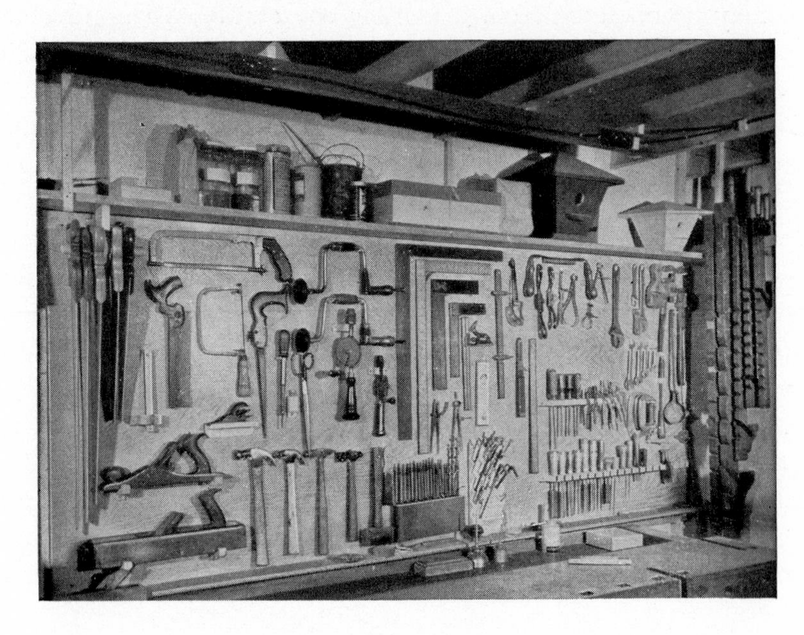

you confidence as you use it. "Good tools, like good friends, will be a joy forever."

Select your tools carefully, and gradually add to your selection as required. The following is a list of hand tools needed for woodworking. Add to this list by increasing the sizes and types of each item.

- 1 claw hammer
- 1 ball-peen hammer
- 1 combination square
- 2 or 3 screw drivers
- 1 jack plane
- 1 ratchet brace
- 1 set auger bits
- 1 combination oilstone
- 1 nail set
- 1 set wood chisels
- 1 folding rule
- 1 crosscut saw
- 1 ripsaw
- 1 hacksaw
- 1 level
- 1 pair combination pliers
- 1 spokeshave
- 1 marking gauge
- 1 pair dividers
- 1 inside caliper
- 1 outside caliper
- 1 wood rasp
- 1 flat file
- 1 triangular file
- 1 rattail file
- several C clamps
- 1 expansive bit

Hand tools are quite necessary, even in a power-equipped shop, for fine finishing and detail work. They should be stored above or near the workbench, as this is the place where they are in constant use.

Learn to handle the tools properly. Treat them well and keep them sharp. Your grinder and oilstone will be of great help to you in keeping your tools sharp. One of the later chapters, on the grinder, will give you information on the correct way to grind and sharpen your tools.

Tool Racks and Storage Cabinets

Storage cabinets of standard sizes and design for both hand tools and power-tool accessories should be installed in your workshop. These may be either purchased or built from plans available in the various craft magazines. Unit sections to fit any storage requirement should be placed near the machine or bench with which they are to be used. Such an arrangement brings orderly method to your workshop activity, preventing much loss of time in hunting for tools stored in a hit-and-miss system. A good tool arrangement improves the appearance of the workshop and keeps the tools in good condition.

Some shop owners prefer open tool panels. The type of rack is very convenient, especially for tools that are in frequent use. Many designs and ideas may be gained from studying the illustrations in this chapter.

Valuable space is often saved for the storage of tools by making use of the space in the walls between the studs. This space may be converted into tool-storage cabinets by adding the necessary brackets and enclosing the sections with plywood doors.

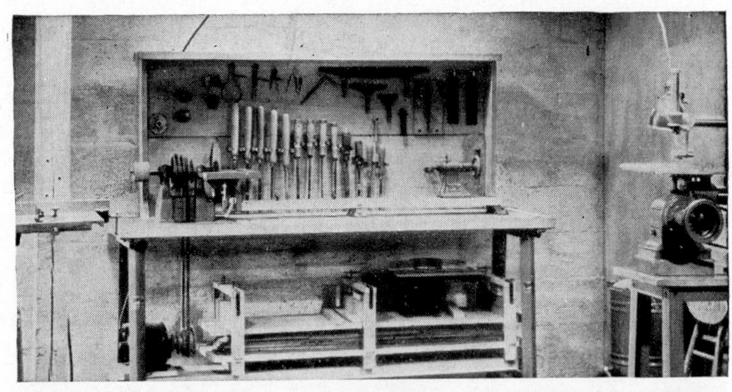

Small cabinets that hang on the wall may save valuable floor space; where floor space is at a premium, this is an important consideration.

The space below power tools and workbenches may often be utilized to advantage. Many craftsmen build cabinets, with storage space throughout, to support their power tools instead of using the usual machine stands.

A panel for lathe accessories within easy reach above the lathe means pleasant, profitable work. The motto, "A place for everything and everything in its place," is good advice to keep in mind throughout your entire home workshop planning.

The main idea, when planning tool storage is to allow plenty of room for the tools which you already have and to have space available for additions to your tool collection.

Keep the tools in a place convenient for their use. All lathe turning tools and accessories should be within easy reach of the lathe. All hand tools should be over or under the workbench. Clamps and gluepot should also be within reach of the bench. Keep the circular-

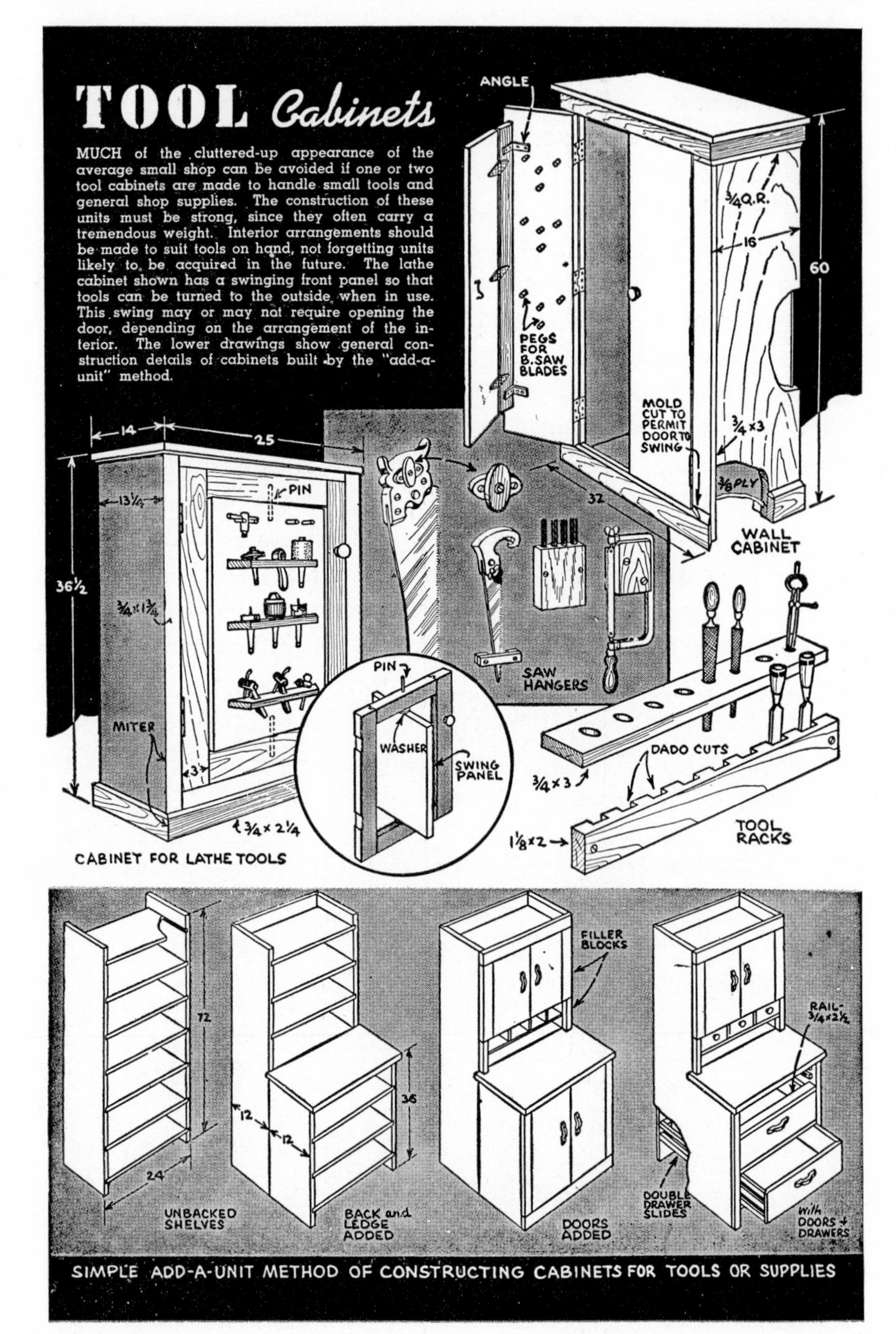
TOOL Cabinets
MUCH of the cluttered-up appearance of the average small shop can be avoided if one or two tool cabinets are made to handle small tools and general shop supplies. The construction of these units must be strong, since they often carry a tremendous weight. Interior arrangements should be made to suit tools on hand, not forgetting units likely to be acquired in the future. The lathe cabinet shown has a swinging front panel so that tools can be turned to the outside when in use. This swing may or may not require opening the door, depending on the arrangement of the interior. The lower drawings show general construction details of cabinets built by the "add-a-unit" method.
ANGLE
3/4 Q.R.
16
60
PEGS FOR B.SAW BLADES
MOLD CUT TO PERMIT DOOR TO SWING
3/4 x 3
3/8 PLY
32
WALL CABINET
14
25
PIN
13 1/4
36 1/2
3/4 x 1 3/4
MITER
3
3/4 x 2 1/4
CABINET FOR LATHE TOOLS
PIN
WASHER
SWING PANEL
SAW HANGERS
DADO CUTS
3/4 x 3
1 1/8 x 2
TOOL RACKS
72
24
12
12
36
FILLER BLOCKS
RAIL- 3/4 x 2 1/2
UNBACKED SHELVES
BACK and LEDGE ADDED
DOORS ADDED
DOUBLE DRAWER SLIDES
With DOORS + DRAWERS

SIMPLE ADD-A-UNIT METHOD OF CONSTRUCTING CABINETS FOR TOOLS OR SUPPLIES

saw blades, molding head, and accessories either in cabinets below the saw or close at hand. Following this procedure will save you many unnecessary steps and make your hobby a real success and pleasure.

Storage of Small Parts

The next step in planning your workshop is to provide storage space for small parts. To save time and effort, these various small parts should be stored separately, in easily accessible locations, and should be arranged so that each part and its size is recognizable at a glance.

For this reason many shop owners employ some form of glass container to make the parts instantly visible. A popular type of jar for the storage of nails and screws is the familiar fruit jar. Many different methods have been devised for holding or storing these jars. Some craftsmen prefer to place the jars on shelves, assorted and marked as to content and size. Others fasten the jar lids to the underside of the shelves and unscrew the jars for removal of the contents.

Small drawers with an index card on the front listing the contents are used by many home workshop owners. Orderly rows of drawers or bins properly indexed make the hardware and small parts easy to locate.

Drawers with small removable sections or open cans are convenient. This arrangement allows the craftsman to select the correct hardware for completing his project and to take the compartment with him to the workbench.

Jigsaw blades may be kept in order by building a special rack consisting of a row of glass test tubes. The different blades are placed in separate tubes, and the entire rack may be mounted on or close to the jig saw for additional convenience.

If you have ever had to look through a large drawer or box filled with odds and ends for a particular size of blade, nail, or the like, you will appreciate the convenience of having all your hardware and small parts kept in order. You will find many additional ideas for the storage of parts and accessories in the illustrations in this and your other craft books. Every home workshop owner has some ideas of his own on this subject, which he will no doubt combine with the ideas presented.

There is no definite set of rules to follow, and the main results to try to achieve are convenience and neatness.

Lumber and Paint Storage

Your supply of lumber must be kept in good condition if you are to secure the maximum use and economy from your efforts. Badly warped lumber means waste. Lumber that is too wet will not cut easily and will dull your tools.

Your supply of lumber should be supported fairly high above the floor, conveniently stacked so that you may obtain the piece you want without disarranging the entire stock pile.

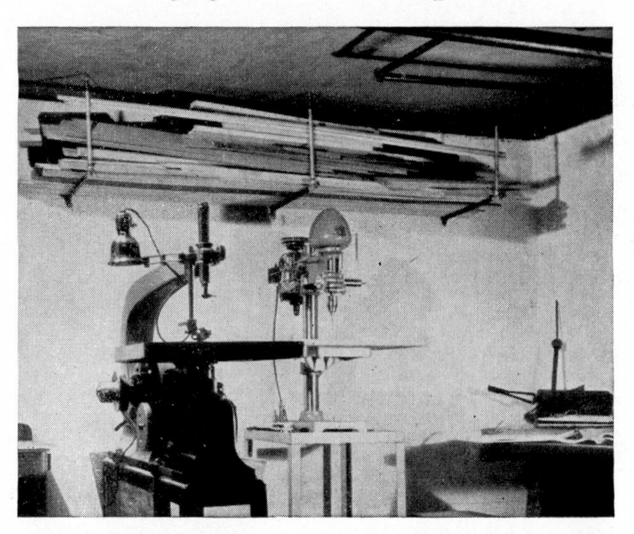

The lumber should be well supported at all points, so that it does not sag and become permanently warped. Space which would otherwise go to waste under the workbench is often used for lumber storage. Some home workshop owners build bins or racks for lumber storage, often from pipes hung from the ceiling and fastened with flanges to the wall of the workshop.

It is much better not to stand lumber on end. It not only has a tendency to warp, but it is unsightly and falls over at the most inconvenient times.

Do not stack the lumber too high, and allow room for ventilation, to be sure of always having clean straight stock with which to work.

The last, but certainly not the least, of the operations to complete a good project is the finish. An important part of doing a nice home workshop project is to finish it as soon as possible. For this, a paint rack or paint-storage place should be available where all paint

can be kept ready for use. There should be a place for brushes, sandpaper, steel wool, and all other articles which may be used in finishing woodwork and metalwork objects.

Paint, brushes, wax, cleaner, etc., must be kept free from dust and dirt. A good suggestion is to secure a few unit bookcases, the type with glass doors, for such storage space.

The cans must be kept tightly closed at all times when not in use. This keeps the finishing materials in good condition and is good economy for the home workshop owner.

Brush keepers are essential for good work, and several types may be constructed by the home workshop owner. The little time and effort involved will be well repaid in a more efficient workshop. One of the simplest types is constructed by taking a 1-gallon can, inserting a rod completely through the can at the required level, and hanging the brushes on the rod by means of a hole through each brush handle. The fluid level should be maintained so that the brush bristles are completely submerged in the liquid. Immediately after being used, all brushes should be cleaned with the proper solvent. Keep the bristles straight by combing with a wire or fiber brush. Keep the brushes and brush keepers in a special compartment in your finishing cabinet. It is preferable to have a door or cover on this part of the cabinet to keep out dust and dirt.

Spraying equipment is becoming more and more popular with the home workshop owner. The cost of such equipment has in recent years dropped to within the small budget, making it possible for many to own such equipment. It would be a good idea to consider it for the future if you are not in a position to purchase it now.

All equipment such as the paint-spray outfit should have its own special cabinet or storage space. The entire problem of storage should be handled efficiently for your own convenience.

The Workshop's Place on the Farm

The workshop is a necessary part of every well-ordered farm, a place where necessary repairs, maintenance work, and new construction may be carried out. Today, more than ever before, the farm workshop holds a position of importance. In a well-equipped farm workshop it is possible to do almost all the necessary repair work, including the sharpening of tools and machinery parts. A few power tools make it possible for the workshop owner to replace any wooden part on his farm implements, buildings, and farm equipment. The farm workshop owner may also build new furniture for his home, modernize the farm buildings, add new units, or make additions to his farm buildings.

Consider for a moment the actual amount of savings which the farmer may realize by doing these jobs himself. Another important consideration is the amount of time saved by having the workshop located right on the farm. Much of the farm equipment which previously was packed into the truck for a trip to the nearest local shop for necessary repair work can now be repaired in the farm workshop.

Unpacking and Setting up the Power Tools

Much of the power equipment which the home workshop owner will buy is delivered or shipped to him in packing crates. All new equipment should be carefully unpacked and installed so that the fine accuracy built into the equipment by the manufacturer will be retained. A nail puller is preferable to a hammer or pinch bar for removing nails from the crate. Care should be taken to avoid damaging the machines by accidentally striking them with a hammer, pinch bar, or other tool. Always remove the top and sides from the crate first. The usual method of crating such machines leaves the bottom of the crate to act as skids for the machinery. The power tools are usually bolted to the bottom of this crate or skids. These bolts should be removed last and the machine lifted from the skids.

After the crate has been removed, the waterproof paper or other wrapping material can be taken off. Boxes or packages containing extras such as chucks, tools, and attachments can be opened. All packing material should be carefully inspected for small parts, instruction books, etc. Any instructions packed with the machinery should be studied before setting up the equipment.

A stiff brush and kerosene can be used to remove the grease and oil employed to prevent the machinery from rusting in transit. After it has been cleaned with kerosene, the machinery should be wiped thoroughly with a clean cloth. All unpainted surfaces should immediately be coated with a film of good machine oil to prevent rusting. If the finished surfaces are kept clean and well coated with oil, the machinery will retain its new appearance indefinitely.

Some home workshop owners, after thoroughly studying their layout problems, bolt their machines to the floor to avoid excessive vibration. Most power machines have lugs at the base for this purpose. In any case, most bench-model machines should be bolted to the bench or to the machine stands provided for them.

Many home workshop machines, if not bolted to the floor, can be fitted with rubber pads to aid in deadening much of the sound transmitted to other parts of the house through the floor.

Some home workshop machines are designed to be portable, and many have casters which may be attached to the base or legs of the stand for this purpose.

Chapter 2. CIRCULAR SAW

Description

The circular saw is the basic machine in any woodworking shop and performs the fundamental operations in straight-line sawing. It is not a difficult machine to run, and plain ripping, crosscutting, and bevel cutting come naturally to most operators. Other jobs requiring more experience or "know how" are easily learned. The most popular sizes for home workshops are the 8- and 10-inch models. The 8- and 10-inch figures express the size representing the diameter of the blade.

Small circular saws are commonly grouped in two main divisions, depending on whether the table tilts or the blade tilts for angle cuts. The simplest and most practical construction calls for a fixed base in which is mounted the saw arbor. With this construction, the saw remains in a fixed position, while the table is arranged to be raised, lowered, and tilted. All inexpensive saws are tilting-table designs.

The second type of construction is the tilting arbor. This system features a fixed table, while the arbor and motor, as a unit, are made to be raised and tilted. Because of the intricate mechanics involved in building a good tilting arbor, these saws are necessarily more expensive than the tilting-table models. Apart from this basic difference in construction, most circular saws are similar as far as controls and other features are concerned. There is a handle to tilt the saw table (or blade), a handle to lock the table at any degree of tilt, and a scale setting to show the degree of tilt. The raising and lowering of the table (or blade) is governed by similar controls, except that some tilting-arbor designs do not have a scale to show the amount of blade projecting above the table.

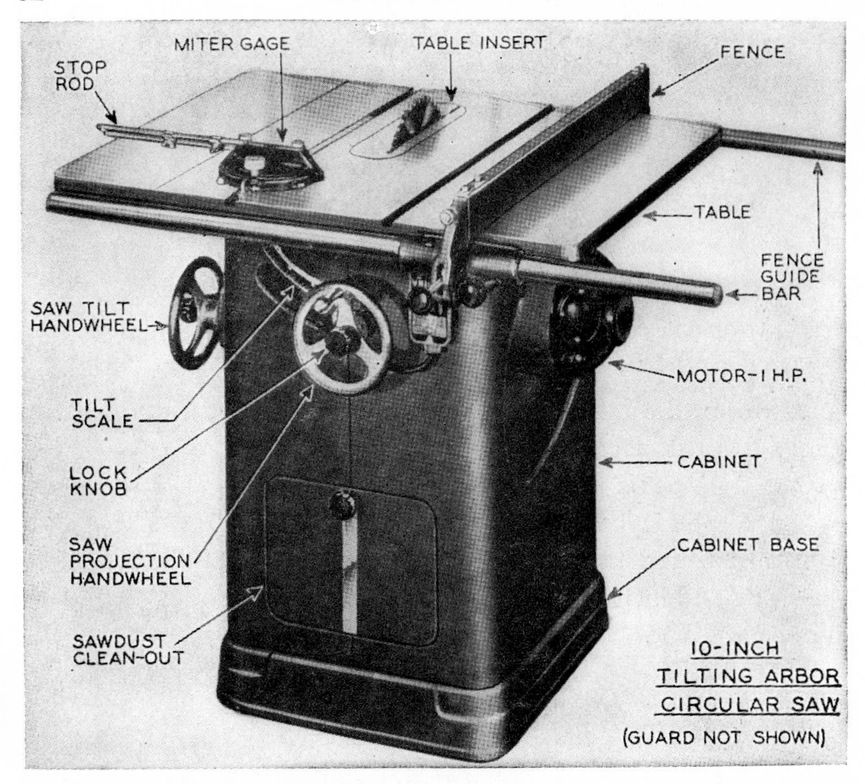

Ripping Fence

The ripping fence is guided by means of bars fastened to each end of the table, with the front bar usually calibrated to show the distance the fence is set from the saw blade. If the saw table is large, the fence must be locked to both the front and rear guide bars in order to be rigid. The lock for the rear end of the fence should be located at the front of the table for convenience. The fence on a small circular saw is often clamped at the front end only, since the short span is sufficiently rigid with one clamp. The ripping fences on the more expensive saws have a microset adjustment to permit fine setting by means of a rack-and-gear movement.

Power and Speed

An 8-inch circular saw requires a ½-horsepower motor for average work, although ⅓ horsepower will suffice if there is not too much heavy work to be cut. A saw of this size is made to operate at a speed of approximately 3,400 rpm, giving a cutting speed of 7,100 surface feet per minute. A 10-inch saw requires ¾ or 1 horsepower if the full capacity of the saw is to be used. This saw runs at approximately 3,100 rpm, which gives a cutting speed of 8,100 surface feet per minute. It is always inadvisable to run any saw faster or slower than the manufacturer recommends. These speeds have been worked out carefully to allow maximum cutting capacity with best blade wear and moderate power consumption.

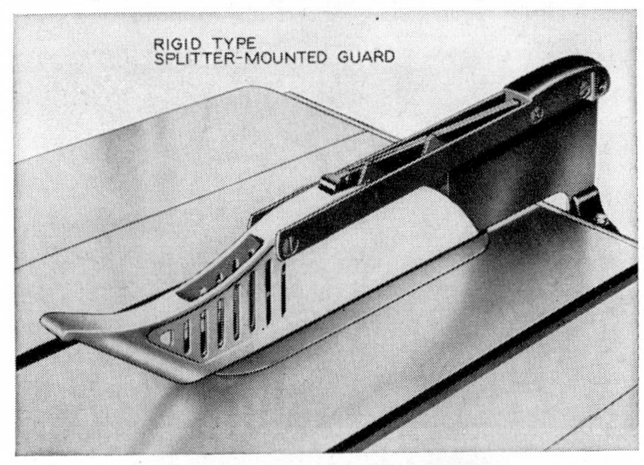

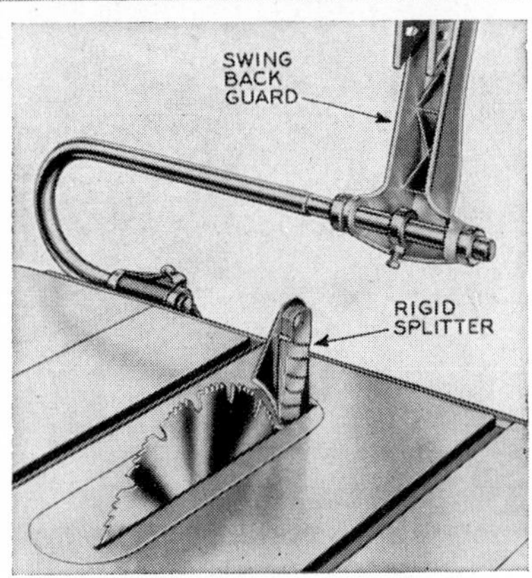

Guard and Splitter

The circular-saw guard is usually a metal basket which is arranged to fall over the blade, rising as the work is pushed under it and into contact with the blade. A splitter is a metal plate mounted directly behind the saw blade. Its purpose is to hold the saw cut or kerf open so that the work will not rub against the saw to cause burning or binding. The splitter is commonly fitted with antikickback fingers, which effectively grip the work and prevent it from being thrown back toward the operator. Guards and splitter are of either the rigid or the swing-back type. For variety work, the swing-back mounting is preferable, since it allows the guard and splitter to be swung out of the way. The mechanics of a tilting-arbor saw usually make it necessary to use a rigid splitter; this is removed when not needed by loosening the screw which holds it in place. Many of the illustrations show the saw guard removed when it should be in place. This has been done only to show the operations more clearly. The saw guard should *always* be used whenever possible.

Tilting Table versus Tilting Arbor

The main feature of the tilting-table saw is sound construction at the lowest possible cost. Advantages of the tilting-arbor saw are concerned almost entirely with the convenience of making angle or bevel cuts—it is much easier to cut an angle on a level table. A second feature of the fixed table is that it is always in the same position, hence allows the use of a fixed outfeed or extension table. For approximately 90 per cent of all saw work, which is plain ripping and crosscutting, the tilting-arbor saw offers practically no advantage over the tilting-table model.

Installation

The saw can be mounted on a bench or on a suitable steel or wood stand. The mounting is sometimes on the same stand with the jointer, since smoothing with the jointer often follows cutting with the saw. The saw-table height should be slightly under waist level, 34 inches from the floor being a good standard. A central location in the floor plan of your home workshop is almost a necessity, since the saw needs plenty of room in all directions. A collection bag or box fitted to or placed under the sawdust chute will catch most of the dust. Tilting-arbor saws are commonly mounted on a cabinet base, which provides a self-contained sawdust box fitted with a convenient cleanout door.

Saw Adjustments

The principal adjustment of the circular saw has to do with the relation between the saw blade, the saw table, and the fence. The fence must be square with the table, and the table must be square with the blade. In making this adjustment, the fence is first aligned parallel with the right-hand table groove, the setting being made by sighting along the side of the fence and the groove. The fence (and table) should then be square with the blade when checked by the following method. Run the saw blade well above the surface of the table and lock in position. Check the distance between a marked tooth of the blade from its forward position in the table insert. Now swing this same tooth to the rear end of the table insert and again check the measurement between it and the fence. These measurements should be identical. If the measurements are not identical, loosen slightly the screws holding the table to the trunions or to the saw base, and tap the edge of the table into the correct position with a wooden mallet. Retighten the screws. Check once more for alignment, also making sure that the saw blade is positioned centrally in the table-insert slot. On some saws the table adjustment is made by turning a single screw which rides against the table trunion.

Other adjustments consist of setting the various scales so that they will read properly. The table should be checked at right angles with the blade by means of a steel square, in order to set the tilting scale correctly. On most tilting-table saws there is a stop screw located under the table, against which the table bumps when it is returned to a level position. This should be set when the blade is checked and found to be square with the table. After checking the squareness of the blade and setting the stop screw to maintain this adjustment, the indicator pointer on the tilting scale should be set at zero. Then the table or blade should be tilted to the 45-degree position, where it will again bump against a stop screw. Check to see if the pointer shows 45 degrees, and if not, adjust the stop screw until an accurate 45-degree setting is obtained.

The depth-of-cut pointer should be set to show the exact projection of the saw blade above the table. The pointer on the fence indicating the ripping width is set by running the fence over until it lightly touches the blade, and then setting the pointer to zero on the calibrated front bar. A recheck on this setting should be made by ripping a board to a predetermined width according to the ripping scale, and then checking the width with an ordinary rule. The miter gauge is also checked for squareness by making a trial cut on a fairly wide board. Check the board with a square, and if it is accurate, set the pointer on the miter gauge to the 90-degree mark. If the miter gauge has a stop link, set the link to maintain the setting. Make a similar check of the 45-degree position, being careful in making the test cut to avoid any creeping of the work.

Lubrication

Circular saws should receive a minimum of lubrication; excess oil or grease simply combines with sawdust and gums the mechanism. A drop or two of oil on moving parts is about all that is needed. Bearings in many cases are sealed and require no attention. Bronze bearings, however, with oilers demand regular lubrication. Polished metal surfaces of a new machine should be thoroughly scrubbed with oil or wax. This will load the pores of the metal with a protective film, and the surfaces can be kept in good condition with an occasional wiping with oil or wax.

Always check the manufacturers' recommendations for lubrication of their particular products.

Saw Blades and Cutters

The average home workshop owner is concerned with two kinds of saw blade, the combination blade and the hollow-ground planer blade. Both these saws rip, crosscut, and miter equally well; hence their adaptability to home workshop needs. Where production work is being done, two other common saw blades—the crosscut saw and the ripsaw—are useful, but each can be used only for the one operation for which it was designed. Other than these four common blades, there are hundreds of specialized saw styles, each designed to work best under a certain set of conditions.

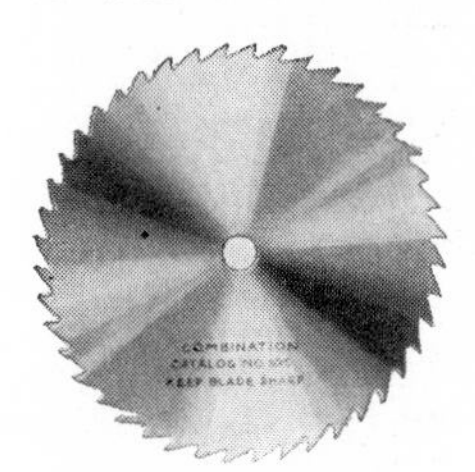

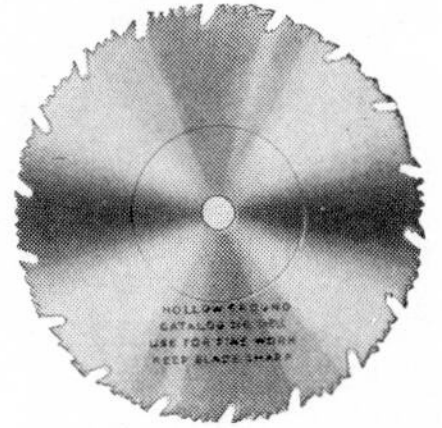

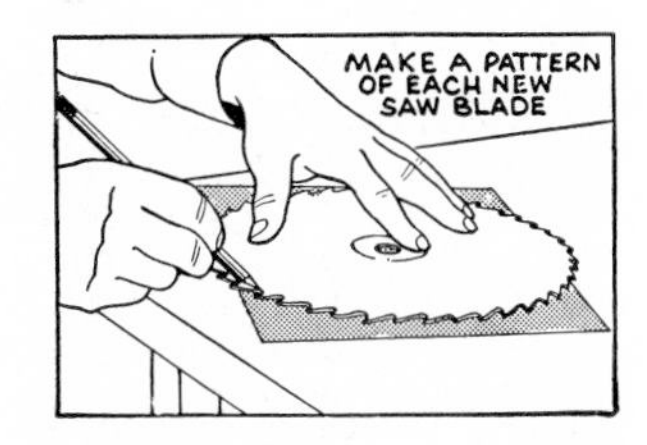

Paper Patterns

The best guide for maintaining any saw blade in good condition is the blade itself. For this purpose it is advisable to make a paper pattern of every saw blade that is acquired. In addition to showing the tooth shape, the pattern should also contain such information as the degree of set, the filing angles, etc. Great exactitude is not usually required, since a slight variation in the tooth shape or bevel will not under ordinary conditions affect the working of the saw. What is more important is that each tooth must be exactly the same. One long tooth or one poorly filed tooth can easily throw the entire blade out of balance.

Crosscut Saw

The crosscut or cutoff saw is intended for cutting across the grain and is useless for ripping. The following illustration shows a typical tooth pattern of this blade and also gives the names applying equally well to any other kind of saw blade. The gullets of the crosscut saw are quite sharp, yet they should have a slight round in order to prevent cracking. The front or face of the tooth is on a line with the center of the saw and is filed to a 15-degree bevel. Where fine, smooth work is being done, the face bevel can be increased to 20 to 25 degrees. The back of the tooth is filed on a 10-degree bevel, this being increased to 15 degrees for fine cutting. This saw is usually spring-set. Setting consists of bending successive teeth in opposite directions to secure clearance as the saw cuts through the wood.

Setting is done after filing, using a setting stake or suitable hand set. The set is alternately right and left on successive teeth. Only the tips of the teeth are set, and the set should not exceed 1/64 inch.

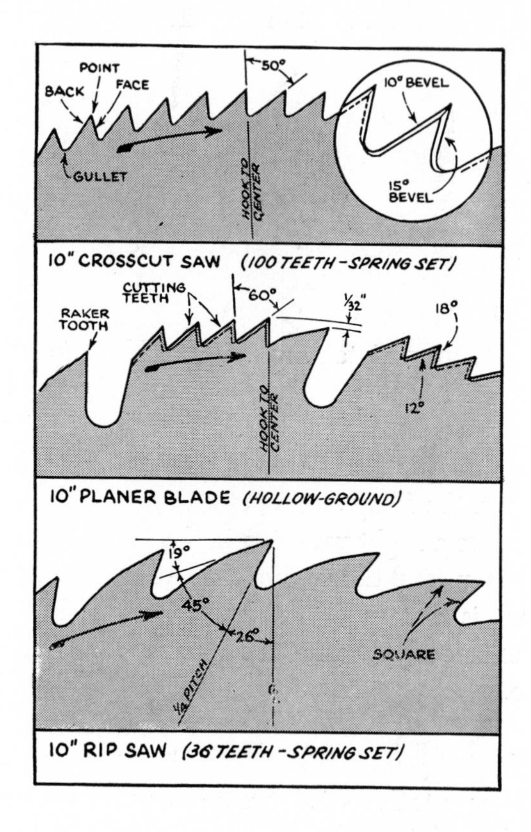

Planer Saw

The planer saw is a hollow-ground blade, the cutting edge of which is shaped as shown in the drawing. The same tooth pattern is also used for flat-ground saws, in which the teeth are set to give the necessary clearance. The hollow-ground blade does not require set, since it is tapered from the edge to the center for clearance. The planer saw has two kinds of teeth, cutting teeth and raker teeth. The cutting teeth sever the wood fibers on either side of the cut, while the raker teeth clean out the remainder of the wood fibers. The raker teeth should be 1/32 to 1/64 inch shorter than the cutting teeth. The cutting teeth are beveled alternately right and left as shown. The raker teeth are filed straight across, front and back.

Ripsaw

Ripsaw teeth are filed to many different patterns. The face of the tooth is on a line tangent to a circle one-third to one-fourth the diameter of the saw. The point of the tooth should be strong—usually not less than 40 degrees, in view of the rough work for which the saw is intended. The teeth are filed square across to give a true chisel point.

Combination Saw

The drawing on page 40 shows a full-size plan of a typical combination saw. This saw is somewhat similar to the ripsaw, except that the teeth are finer and beveled on the back, so that the saw will cut across the grain as well as with the grain. The various steps in sharpening a blade of this kind are shown in the drawing. Where jointing has removed a considerable portion of the tooth point, the blade is first filed and then set.

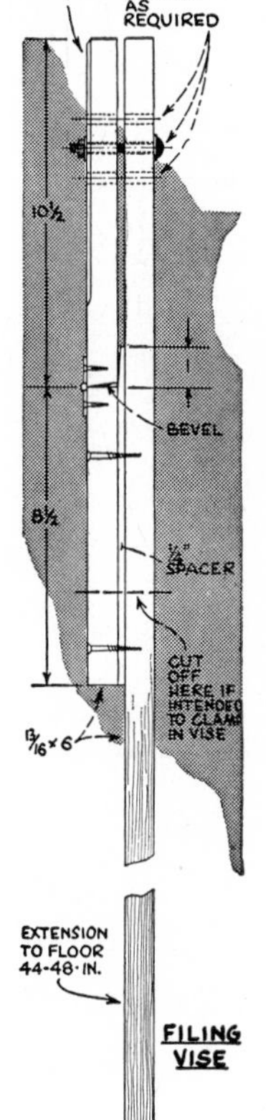

Filing Vise

A suitable vise for filing saws in the home workshop may be constructed as shown in the drawing and accompanying photograph. This can be made up

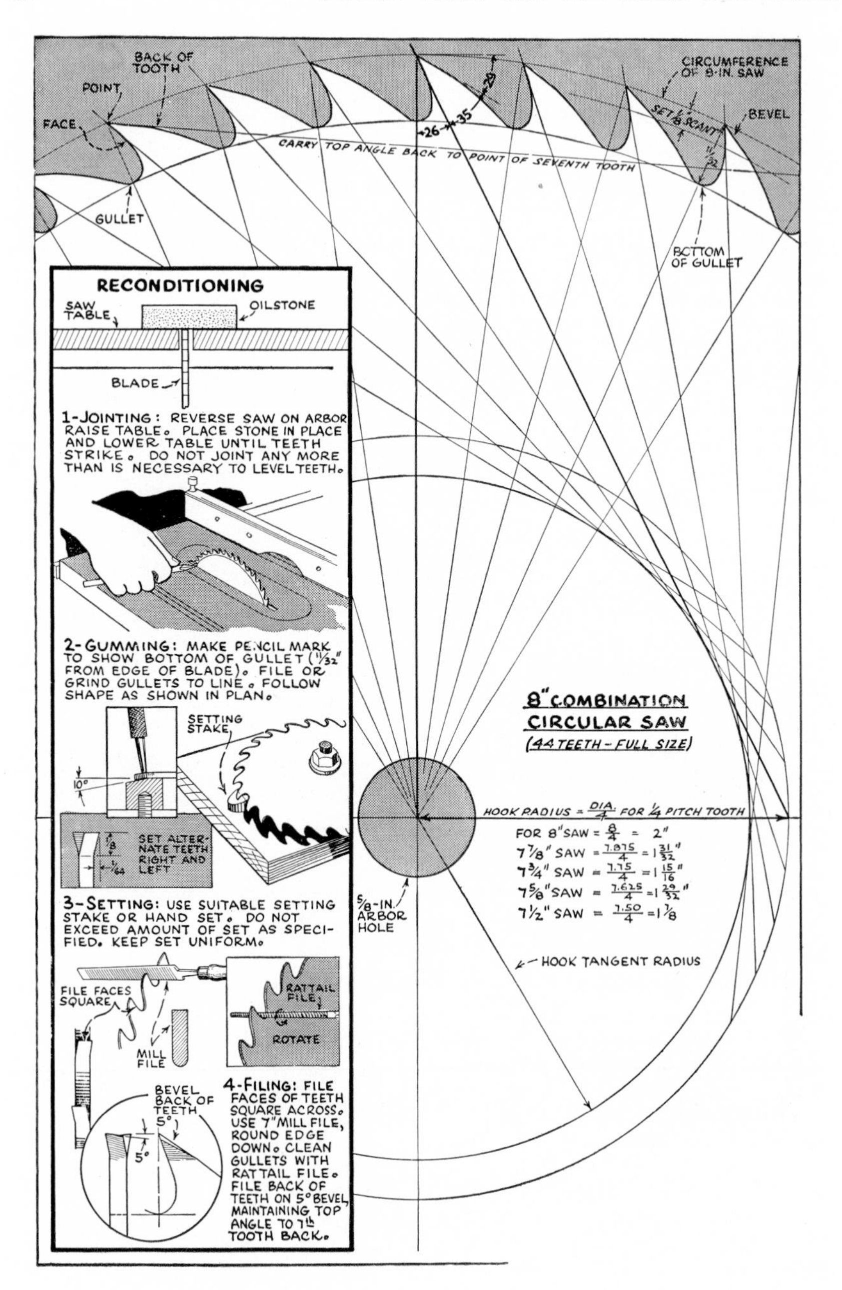

BACK OF TOOTH
POINT
FACE
GULLET
CIRCUMFERENCE OF 8-IN. SAW
SET 1/8 SCANT
BEVEL
CARRY TOP ANGLE BACK TO POINT OF SEVENTH TOOTH
BOTTOM OF GULLET
RECONDITIONING
SAW TABLE
OILSTONE
BLADE
1-JOINTING: REVERSE SAW ON ARBOR RAISE TABLE. PLACE STONE IN PLACE AND LOWER TABLE UNTIL TEETH STRIKE. DO NOT JOINT ANY MORE THAN IS NECESSARY TO LEVEL TEETH.
2-GUMMING: MAKE PENCIL MARK TO SHOW BOTTOM OF GULLET (11/32" FROM EDGE OF BLADE). FILE OR GRIND GULLETS TO LINE. FOLLOW SHAPE AS SHOWN IN PLAN.
SETTING STAKE
10°
SET ALTERNATE TEETH RIGHT AND LEFT
3-SETTING: USE SUITABLE SETTING STAKE OR HAND SET. DO NOT EXCEED AMOUNT OF SET AS SPECIFIED. KEEP SET UNIFORM.
FILE FACES SQUARE
MILL FILE
RATTAIL FILE
ROTATE
BEVEL BACK OF TEETH 5°
5°
4-FILING: FILE FACES OF TEETH SQUARE ACROSS. USE 7" MILL FILE, ROUND EDGE DOWN. CLEAN GULLETS WITH RATTAIL FILE. FILE BACK OF TEETH ON 5° BEVEL, MAINTAINING TOP ANGLE TO 7th TOOTH BACK.
8" COMBINATION CIRCULAR SAW
(44 TEETH - FULL SIZE)
HOOK RADIUS = DIA./4 FOR 1/4 PITCH TOOTH
FOR 8" SAW = 8/4 = 2"
7 7/8" SAW = 7.875/4 = 1 31/32"
7 3/4" SAW = 7.75/4 = 1 15/16"
7 5/8" SAW = 7.625/4 = 1 29/32"
7 1/2" SAW = 7.50/4 = 1 7/8
5/8-IN. ARBOR HOLE
HOOK TANGENT RADIUS

to clamp in a vise, or, by making the lower arm sufficiently long, it can be clamped to the side of an upright object. Filing equipment should include a 6- or 7-inch taper file for crosscut saws, a 7-inch mill file with one round edge for ripsaws and combination saws, and a round taper file for cleaning out gullets.

Grinding Saw Blades

The various saws can be ground or filed mechanically by using a suitable setup. The drawing which follows shows how a ¼-inch-wide grinding wheel is used for gumming ripsaws and combination blades. The cut should be light to avoid burning. The saw must be free of gum or pitch, which might cause an inaccurate setting against the guide pin. Pitch or gum on a saw blade can be removed

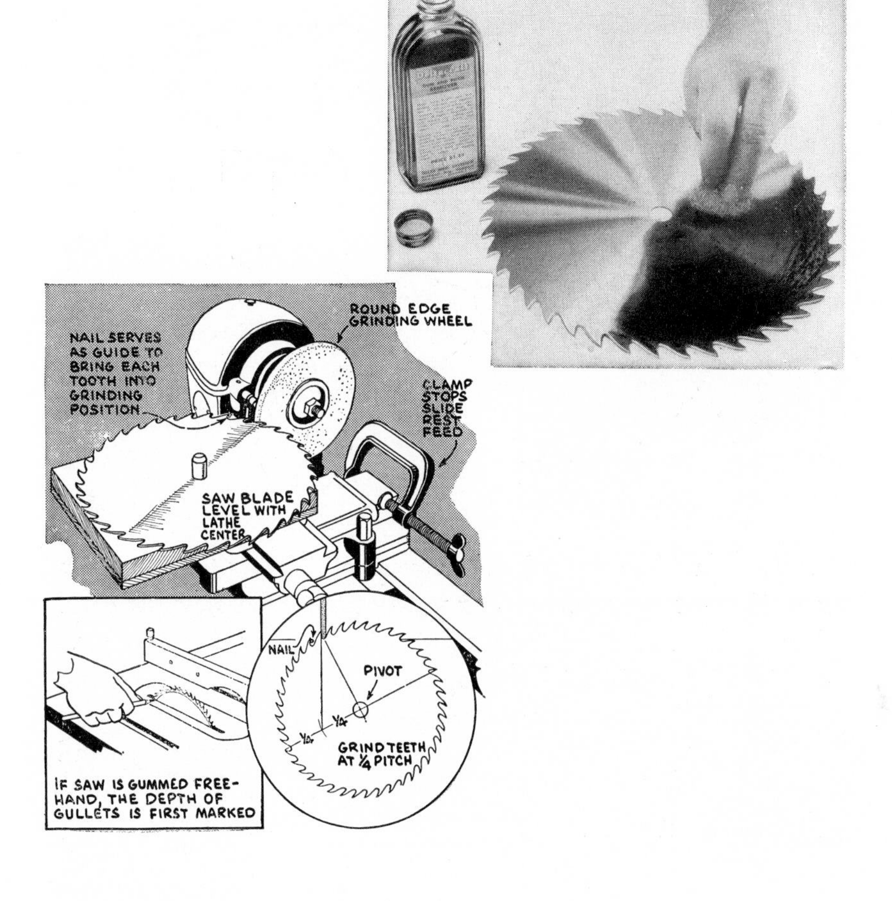

mechanically with a knife, or it can be softened with a prepared pitch solvent, as shown in the illustration, and then wiped off with steel wool. After the gullets and tooth faces are ground, the position of the slide rest can be changed to grind the backs of the teeth.

The Dado Head

A dado head is made up of two outside saws and three or four inside cutters. Various combinations of saws and cutters are used to cut grooves from ⅛ to 1¾₁₆ inch. The outside cutters are heavily swaged and must be arranged so that this heavy portion falls in the gullets of the outside saws, as shown in the drawing. The drawing

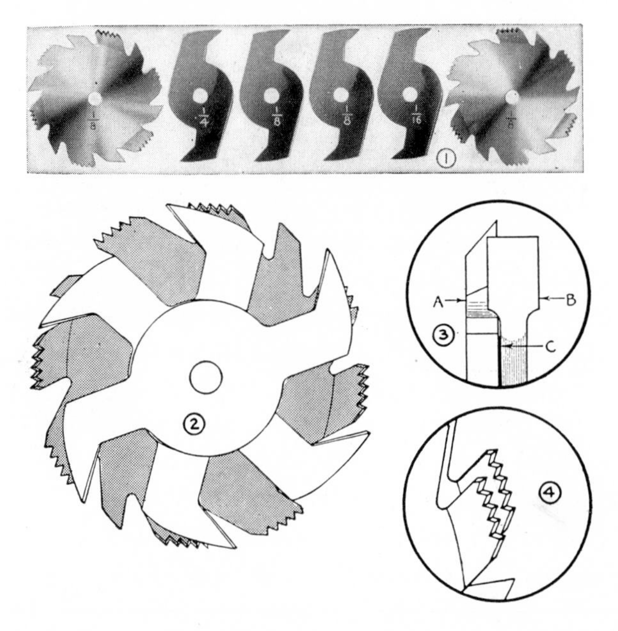

also shows how the saw and cutter overlap, *A* being the inside saw, *B* an inside cutter, and *C* a paper washer, or washers, which can be used as needed to control the exact width of the groove to be cut.

A ¼-inch groove is cut by using the two outside saws and fitting the ground teeth directly opposite each other, in order to allow clearance for the slight set of the saw teeth. Dado heads usually can be returned to the factory for resharpening, and this procedure is advisable in most cases.

The Molding Head

The molding head consists of a cutterhead in which can be mounted various shapes of steel knives, as shown in the illustration. A special fence is required, this being cut out at the center to give clearance to the cutterhead when the knives are at their highest cutting point. As an alternate, a cutout wood facing can be clamped or screwed to the standard fence. Each of the three knives in a set is fitted into a groove in the cutterhead and securely clamped with a locking screw. The knife groove should be kept free of sawdust, which would prevent the individual cutters from seating properly.

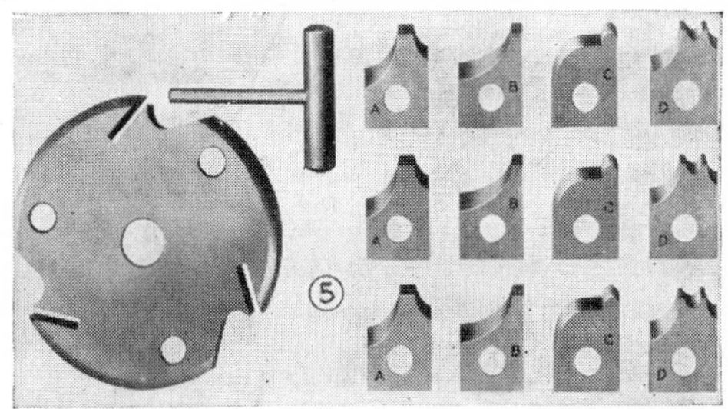

Molding-head knives are made from high-speed steel and will cut many thousands of feet of molding before becoming dull. They are ground in such a manner that sharpening is accomplished by simply whetting the flat side of the knife and then removing the burr thus formed from the beveled edge. Extremely dull knives can also be ground on the bevel, but this is seldom worth while, in view of the low cost of new knives. Grinding is often useful, however, in re-shaping a straight knife to some particular pattern which may be needed. Remember that all three knives making up the set must be shaped identically, or they will be unbalanced and most of the load will fall on the higher knife. Grinding should be done dry, and the knife should be cooled frequently in water to prevent burning.

Abrasive Wheels

Abrasive wheels for use on the circular-saw arbor can be obtained in a number of different grades, thicknesses, and diameters. For average home workshop use, 8-inch diameter, $3/32$-inch-thick, resin-ous-bonded wheels are the most satisfactory. Almost any material can be cut with abrasive wheels. Aluminum oxide wheels are used for cutting steel and nonferrous metals, while silicon carbide wheels work best for glass, porcelain, plastics, hard rubber, and other materials. Cutting operations are performed dry and at the regular saw speed of about 6,500 surface feet per minute. For production work the speed can be increased to 10,000 feet per minute, but this has no particular advantage beyond prolonging the life of the wheel. Wheels are mounted on the circular-saw arbor in the same way as any blade, with the addition of heavy paper washers on either side. These

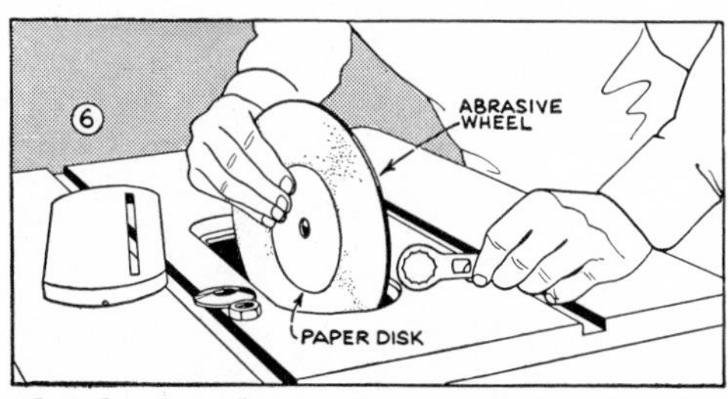

washers act as shock absorbers. A guard should always be used to protect the operator against accidental wheel breakage. This, however, is not likely to occur if the work is properly guided with the rip fence or miter gauge. If a regular abrasive-wheel guard is not available, a passable substitute can be made by lining the regular saw guard with strong cardboard or sheet metal, the idea being that if the wheel should break, it cannot get out of the guard.

Plain Sawing

Plain sawing includes ripping and crosscutting, plus a few other standard operations of a fundamental nature. It is highly important that the beginner learn and consistently use a safe technique in making these cuts. The methods outlined here feature safety and are intended specifically for home workshop use. However, some variations in operating techniques will result from personal preference, as well as from the mechanical features and size of the saw being used.

Ripping

Ripping is the operation of making a lengthwise cut through a board. One edge of the work rides against the guide fence, while the flat side of the board rests on the table. These contacting surfaces of the work must be reasonably straight and true. It can easily be seen that if the work has an irregular edge, it will be impossible to guide it in a straight line through the saw. Then, when the work departs from a straight and true feed, the saw blade will become jammed in the saw cut, leading to bucking of the work and, if the work is light, an actual kicking back of the work toward the operator. The danger in the kickback is that if the hands are near the saw blade at the time, one or both hands may be jerked loose or thrown into the blade. The approved sawing method is therefore aimed at preventing kickbacks; then, as an added precaution, the hands are kept in the clear "just in case." Kickbacks will not occur if the saw is sharp and has good set, and if the work has reasonably true surfaces to guide it along the fence and support it without rocking.

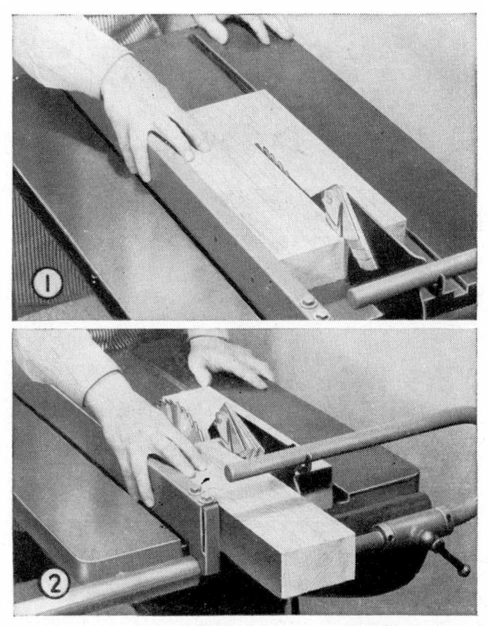

The start of a ripping cut on a long board demands no particular method. Stand where you like behind the saw, hold the work with both hands, and push it along the fence and into the saw blade. At the stage shown in the first illustration, the left hand is removed from the work, and the feed is continued with the right hand only. If the cut is 3 inches or wider, the right hand can safely feed the work right past the blade, as shown in the second illustration. After the work is beyond the saw, the feed hand is removed from the work. When this is done, the work will either stay on the table, tilt up slightly, and be caught by the splitter, or, if no splitter is used and if the work is long, it will tilt up and slide off the table to the floor. Alternately, the feed can continue to the end of the table, after which the work is lifted and brought back along the *outside* edge of the fence. The waste stock remains on the saw table and is not touched with the hands until the saw is stopped, unless it is a large piece allowing safe removal. If the ripped work is less than 3 inches wide, a push stick should be used to complete the feed, bringing this into use at the stage shown in the first illustration.

How Not to Rip

The fourth illustration shows a half-dozen common errors in ripping. (1) Half-rolled sleeves or any dangling clothing are always

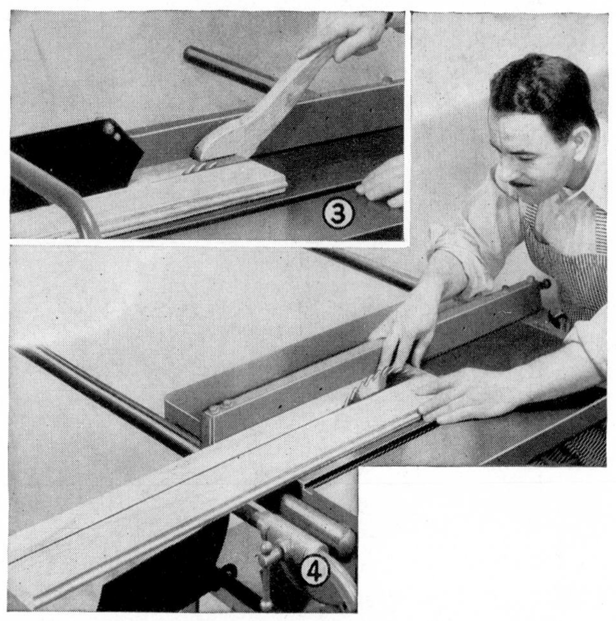

dangerous. (2) The ripped stock is less than 3 inches wide and should be fed with a push stick. (3) Work of this length should preferably employ a different technique, since the strain of holding down against the long overhang is too much for safe operation. (4) With left-hand feeding, the work is in a dangerous position if a kickback should occur. (5) The blade is much higher than necessary—it should be no more than ¼ inch above the work. (6) The saw has a splitter, which should be used.

The third illustration shows the same operation correctly performed.

Guard and Splitter

Safety codes and competitive sales pressure have put guards on practically all small circular saws. If you are a beginner, it is advisable to use the guard for early protection, and this training period with a guard will undoubtedly reveal its uses and limitations better than any amount of print.

The splitter is the best safety device and should be used whenever possible. A splitter is particularly useful and practical if it is the swing-back type, but even the fixed type is worth the little time needed to attach or remove it. The splitter is practical only when fitted with antikickback fingers which actually work. A splitter holds

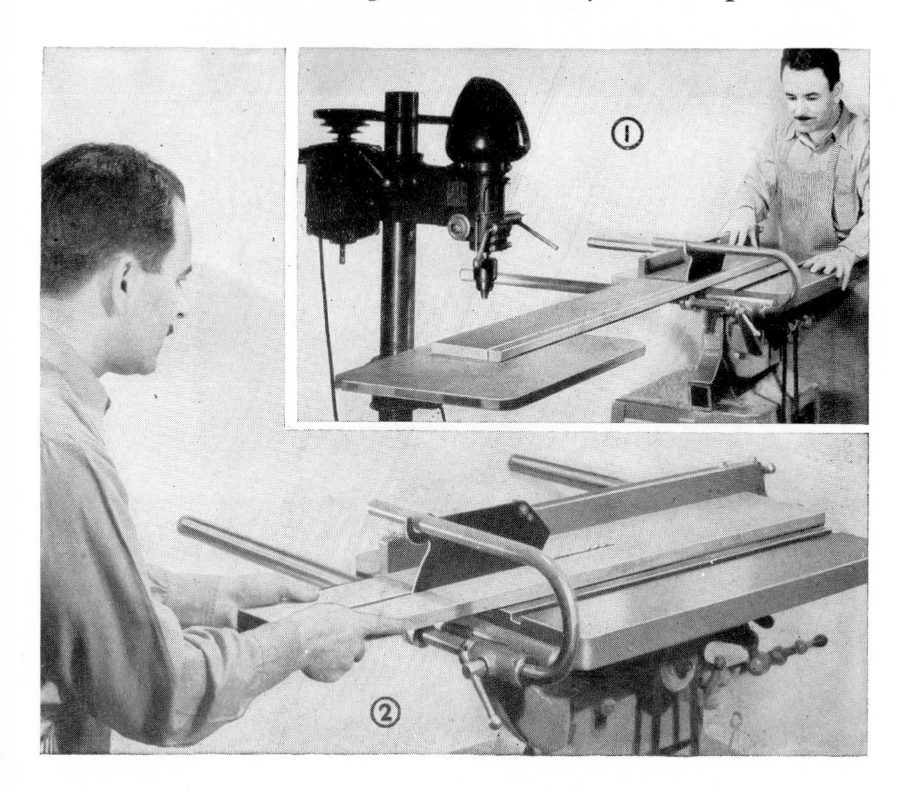

the saw kerf open, it prevents kickbacks, it takes some of the weight off long overhangs, it prevents long ripped work from falling to the floor at the end of the cut.

Ripping Long Work

Long cuts can be easily handled with the use of some type of outfeed table to support them. An approved technique used by many home craftsmen is the "pull-through" feed. This technique is especially practical when a splitter is used, because the splitter holds the work securely on the table while the operator walks around the saw. If you make regular use of a splitter, the pull-through feed is recommended for all ripping of medium or long work. Obvious advantages include perfect safety while using both hands to control the work and the waste stock all the way through the cut and off the table. The disadvantages of this method are that it takes a little practice to keep the work smoothly against the fence, and that the stop-and-go feed will sometimes show a saw burn.

③

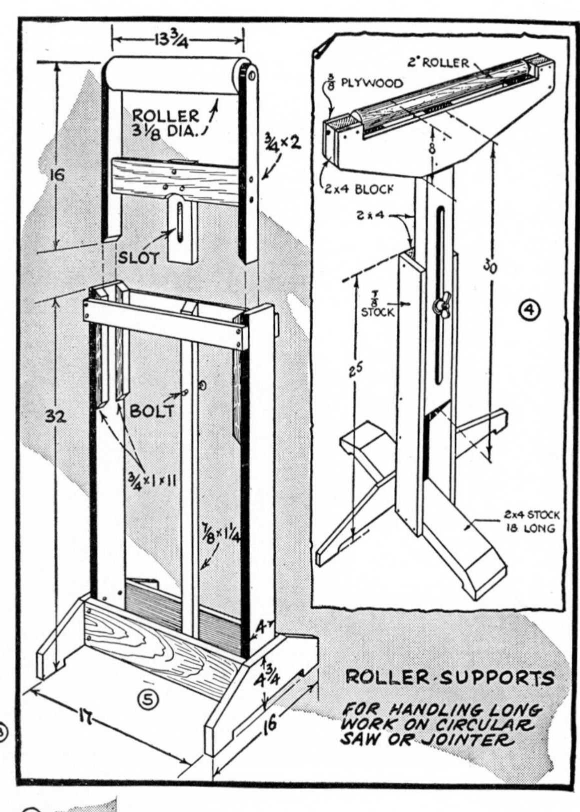

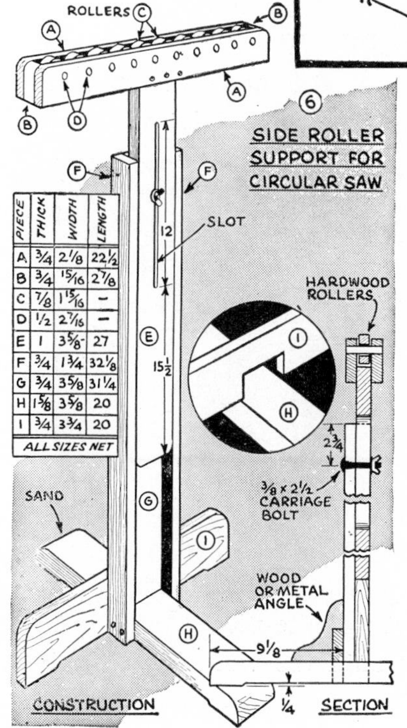

PIECE	THICK	WIDTH	LENGTH
A	¾	2⅛	22½
B	¾	15/16	2⅞
C	⅞	1 15/16	—
D	½	2 7/16	—
E	1	3⅝	27
F	¾	1¾	32⅛
G	¾	3⅝	31¼
H	1⅝	3⅝	20
I	¾	3¾	20
ALL SIZES NET			

Roller Supports

Roller supports are an obvious advantage in supporting long work. If your saw is the tilting-table variety, the roller support must be adjustable for height. In most tilting-arbor saws the table is stationary, and this feature allows the use of a fixed support without height adjustment or the use of a permanent outfeed table. Side supports are also useful in handling long work when crosscutting. The support is used parallel with the saw, the work riding hardwood rollers which turn on dowel pins.

Crosscutting

Square crosscutting is done by placing the work against the miter gauge and advancing both the gauge and the work toward the saw blade. The gauge may be used in either table groove, most operators preferring the left groove for average work. All crosscutting operations are more conveniently worked with greater safety if the miter gauge is fitted with an auxiliary wood facing. This should be at least 1 inch wider than the maximum depth of cut and should extend 12 inches or more on either side of the blade. If desired, the height of the wood facing can be cut down to about 3 inches over the miter gauge in order to permit a more comfortable handgrip.

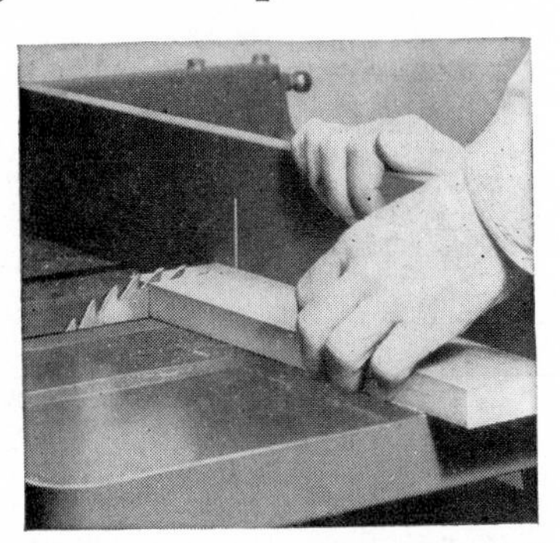

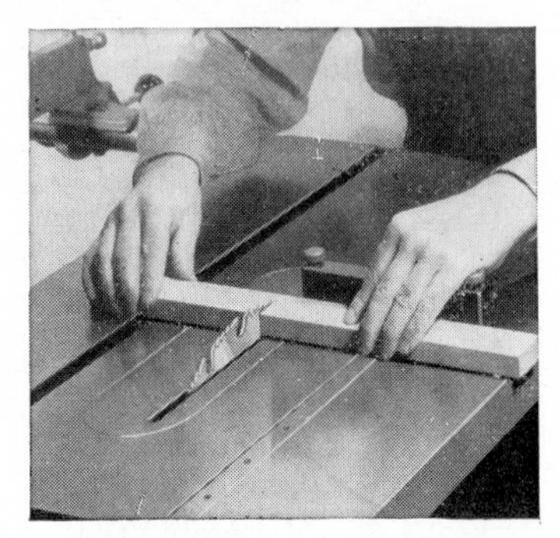

Most crosscuts are done with one hand. The right illustration shows an unsafe two-hand feed. One of the cardinal rules in running a circular saw is never to hang onto or touch a free piece of work. Hold the supported piece, not the free piece that is cut off. The feed in crosscutting continues until the work is cut in two, after which the gauge and work are pulled back to the starting position. Get into the habit of giving the work a little sidewise movement before starting the pull back, to shift it slightly away from the saw blade.

The next illustration shows something you should *never* do, that is, pick free work off the table. A smart operator never touches a cutoff unless it is at least a foot long.

Short and Long Work

Extremely short work is always dangerous to handle, and extra precautions should be taken to assure safety. The work shown in the next illustration should not be cut off at all with miter gauge alone, because it would have practically no support. With wood facing, the work is well supported and can be cut with a normal handgrip if desired. However, the use of a wooden block as a hold-down makes the operation safer.

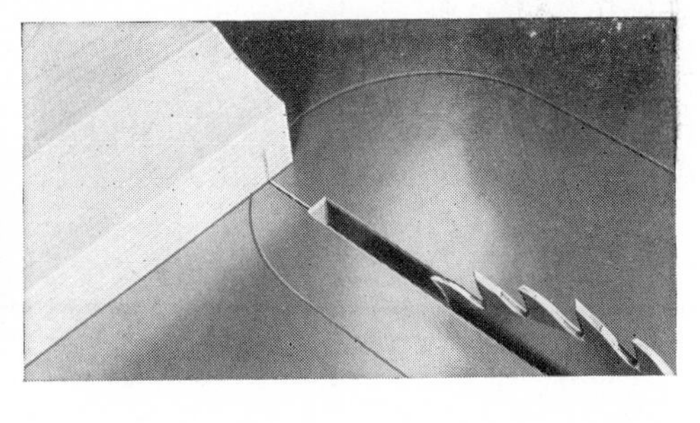

A long piece of work is best cut with a wood facing on the gauge, the operator feeding with both hands positioned at the ends of the facing. A wide piece of work is easily handled by reversing the miter gauge, holding the work against the gauge, and following through with hand pressure holding the work firmly against the face of the gauge.

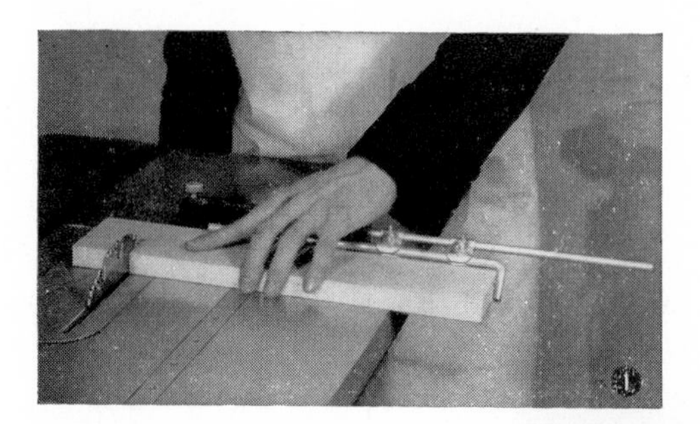

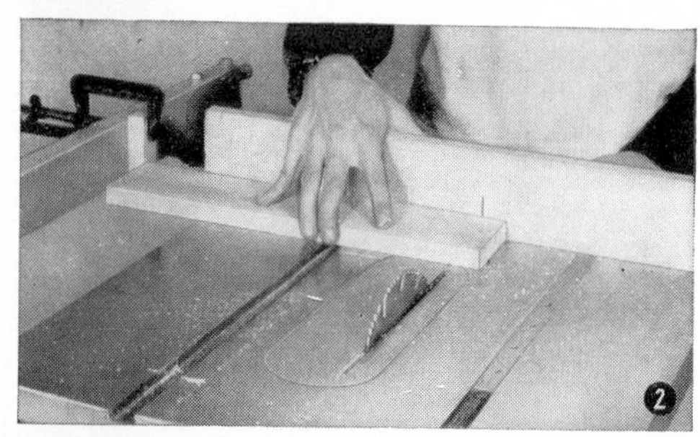

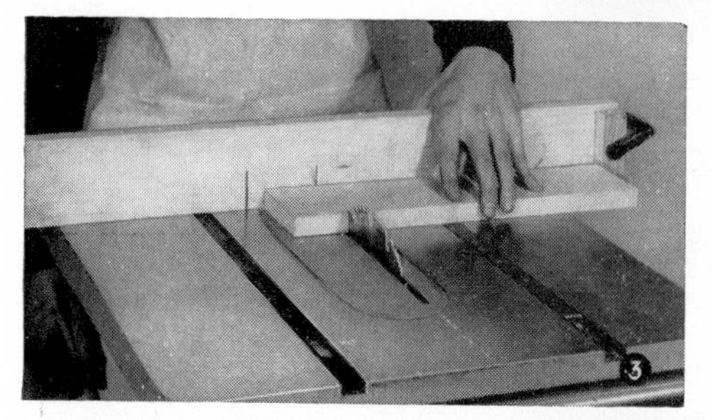

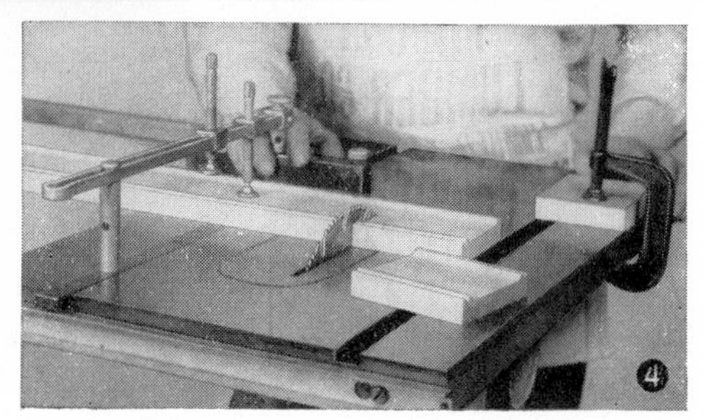

Cutting to Exact Length

Most crosscutting is done to produce a piece of exact-length material. In many instances cutting is done to a pencil mark, and in this case it is best to position the work against the miter gauge before starting the saw. If you use a wood facing, accurate setting of the work is easily done with the saw running, since the pencil mark on the work can be set to the saw kerf in the wood facing. Another useful device is a mark scribed on the table insert in line with the side of the saw blade. When more than one piece is to be cut to the same length, the work should be set by some type of mechanical stop. One method is the use of the standard stop rod attached to the miter gauge. The stop rod cannot be used in connection with a wood facing; the stop in this case must be a wood block fitted to the fence or to the facing. Such a stopblock may also be clamped directly to the saw table. See the four illustrations opposite.

An important point in the use of a stop is that it must never bind the free end of the work being cut. The next two illustrations show the *wrong* and the *right* way of making such a cut. Note how the use of the stop rod on the free end of the work will tend to cause a twisting action and consequent kickback at the end of the cut. With the stop rod correctly used on the supported end of the work, this does not happen.

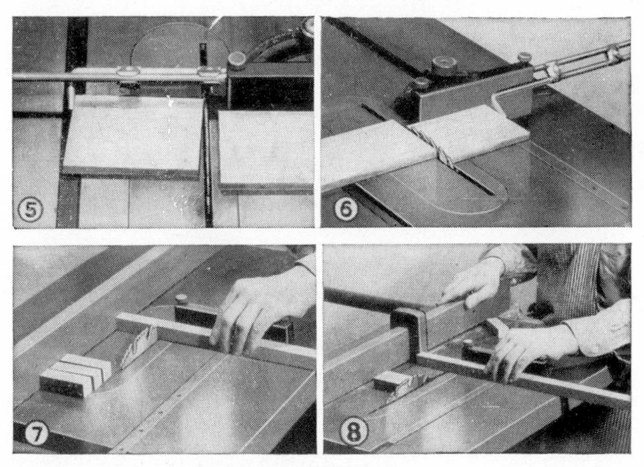

Another example of the *right* and *wrong* way to use stops is shown in the next two illustrations. Number 7 is wrong, as the work will jam between the blade and the fence. Number 8 is correct—the stopblock allows accurate setting but gives clearance to the work in the cutting operation.

Miters

Miters are cut in much the same manner as a square crosscut, using the miter gauge in either table groove. The gauge can be used in either a closed or an open position. The closed position is recommended for all small cuts, because it allows a better contact area.

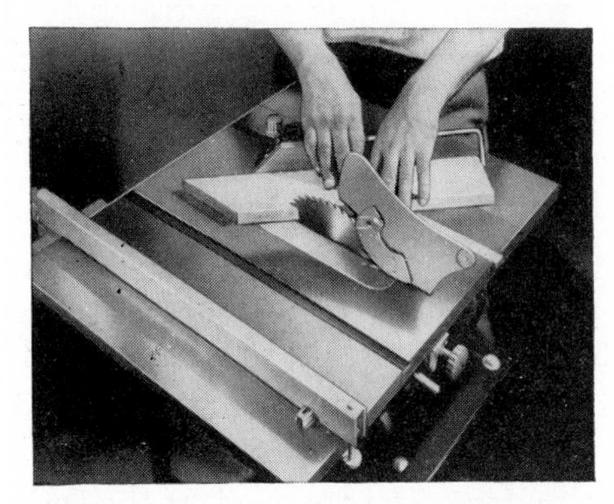

The closed position is illustrated in the above photograph.

All miter cuts tend to creep slightly during the course of cutting. Under average circumstances the creeping is toward the blade. In any case, creeping can be largely eliminated by holding the work firmly and feeding rather slowly.

Resawing

Resawing is the operation of ripping a thick board to make a thin board. If the work does not exceed the capacity of the saw, the cut can be treated like a regular ripping operation. However, the job usually consists of cutting from both sides, and a final band-saw cut may be needed to separate the two parts. When two cuts are needed, the saw projection is set a little over half thickness, and the first cut is made. This part of the job is safe and easy to do. The second cut, which separates the work, is more difficult to handle, and it is recommended that homecrafters use a setup requiring little exposure of the hands to possible danger. In order to accomplish this, hold-downs should be fashioned and a push stick used. On work where a smooth cut is not essential, it is often more practical to leave a narrow rib of uncut wood through the center, completing a cut on the band saw.

Rabbeting

This operation is performed by making two ripping cuts of suitable depths to remove a corner of the work. Various techniques are used; the work should be pencil-marked and the fence and saw depth setting made to the marks before starting the saw. The cut which requires sawing with the work on edge should be made first. This cut is set a little short of the pencil mark. The second cut, in which the work is run flat, is set a little deeper, cleaning the corner.

Rabbets may also be cut with one pass by using the dado head.

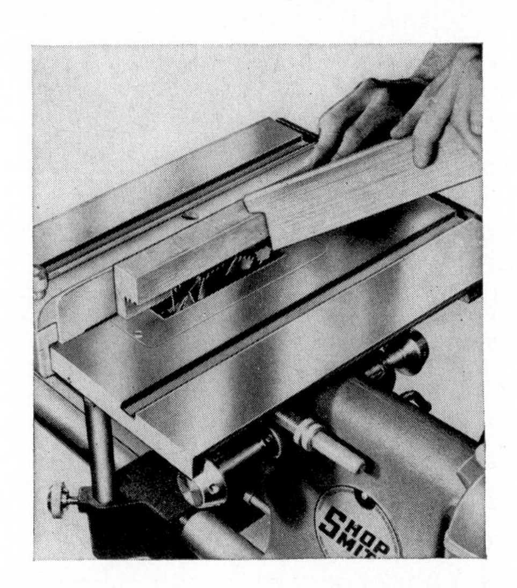

Special Operations

Special operations performed on the circular saw include taper ripping, pattern sawing, cove cutting, the sawing of compound angles, etc. These operations are easy and safe to do, and, while the nature of the work is different, the actual handling of the saw does not vary greatly from plain ripping and crosscutting.

Taper Ripping

Taper ripping is most commonly used in producing the tapered leg used in furniture construction. A special jig is required, this being made up to suit the work. The work is first dressed to net size and squared perfectly. The jig used to make the cut is designed to make use of either the rip fence or the miter slot in the saw table.

Cove Cutting

The cove-cutting operation consists of making a concave cut in the work, as required, for instance, for rounded corners in modern furniture construction or for making moldings when other equipment is not available.

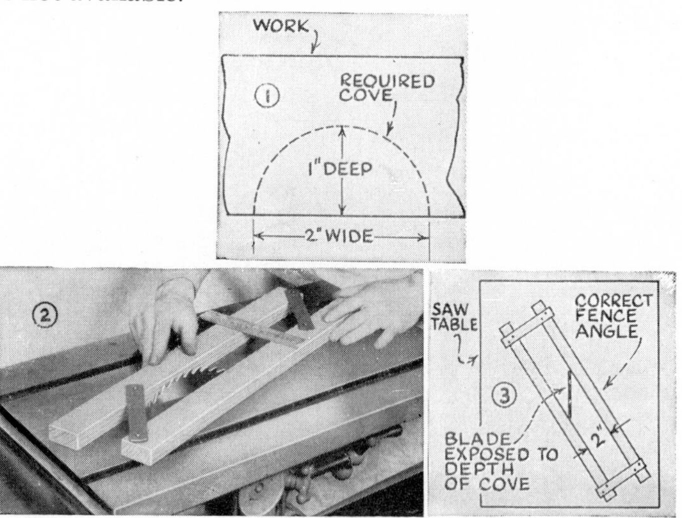

The work is done by clamping a straight guide fence to the saw table, out of parallel with the blade, and then running the stock against this fence, taking a number of light cuts until the desired depth is obtained. The proper angle of the fence is determined by using a parallel rule or four strips of wood nailed up to make a frame. The wider the angle from the saw blade, the wider the cove cut will be. For a job requiring a cove cut 2 inches wide by 1 inch deep, for example, first set the saw at the required projection of 1 inch, place the wood frame or parallel rule over the projecting blade, and turn it until it just touches the front and rear tooth of the blade. Rotate the saw by hand, making sure that the teeth just touch the frame. This determines the proper angle of the fence, which is then set by measurement, so that the center line of the work will intersect the center line of the saw blade.

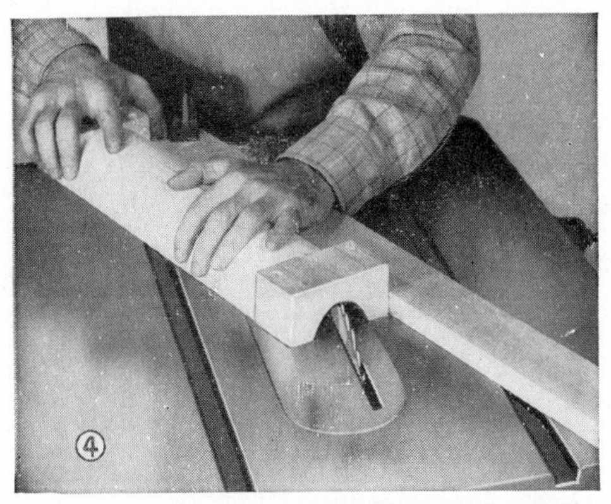

In cutting the cove, the blade is set so that it projects about ⅛ inch above the table, and successive cuts are made, raising the blade ⅛ inch between cuts. The cove cut produces an ellipse, and it is necessary to sand it with sandpaper over a suitable rounded shape in order to smooth the surface. In producing a rounded member to be used in furniture construction, the work may first be prepared on the lathe as a split turning, after which the cove cut is used to produce the rounded inside surface. The work may then be sawed in two to

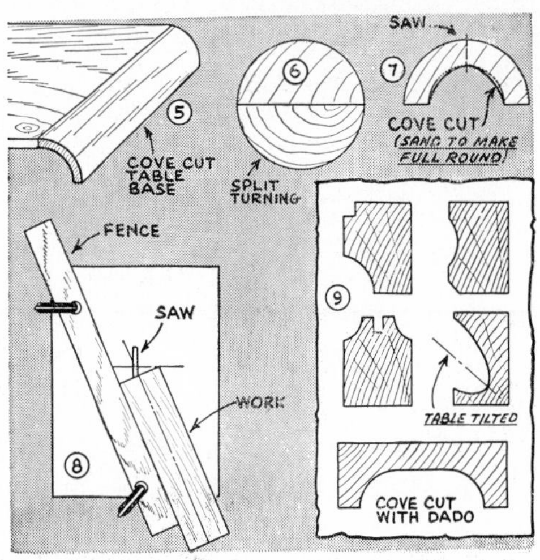

make two quarter rounds. The saw blade preferably for cove cutting is a combination or ripping blade with a considerable amount of set. The blade must be kept sharp. Cuts of the same nature produced with a molding head can be run in one or two passes of the work, this setup being most practical if a large number of shapes are to be made.

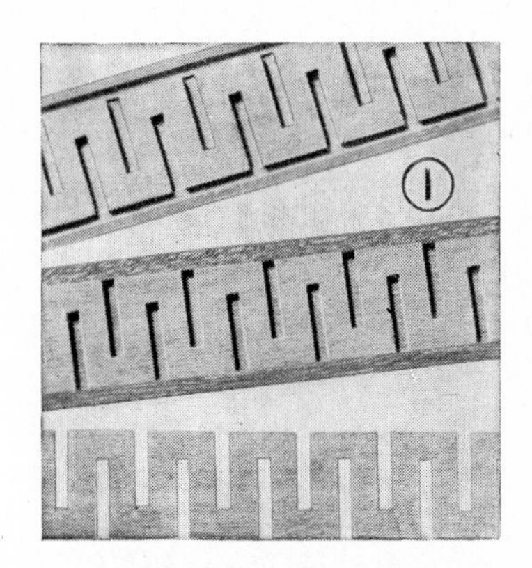

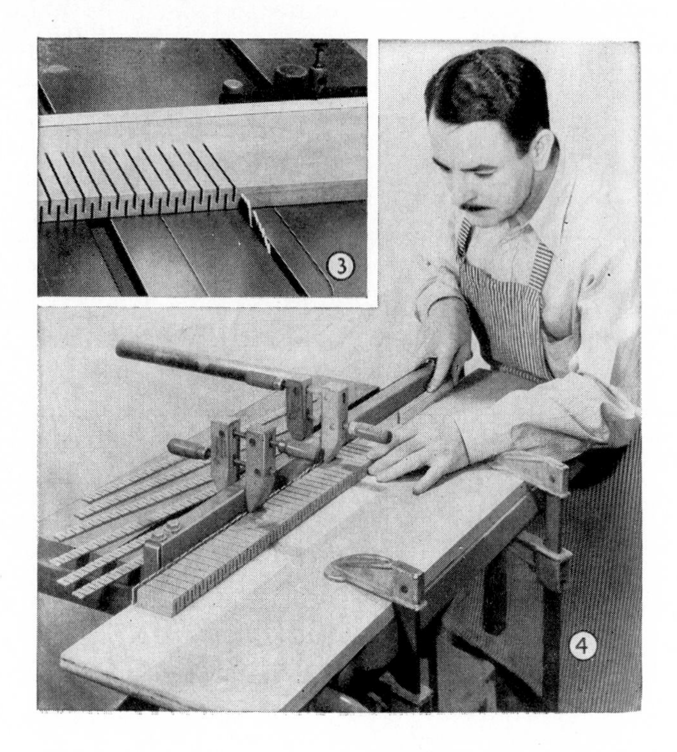

Saw-cut Moldings

It is not generally known that quite a few attractive moldings can be made with saw cuts only. The zigzag shape is commonly called a "dentil molding," although this term has a broad application and may include many different shapes. See illustrations opposite.

The setup is made by fastening a wood facing to the miter gauge. A nail driven into the wood facing acts as a guide pin, the distance from nail to blade determining the spacing of the saw cuts. The saw is set at a suitable projection, and repeat cuts are made with the work turned alternately face up and face down. The actual molding is then made by ripping narrow strips from the work. A ripping operation on work as narrow and delicate as this requires a special setup. The saw table should be fitted with an auxiliary wood table to give the work full support, lest the work be pulled down through the narrow opening in the table insert. Two small parallel clamps will serve as hold-downs, and the job should be done with a planer blade in a sharp condition to assure clean-cut moldings. The molding can be used as an overlay, or it can be mounted on a heavier backing piece of contrasting color.

Jigs and Fixtures

Numerous jigs and fixtures are used in circular-saw work. A few of these are so universal in application as to be considered an essential part of the circular saw. These jigs include the tenoning jig and other fixtures which, while less extensive in scope, are often extremely handy in accomplishing some particular job or special setup.

Sliding Table Jig

The sliding jig is normally referred to as shaper equipment, but it can be used equally well on the circular saw and is excellent for holding work which cannot be guided with either the fence or miter gauge. See number 1, next page.

It is easy to build a duplicate jig, using a wood table, suitable hold-down clamps, and a miter-gauge bar to ride in the saw-table groove.

Perfect miters are difficult, since the work tends to creep along the miter gauge as it is being cut. Another difficulty is that both right- and left-hand cuts are required, and frequently they do not fit exactly, owing to an error of the operator in swinging the miter gauge from one position to the other. These difficulties are eliminated by various methods, one of which is shown in illustration 2.

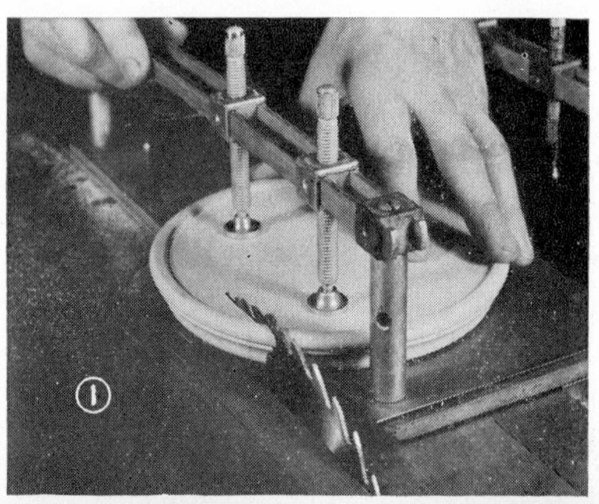

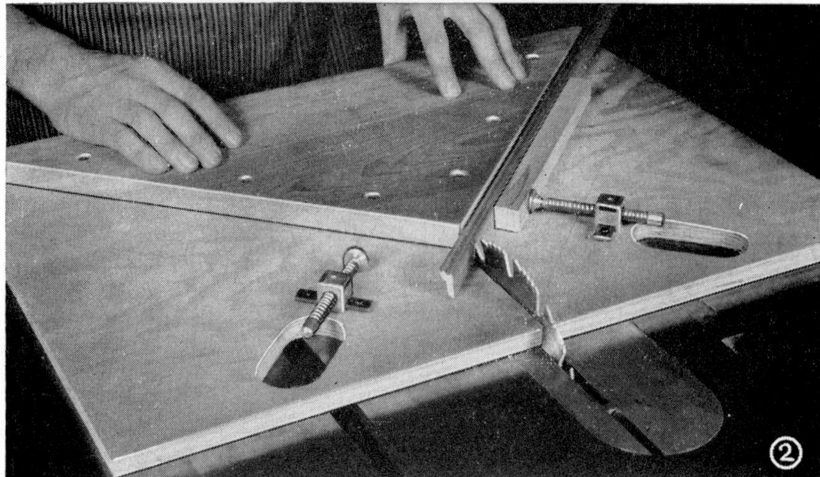

The jig shown consists of a ¾-inch plywood table, with a triangular piece of wood finished to an exact 90 degrees and screw-fastened in place. Clamps are mounted to secure the moldings rigidly to the jig, and the entire fixture is guided into the saw blade by means of the bar following the table groove. Since the fixture is never moved from one side or the other, and the saw settings are never changed, the moldings will fit together, forming a perfect 90-degree miter.

Tenoning jigs or practical homemade substitutes are invaluable for holding and supporting stock while cutting tenons. These jigs not only eliminate imperfections due to faulty holding of the work by the operator, but they also render the operation practical from the standpoint of safety.

The Molding Head

The making of a variety of moldings with the molding head in the circular saw is a fast, safe, and clean operation. There are many different knife shapes available, making it possible for the operator to produce almost any kind of molding, as well as glue and drawer joints.

Where the saw is not equipped with a cutout molding fence, it will be found necessary to add wood facings to one or both sides of the regular rip fence. If the work is not too thick, it can be run against a facing clamped to the regular fence.

A large portion of all work done with molding cutters is straight-line work. Where the cut is along the side of the work, the operation is much the same as using a saw or dado head. The fence is adjusted to the proper width, while the saw table or molding head is adjusted to the right height. Work may be shaped flat on the table, or it may be shaped by standing the stock on edge and projecting it into the cutter. Edge work is generally less preferable than running the work flat on the table. When work is being molded on edge, the cut must not entirely cover the edge, as some stock must be left to follow through against the surface of the table. In all cuts attention must be given to the grain, making the cut in the same direction as the grain whenever possible.

The usual manner of producing strip moldings is to mold the edge of a wider board and then rip off the molded portion. Moldings may require a combination of cuts, and they are then run in successive stages, changing the knives or readjusting the cutterhead for each step.

Making Ornamental Moldings

A wide variety of ornamental moldings which give the appearance of hand-carved work can be made with molding cutters. Typical examples are shown in illustrations *A* through *L*. The work consists simply of a repetition of a suitable molding cut, the cuts being spaced mechanically by means of a guide pin or guideboard. A guideboard makes the best setup, because many of the shapes cannot be spaced accurately with a pin set to the work itself. The guideboard is a separate strip having saw cuts into which the pin fits when each successive part of the molding is being cut. The saw kerfs are spaced evenly in the guideboard, the space being determined by the molding cutter used and the pattern desired. The guide pin is a thin strip of wood let into a saw kerf cut in the miter-gauge facing. The pin can be located in any position, since the spacing is determined by the guideboard and not by the work itself. As will readily be seen, the cuts are merely a matter of cutting and spacing until the full length of the work is machined.

After a wide molding is complete, it can be ripped into suitable

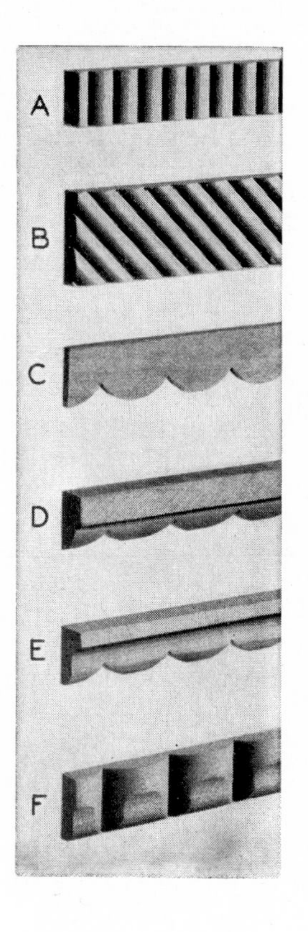

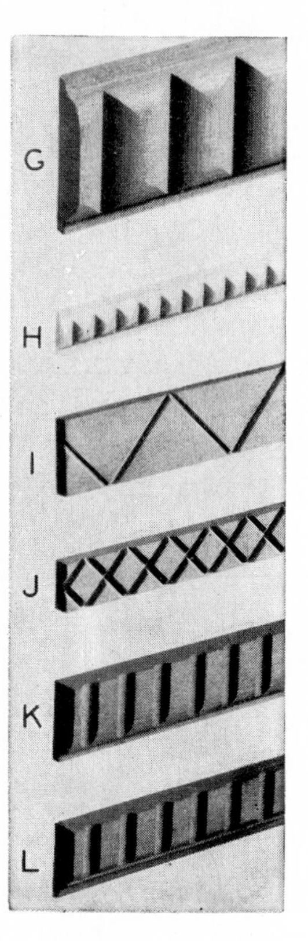

strips and further ornamented by running molding cuts lengthwise of the strip in the ordinary manner. Molding *C* is a thin slice of the bead shape; shapes *D, E, F,* and *G* are thicker slices with lengthwise molding cuts added. Molding *B* is a small bead shape cut with the miter gauge at 45 degrees. *H* is a small bead shape with the same cut returned along the edges to produce a rounded diamond. Molding *I* is worked with the V cutter, as is *J*. *K* and *L* are cut with a different style cutter, with a running molding added at the bottom. All the moldings shown are worked in the same general manner by forming a wide strip and then ripping it into suitable narrow moldings.

Another method of using the guideboard is to fasten it to the top of the work. This type of guideboard is especially useful for production work, since it is not touched by the molding cutter.

Each edge of the guideboard can have a different spacing of saw cuts to suit some specific molding.

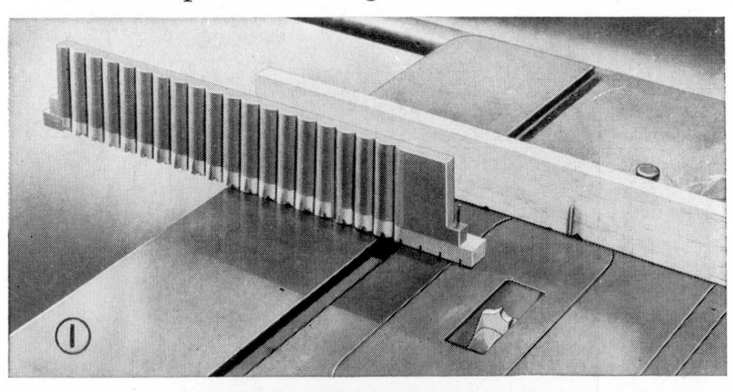

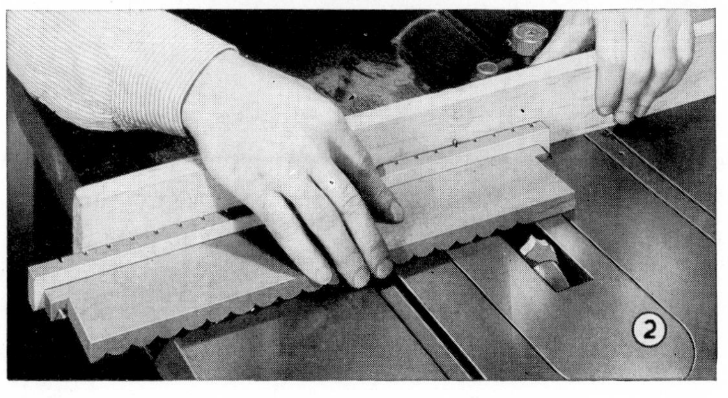

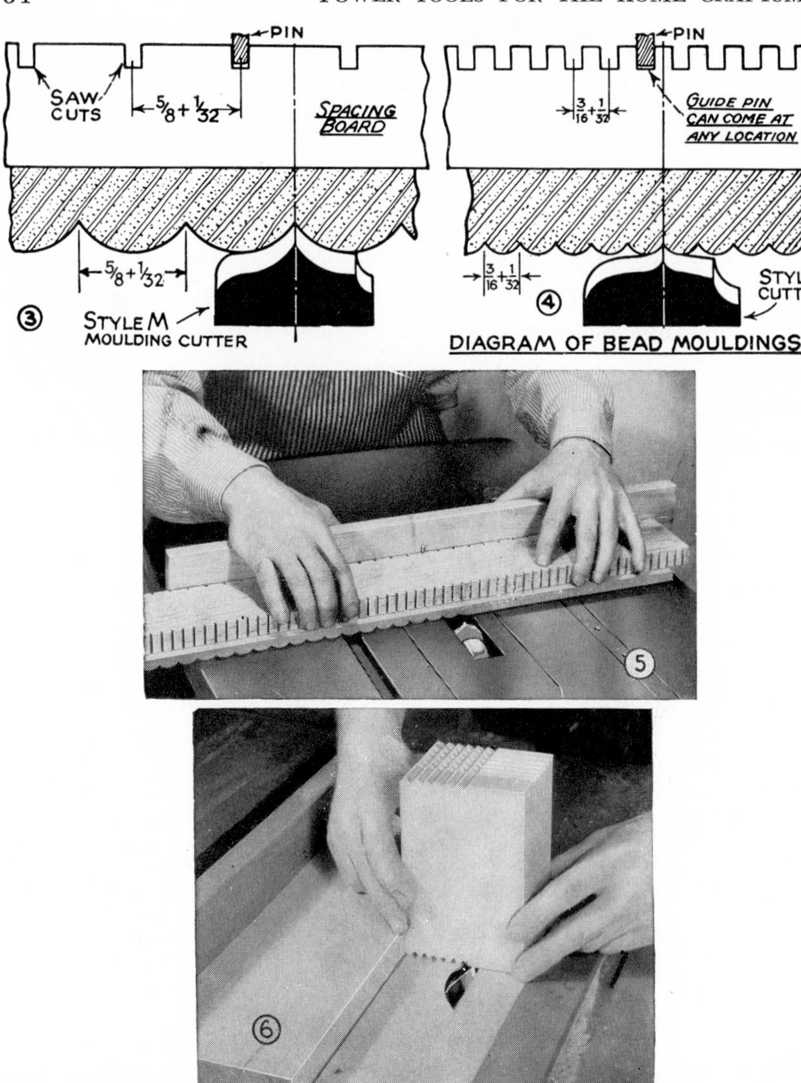

Molding cutters should be sharp for this type of work, because it is cross-grain cutting. Like other cuts of this nature, the end of the cut may tend to splinter out, especially when the top-guide method is used, since this does not offer a fresh backing for each cut. A simple trick to produce a smooth cut on cross-grain work is to back-cut. Back cutting is done by starting the work on the far side of the cutter and then pulling it toward you—exactly the reverse of pushing a piece of work into the cutter. If you use this method, you may expect a mild kickback at the start of the cut; then feed slowly backward.

Another method of spacing which is sometimes useful for occasional work is the use of a waste board. After each molding cut is made, the waste board is run over the jointer to slice off ¼ inch or whatever spacing is needed. This changes the distance between the cutter and the fence with each successive cut. Other setups can be made with stops and spacing strips, but all are inferior to the saw-cut guideboard.

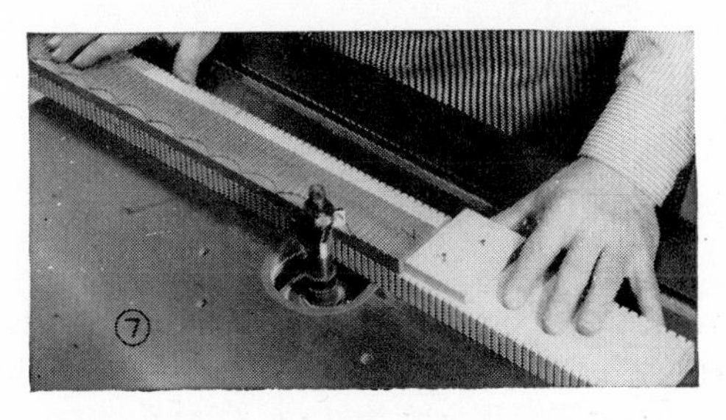

Special wood table inserts are usually employed in the saw table in order to provide full support for the work. This is a necessary safety measure in handling small work, but it is not needed when molding long strips. Including ornamental cuts run on both the drill press and the shaper, the ornamental-molding possibilities are limited only by the imagination of the operator.

The Dado Head in Use

The application of the dado head is easy to understand—it is simply a thick saw used for making various widths of grooves and rabbets. The dado head must be kept in good condition in order to do good work. The outside saws should not be used for general cutting, since wear on any one part affects the performance of the entire head. The inside cutters used alone produce a very rough cut and are not recommended for any other use.

A typical application of the full dado head is the cutting of a ¾-inch-wide groove. The work is backed by the miter gauge, and in

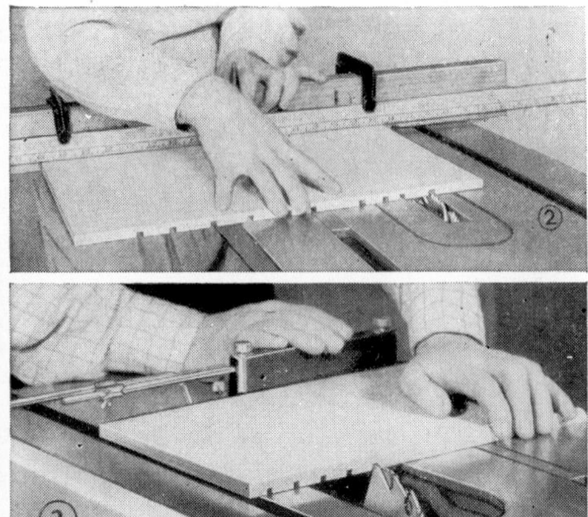

all respects the operation is similar to working with a single saw, except that a slightly slower feed rate is recommended for smooth cutting. In making a series of grooves, a yardstick clamped to the miter-gauge facing makes a practical guide for setting the various cuts. Another method of spacing regular repeat cuts is to engage the end of the stop rod in one of the grooves previously cut. A better method, however, is the use of the guideboard previously described.

Tenons are easily and quickly made with the dado head. The widest combination of blades and rakers is generally used, this being wide enough to cut the average stub tenon in one pass of the work. The work should be set with a stop rod, and the feed should be slow, in order to prevent a natural tendency of the work to creep away from the saw.

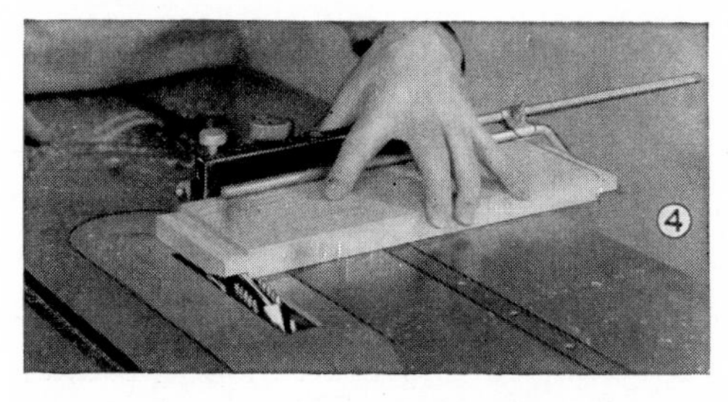

Where the tenon is larger than the width of the dado head, the inside cut should be made first and the work stepped over to make the necessary extra cuts. Wide tenons or grooves can be made speedily by using a notched stopblock. Each of the steps in the block advances the work $^{11}/_{16}$ inch, permitting the maximum width of cut to cover the required area in the least possible number of passes.

A groove cut with the dado head which stops short of one or both ends of the work is called a "blind dado." Cuts of this kind are commonly used in making splined joints. Stops to locate the beginning and end of the cut are necessary. The position for these cuts is located by holding the work alongside the saw in the required position. In many cases the ending stop can be eliminated, using just a pencil mark, but the starting stop is always needed. The reason for this is that there is a fairly strong kickback of the work when it is lowered over the saw, and the stop is needed to support the work and prevent it from being thrown off the table.

Rabbeting with the dado head is similar to a ripping operation with a single saw. The head is made up to a width which would remove more than the required amount of wood. The work is then pushed into the head to cut the rabbet in one pass. This procedure is not recommended for large rabbets, but it is fast and useful for small cuts. Always remember that in dado work the insert hole is fairly large, and that a short piece of work might easily drop into the hole. The use of the tenoning jig to hold small pieces of work will eliminate this danger.

How to Make Wood Joints

The saw cuts needed to fashion wood joints comprise a large part of all circular-saw work and offer the greatest opportunity for the operator's skill. The blade recommended for this type of work is the hollow-ground saw, because it makes a cleaner cut, can be set more accurately to guidelines, and requires less cleaning or finish work to assure a good tight joint.

Splined joints are used in construction to strengthen plain butt and miter joints. Various applications of this joint are shown in the following illustrations. The groove for the spline is commonly cut with the dado head, ¼ inch being the usual standard for ¾- to 1-inch stock, although a ⅛-inch spline is sometimes used, especially for miters. A spline introduced into the miter joint after the joint has been assembled makes a keyed, or slip-feather, miter.

The tenon for the mortise-and-tenon joint can be cut in a number of different ways, depending on the equipment available and the nature of the joint. The method of working to pencil-line layout marks is practical when only one joint is to be made. If two or more are to be matched, however, a procedure of making the required setting for each step, making the similar cuts on component parts, and then proceeding to the next setting should be followed. Various other methods of cutting tenons with the dado head will be acquired with experience and will become standard procedure as the crafter becomes more adept at using his various power tools and accessories.

Many common styles of the lapped, or halved, joint are shown in the following illustrations. The first step in making a lapped joint is to set the saw projection equal to one-half the work thickness, testing on a piece of scrap stock. The width of the cut is usually set off by pencil lines, although a stopblock and spacer can be used to advantage for repeat work. A single joint is commonly cut by working two pencil marks, walking the saw across in successive cuts to obtain the required width. Production work makes use of the dado head in order to reduce the number of passes required.

Miter joints are worked flat or on edge, as shown in the drawing. The setting of table, blade, or miter gauge, as required, is commonly a full 45 degrees and should be checked for accuracy on a piece of scrap wood before cutting the joint.

A common form of splined miter joint shows the spline at both ends. The spline should be ⅛ inch thick by about $\frac{9}{16}$ inch wide for standard ¾-inch stock. Three-ply birch plywood makes excellent spline stock. If solid lumber is used, the grain should preferably run the short way to give added strength across the joint.

In constructing a blind splined miter, the spline is stopped short of one edge, a stopblock being needed to control the length of the spline groove.

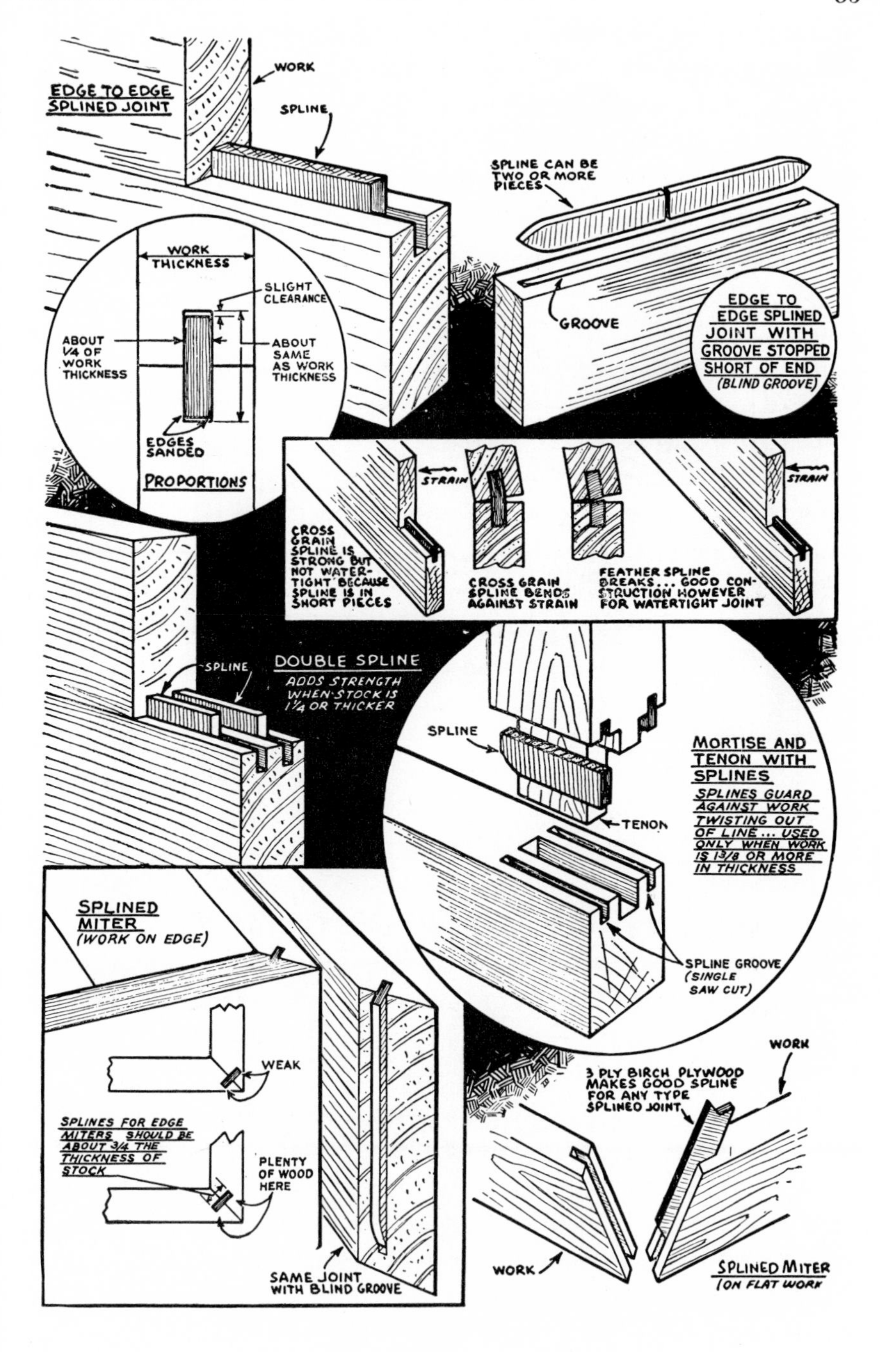
EDGE TO EDGE SPLINED JOINT
WORK
SPLINE
WORK THICKNESS
SLIGHT CLEARANCE
ABOUT 1/4 OF WORK THICKNESS
ABOUT SAME AS WORK THICKNESS
EDGES SANDED
PROPORTIONS
SPLINE CAN BE TWO OR MORE PIECES
GROOVE
EDGE TO EDGE SPLINED JOINT WITH GROOVE STOPPED SHORT OF END (BLIND GROOVE)
STRAIN
STRAIN
CROSS GRAIN SPLINE IS STRONG BUT NOT WATER-TIGHT BECAUSE SPLINE IS IN SHORT PIECES
CROSS GRAIN SPLINE BENDS AGAINST STRAIN
FEATHER SPLINE BREAKS... GOOD CONSTRUCTION HOWEVER FOR WATERTIGHT JOINT
SPLINE
DOUBLE SPLINE
ADDS STRENGTH WHEN STOCK IS 1 1/4 OR THICKER
SPLINE
TENON
MORTISE AND TENON WITH SPLINES
SPLINES GUARD AGAINST WORK TWISTING OUT OF LINE... USED ONLY WHEN WORK IS 1 3/8 OR MORE IN THICKNESS
SPLINE GROOVE (SINGLE SAW CUT)
SPLINED MITER (WORK ON EDGE)
WEAK
SPLINES FOR EDGE MITERS SHOULD BE ABOUT 3/4 THE THICKNESS OF STOCK
PLENTY OF WOOD HERE
SAME JOINT WITH BLIND GROOVE
WORK
3 PLY BIRCH PLYWOOD MAKES GOOD SPLINE FOR ANY TYPE SPLINED JOINT
WORK
SPLINED MITER (ON FLAT WORK

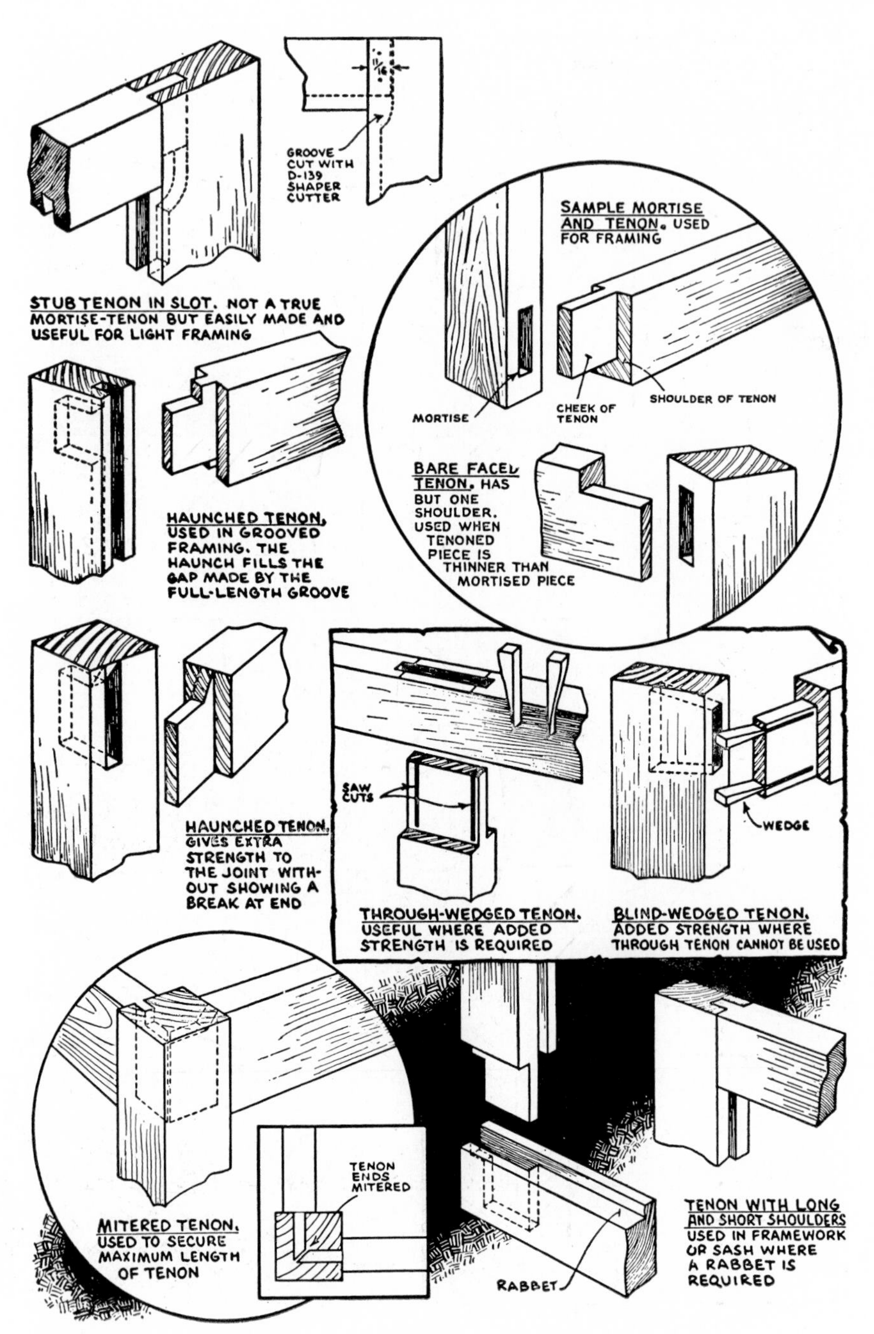
GROOVE CUT WITH D-139 SHAPER CUTTER
STUB TENON IN SLOT. NOT A TRUE MORTISE-TENON BUT EASILY MADE AND USEFUL FOR LIGHT FRAMING
SAMPLE MORTISE AND TENON. USED FOR FRAMING
MORTISE
CHEEK OF TENON
SHOULDER OF TENON
HAUNCHED TENON. USED IN GROOVED FRAMING. THE HAUNCH FILLS THE GAP MADE BY THE FULL-LENGTH GROOVE
BARE FACED TENON. HAS BUT ONE SHOULDER. USED WHEN TENONED PIECE IS THINNER THAN MORTISED PIECE
HAUNCHED TENON. GIVES EXTRA STRENGTH TO THE JOINT WITHOUT SHOWING A BREAK AT END
SAW CUTS
WEDGE
THROUGH-WEDGED TENON. USEFUL WHERE ADDED STRENGTH IS REQUIRED
BLIND-WEDGED TENON. ADDED STRENGTH WHERE THROUGH TENON CANNOT BE USED
TENON ENDS MITERED
MITERED TENON. USED TO SECURE MAXIMUM LENGTH OF TENON
RABBET
TENON WITH LONG AND SHORT SHOULDERS USED IN FRAMEWORK OR SASH WHERE A RABBET IS REQUIRED

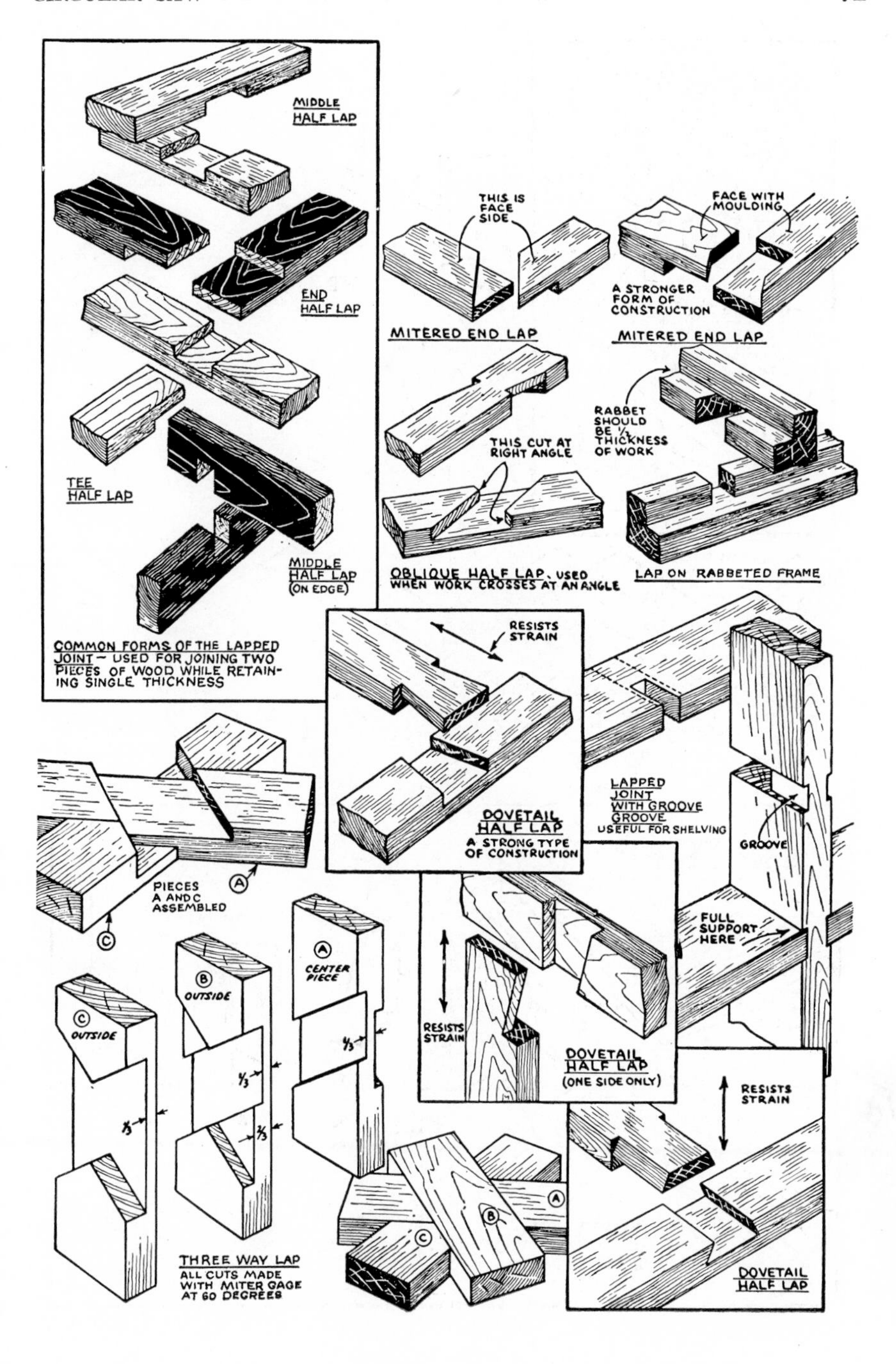
MIDDLE HALF LAP
END HALF LAP
TEE HALF LAP
MIDDLE HALF LAP (ON EDGE)
COMMON FORMS OF THE LAPPED JOINT — USED FOR JOINING TWO PIECES OF WOOD WHILE RETAINING SINGLE THICKNESS
THIS IS FACE SIDE
MITERED END LAP
FACE WITH MOULDING
A STRONGER FORM OF CONSTRUCTION
MITERED END LAP
THIS CUT AT RIGHT ANGLE
OBLIQUE HALF LAP, USED WHEN WORK CROSSES AT AN ANGLE
RABBET SHOULD BE 1/2 THICKNESS OF WORK
LAP ON RABBETED FRAME
RESISTS STRAIN
DOVETAIL HALF LAP
A STRONG TYPE OF CONSTRUCTION
LAPPED JOINT WITH GROOVE
GROOVE
USEFUL FOR SHELVING
GROOVE
FULL SUPPORT HERE
PIECES A AND C ASSEMBLED
A
C
C OUTSIDE
B OUTSIDE
A CENTER PIECE
1/3
2/3
RESISTS STRAIN
DOVETAIL HALF LAP (ONE SIDE ONLY)
RESISTS STRAIN
THREE WAY LAP
ALL CUTS MADE WITH MITER GAGE AT 60 DEGREES
B
DOVETAIL HALF LAP

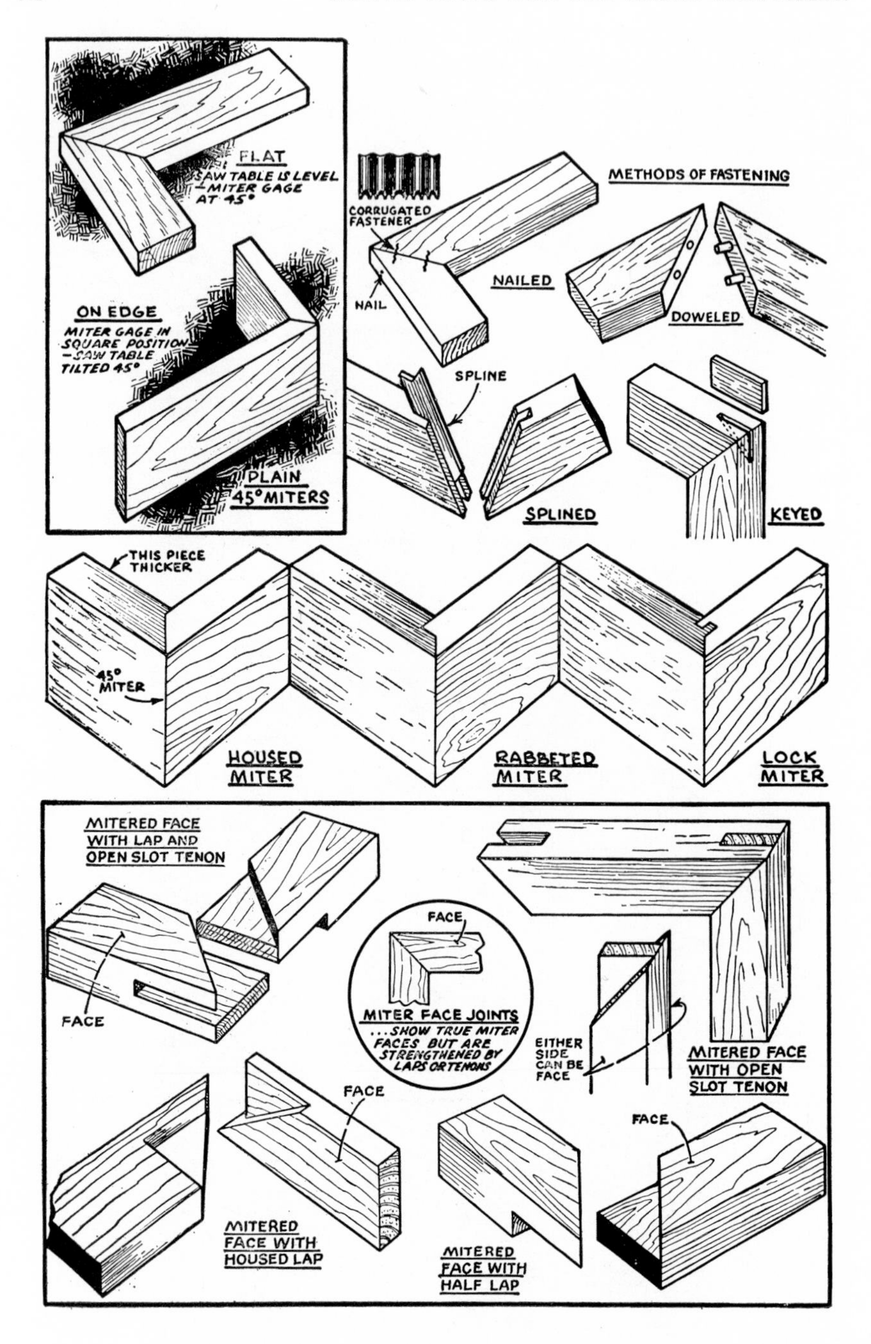
FLAT
SAW TABLE IS LEVEL —MITER GAGE AT 45°
ON EDGE
MITER GAGE IN SQUARE POSITION —SAW TABLE TILTED 45°
PLAIN 45° MITERS
METHODS OF FASTENING
CORRUGATED FASTENER
NAIL
NAILED
DOWELED
SPLINE
SPLINED
KEYED
THIS PIECE THICKER
45° MITER
HOUSED MITER
RABBETED MITER
LOCK MITER
MITERED FACE WITH LAP AND OPEN SLOT TENON
FACE
FACE
MITER FACE JOINTS ...SHOW TRUE MITER FACES BUT ARE STRENGTHENED BY LAPS OR TENONS
EITHER SIDE CAN BE FACE
MITERED FACE WITH OPEN SLOT TENON
FACE
FACE
MITERED FACE WITH HOUSED LAP
MITERED FACE WITH HALF LAP

The familiar box joint, seen on many varieties of small boxes, can be used to advantage for much of the work that falls within the scope of the home workshop. The joint presents several gluing surfaces, besides being neat in appearance. The joint, in any suitable size, can easily be made up on the circular saw fitted with the dado head.

Circular-saw Projects

There are many home workshop projects which can be constructed almost entirely with the circular saw, that is, the circular saw can perform at least 90 per cent of the power-tool operations required. An example of this construction is the chest of drawers shown in the following illustrations.

The chest is of modern design, having slanting drawer fronts with a finger groove under the lower edge of each drawer, making the use of ordinary hardware unnecessary. The sides, top, and drawer fronts may be constructed from ¾-inch plywood panel or from solid lumber glued edge to edge to make up the required width. The top and sides are joined together by means of a blind splined miter joint. Photographs 5 and 6 show a temporary fixture clamped to the saw table and used to cut the groove for the spline. An auxiliary wood facing is clamped to the regular rip fence, while the 45-degree upright fixture aids in holding the panel at the correct angle for cutting the spline groove. An alternate method is to tilt the saw table (or blade) to 45 degrees and make the required cut with the panel in a level position. Photograph 4 shows the finger groove being cut on the forward edge of the frames, using the molding head and a suitable molding cutter.

The frames themselves are cut from solid stock, and the corner joints of the frames are mortise-and-tenon joints. The frames are glued into blind-front dado grooves in the side panels. The back is a ⅛-inch sheet of pressed wood rabbeted into the edge of the sides and top. The drawers employ standard drawer-joint construction—

the bottoms are pressed wood set into grooves cut in the drawer front and sides. Remember to take into consideration the angle of the drawer fronts when cutting the groove for the bottom. Glue blocks below the lower frame help to maintain the rigidity of the chest of drawers.

If the chest is constructed from light wood such as birch or maple,

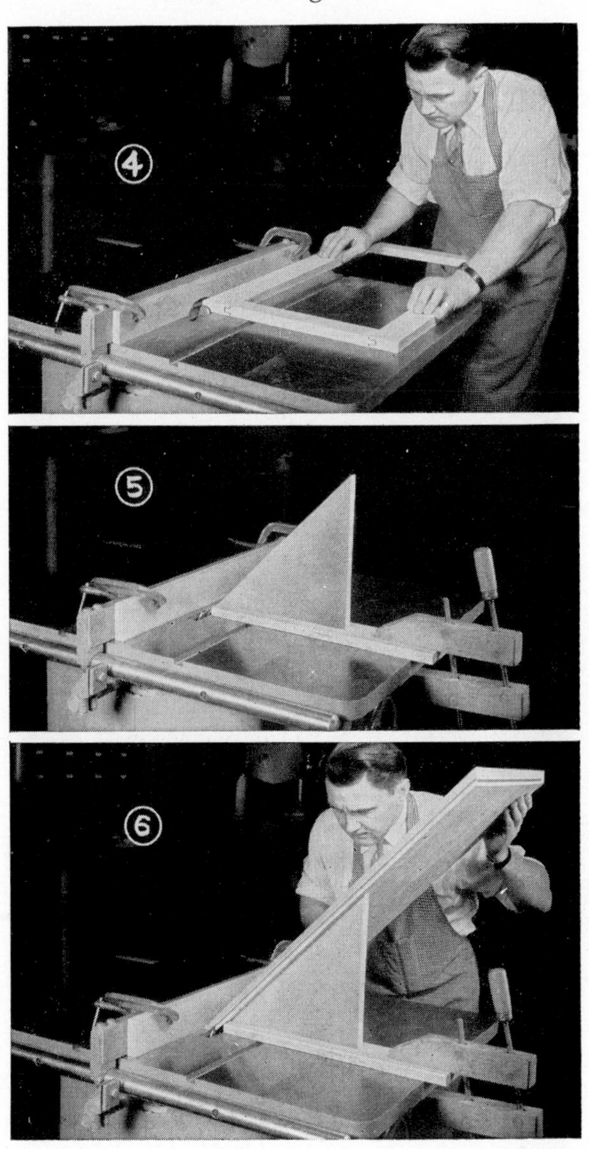

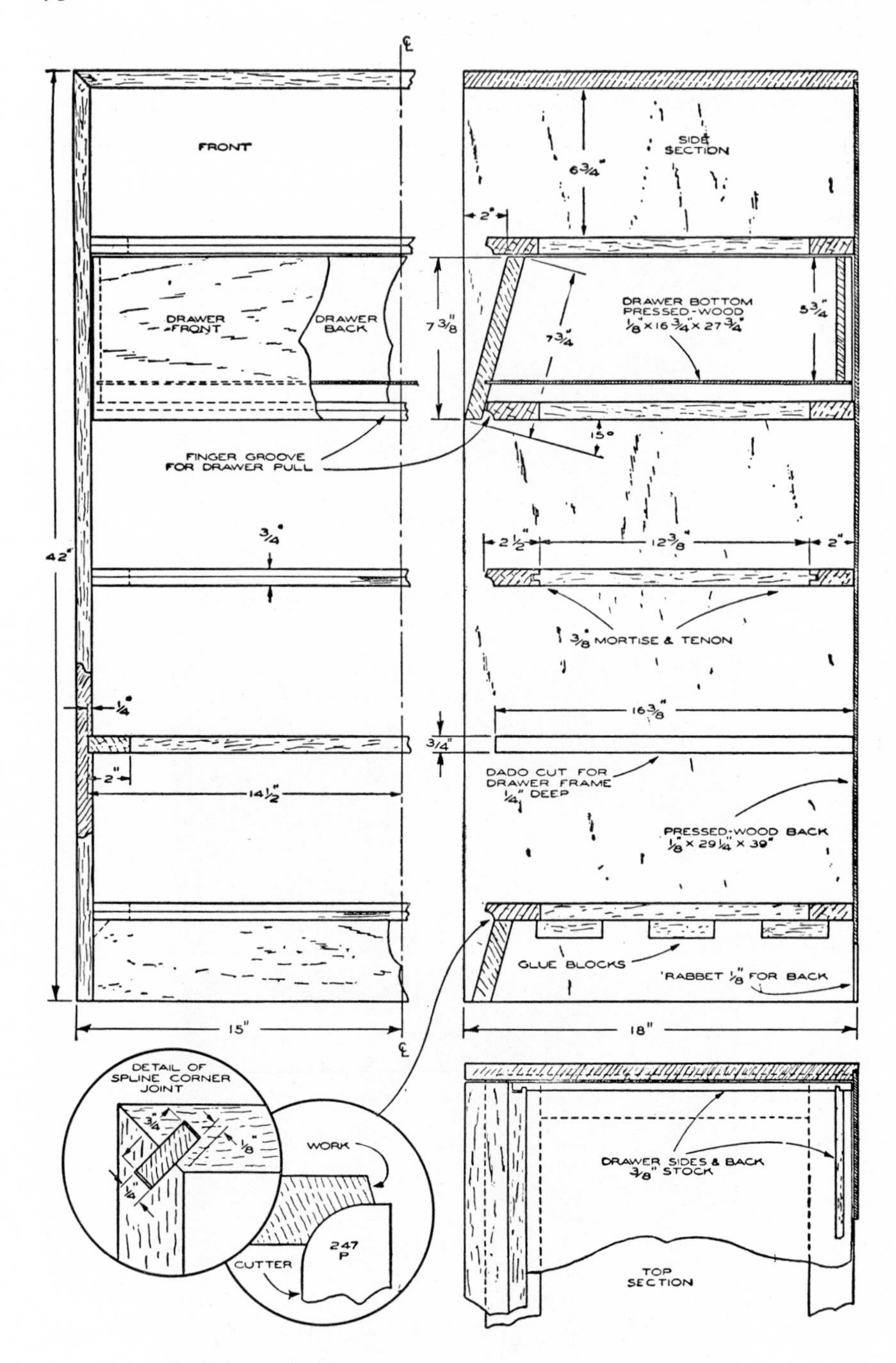

FRONT
SIDE SECTION
6 3/4"
2"
DRAWER FRONT
DRAWER BACK
7 3/8"
7 3/4"
DRAWER BOTTOM PRESSED-WOOD 1/8" x 16 3/4" x 27 3/4"
5 3/4"
15°
FINGER GROOVE FOR DRAWER PULL
3/4"
2 1/2"
12 3/8"
2"
42"
3/8" MORTISE & TENON
1/4"
16 3/8"
3/4"
2"
14 1/2"
DADO CUT FOR DRAWER FRAME 1/4" DEEP
PRESSED-WOOD BACK 1/8" x 29 1/4" x 39"
GLUE BLOCKS
RABBET 1/8" FOR BACK
15"
18"
DETAIL OF SPLINE CORNER JOINT
3/4
1/8"
1/4"
WORK
247 P
CUTTER
DRAWER SIDES & BACK 3/8" STOCK
TOP SECTION

a natural finish consisting of one or two coats of white shellac followed by good spar varnish will assure an attractive piece of furniture. If the sides and top are constructed from plywood panels, be sure to cover the exposed forward edges with thin strips of solid lumber.

You will note that many of the wood joints, moldings, and miters previously described in circular-saw operations have been employed in the construction of this project. The project itself offers an excellent test of the operator's skill in actually working out the problems and procedures already described.

Chapter 3. THE JOINTER

Description

The jointer is a planing machine, used mainly to finish edges and surfaces of boards cut on the circular saw. A typical machine with principal parts named, with the exception of the cutterhead, is shown in the following illustration. The size referred to in the naming of a jointer is based on the length of the knives carried in the cutterhead, that is, the maximum width of a board which the machine can surface at one time.

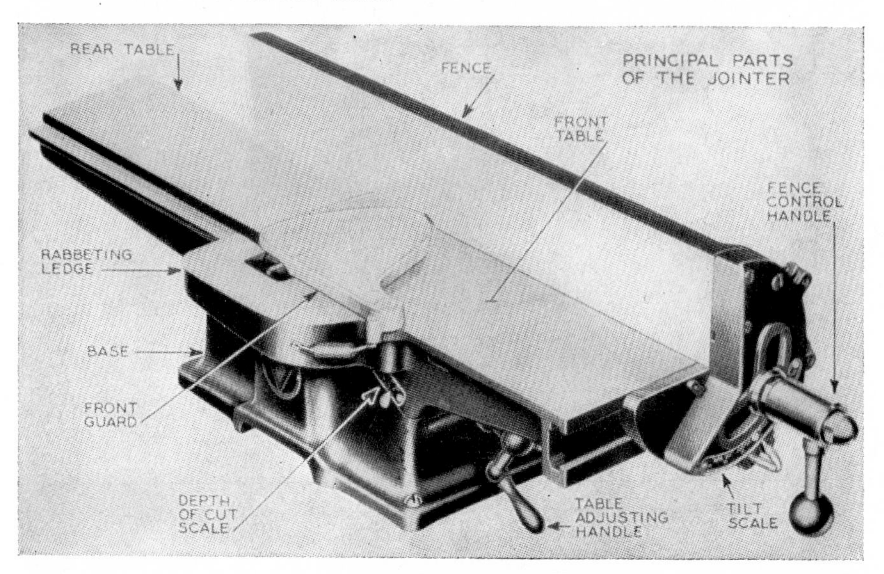

Adjustments

In order to do satisfactory work, the rear table must always be exactly level with the knives in the cutterhead. To make the adjustment, release the locking handle at the back of the jointer, and then raise or lower the rear table until it is level with the knives. An accurate straightedge at least 10 inches long should be used. The initial check is made on any one knife, which should be in such a position that its cutting edge is at the highest point of the cutting circle. The projection of each knife is checked in a similar manner. The adjustment should be checked at both ends and also at the center of each knife, in order to determine whether any knife is improperly mounted in the cutterhead. If a knife is found out of alignment, the screws which hold it in place should be loosened slightly so that the knife may be pried up or tapped down to its proper position. Once the rear table has been adjusted perfectly level with the knives, it is locked in place by means of the locking handle and is not touched again until further adjustment is required after sharpening the knives or after the rear table has been lowered for some special operation, such as chamfering. The effect of an improperly adjusted rear table is shown in illustration 2. If the rear table is higher than the knives, the work will be cut on a taper; if the rear table is lower than the knives, the work will be gouged at the end of the cut. After setting the rear table with a straightedge, a secondary check may be made by setting the machine in motion and running a piece of wood slowly over the knives for a distance of a few inches. It should slide onto the rear table perfectly, the work neither bumping the table nor being above it.

After the rear table has been adjusted perfectly, a chisel mark may be made across the break in the two castings, so that the table, after any later changes, may be returned to its former adjustment with little effort.

The depth-of-cut pointer must be set so that it will show the correct cut on the scale. To adjust this, make a test cut of exactly ⅛ inch, and then set the pointer to this mark on the scale. All other markings should then be correct. The depth-of-cut pointer will require slight adjustment each time the knives are sharpened. The tables on a jointer usually ride in machined dovetail ways on the base casting. An adjustment is usually provided to take up any wear on the dovetail ways. It is seldom necessary to make this adjustment on the rear table, since the rear table remains in a fixed position most of the time. It will very rarely show any wear during the life of the jointer. On the front table it may be necessary after long use to make this take-up adjustment. This is usually done by turning the gib screws found at the back of the jointer.

The fence should then be adjusted so that it is exactly perpendicular to the table, as shown in the illustration.

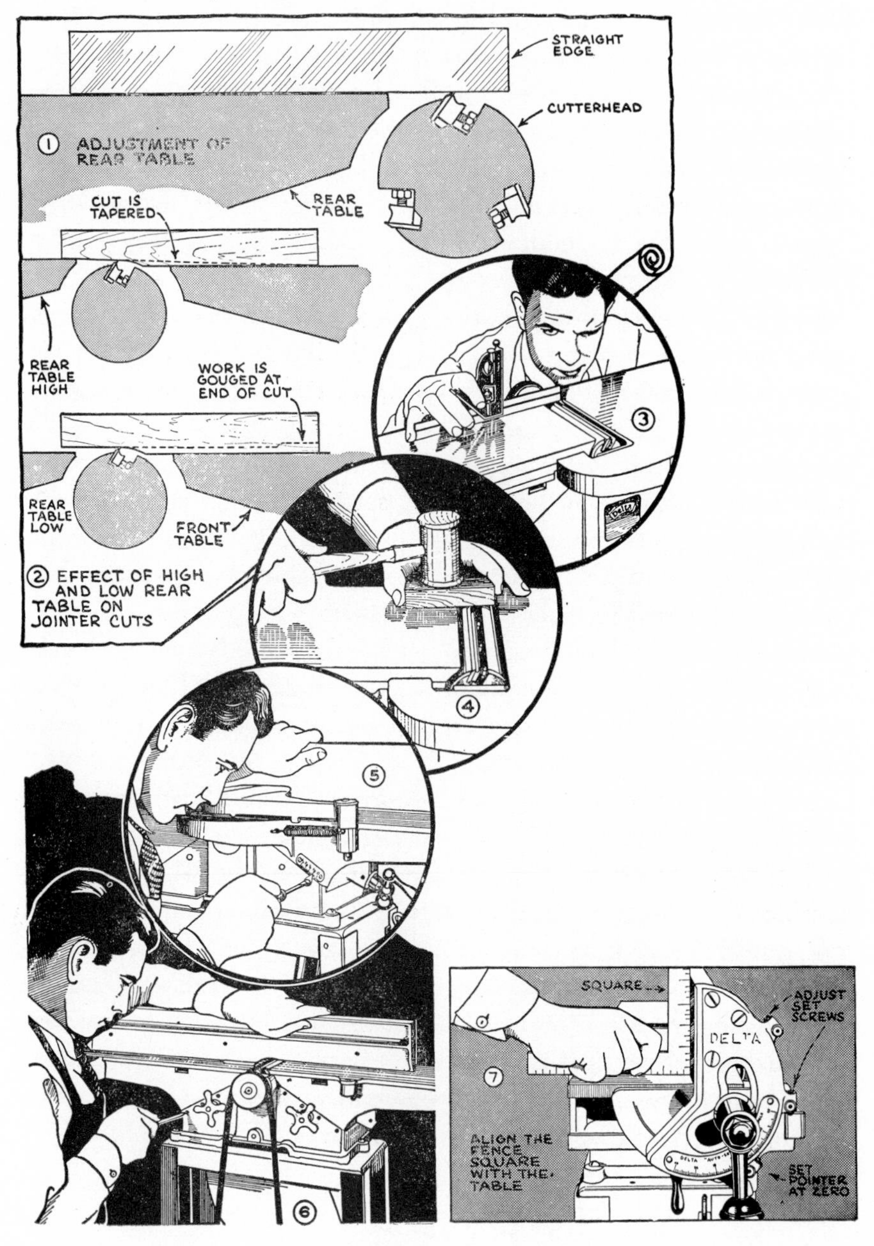

The adjustable pointer is then set at zero on the tilt scale. If the jointer fence is fitted with automatic stops at the 0 and 45-degree positions, these should be carefully checked and adjusted.

Even if the adjustments described are checked at the factory, they should be rechecked by the operator before the machine is used. Once they are checked, they should require no attention until the knives in the cutterhead are sharpened, or until long wear makes readjustment necessary. It is worth noting here that in the manufacture of these machines, the front and rear tables are ground together when they are mounted on the base casting, so that the tables are in perfect alignment when the machine is bought.

Sharpening Jointer Knives

Jointer knives are ground at an angle of 36 degrees. When they are mounted in the cutterhead, the bevel on the rear edge of the blade usually projects about 1/16 inch above the surface of the cutterhead. Since the knives are quite narrow, it is necessary when grinding to have a block in which to hold the blade. Such a block can be made from hardwood by running a saw cut at the required angle in the edge, just deep enough so that the beveled edge projects a slight amount to provide clearance. The saw kerf to hold the blade should provide a snug fit; however, if any looseness is apparent, the knife can be held securely by means of screws.

The blades may then be sharpened on any one of several different machines. They may be sharpened on the grinder by adjusting the tool rest to the required angle, clamping a guideblock in position to ensure a straight cut across the knife, and then working each knife in turn, taking a very light cut. A strip of paper is then pasted to the holding block, in order to set the next cut without changing the original position of the guideblock. Two or three very light cuts will usually bring all the knives to a perfect edge. It is imperative that abrasive cuts on high-speed steel knives should be very light—heavy cuts will invariably burn the knives and render them useless.

A second method of grinding jointer knives is to use the cup wheel on the drill press. The knives are inserted with the flat edge of the bevel facing the top of the holding block instead of the side.

A third method employs the use of the circular saw, with a grinding wheel mounted on the arbor. The holding block can be clamped rigidly in the sliding jig and fed past the grinding wheel accurately by using the slot in the saw table.

Whatever method is used, best results will be obtained if the grinding is done with successive light cuts, taking each knife in turn until all edges are sharp.

Grinding is not always necessary to sharpen the jointer blades, since careful honing at regular intervals will maintain a sharp cutterhead for some time. To hone the knives, partly cover a fine carborundum stone with paper, so that it will not mark the table. Place the stone on the front table. Turn the cutterhead until the stone rests flat on the bevel. Lock the head in this position by clamping the V belt to the stand or some other convenient location. Whet the knife by stroking the stone lengthwise with the blade, treating each knife with the same number of strokes.

Jointer knives can be sharpened and brought to a true cutting circle by jointing their edges while the head is revolving. In this operation the stone is placed on the rear table and the table lowered until the stone barely touches the knives. Be certain to check this setup by turning the cutterhead by hand before turning on the power. Joint the knives lightly.

Setting the Knives

One of the best methods of setting jointer knives in the cutterhead is with a magnet. A powerful magnet is placed on the rear table overhanging the cutterhead opening. The cutterhead is revolved until the cutting edge of the knife is at the highest point in its cutting circle. The knives are then loosened in the cutterhead, the magnet draws them flush with the rear table and against the magnet, and the knife is then tightened in its correct position in the cutterhead.

Jointer Operation

Jointing an edge is the simplest and most common operation which can be performed on the jointer. Illustration 1 shows the start of a cut. The guide fence is square with the table. The guard has been removed to show the cutting action. The depth of cut is approximately ⅛ inch. The best-face side of the work is against the fence.

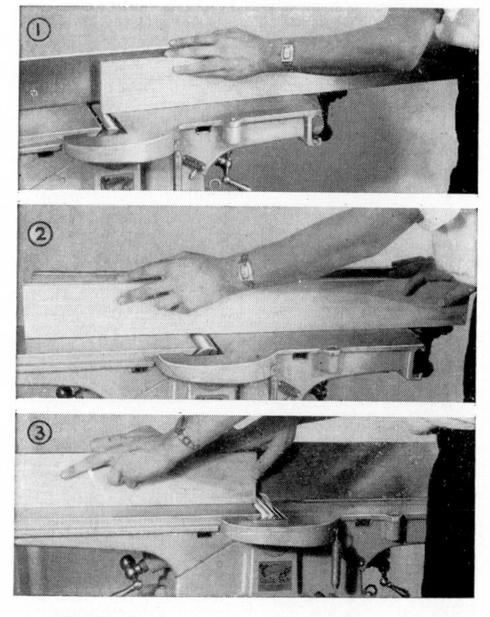

Illustrations 2 and 3 show successive stages of the cut as the work is being pushed over the revolving cutterhead. The hand over the rear table presses the work down firmly, so that the newly planed surface will make perfect contact with the rear table. The hand over the front table, which is usually the right hand, exerts no downward pressure but simply advances the work to the cutterhead. Side pressure against the guide fence is exerted by both hands as the work is advanced for the cut.

Some operators never pass either hand directly over the knives. In working by this method, both hands are over the front table at the start of the cut. As soon as the stock is resting solidly on the rear table, the left hand is lifted and placed on this portion of the work. As the right hand approaches the cutterhead, the work is held down tightly with the left hand, while the right hand is lifted and placed on the stock over the rear table. Both hands are now over the rear table, and the remainder of the cut is completed from this position.

A second method finds both hands on the front table at the start of the cut, and both hands pass over the cutterhead as the feed is made. While there may be some mental hazard in advancing the hands over the cutterhead, actually there is no danger involved, provided that certain conditions are carried out: the feed should be made carefully, the stock being cut should not be too narrow or too short, and a hold-down block should be used when the work is being surfaced flat. It is faster and easier to make the feed in this manner. The right hand, always in position at the end of the work, offers positive protection against the most common and most dangerous jointer hazard—the kickback. The first method is safer when surfacing, especially when the stock is less than 1 inch thick.

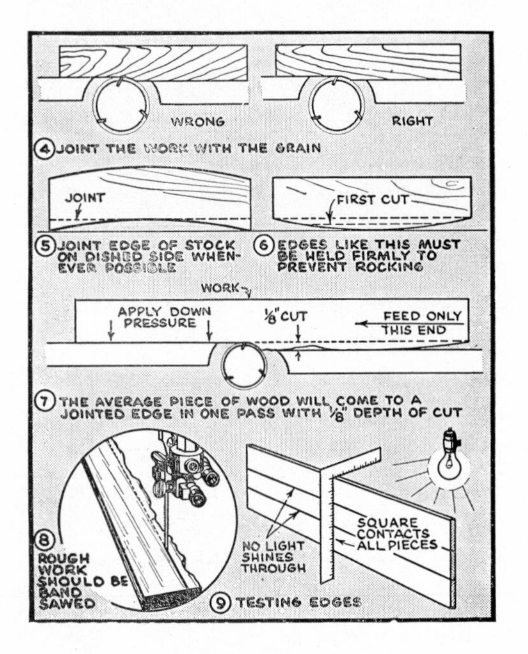

Illustrations 4 through 9 show important points to observe in jointing an edge. Always work with the grain whenever possible. When it is necessary to joint a curved edge, as shown in illustration 6, pick out the central portion of the curve, and make the first light cut on this portion of the wood. It can be seen that the stock has no fixed base line; hence it must be held firmly for this first cut. With a partial base made in this manner, succeeding cuts can be made to bring the edge to a true surface.

Side pressure is always required in order to keep the work in perfect contact with the jointer guide fence and is very important when jointing wide stock. Where a considerable amount of wide work is to be handled on edge, it is advisable to fasten a high auxiliary fence to the regular fence, in order to supply a more positive and accurate means of support.

Jointing work on end can be done in the same manner as jointing with the grain. The one big difference is that the surface should be formed with several light cuts. A single heavy cut will invariably tear the grain at the end of the cut unless the knives are very sharp. There is, however, a method of working that will avoid this. A short cut can be made at one end and the work then reversed and fed from the opposite end to blend with the first cut. This method has the disadvantage of a possible poor blend of the two cuts, unless the rear table and guide fence are set to hairline perfection. Where the work is to be jointed on all four edges, it can readily be seen that if the concluding cuts are with the grain, they will remove any splintered edges formed by the initial cuts across the end grain. Stock less than 8 inches wide should not be end-jointed unless some sort of guiding fixture is used.

Surfacing, or planing a working face, is the most difficult standard jointer operation. The work may have two main defects, warp and wind. Warped lumber is dished from side to side across the board. Lumber with wind is twisted throughout its length. Testing for wind can be done by sighting across straightedges placed across each end of the work or by rocking the work on a flat surface. Where the stock is to be dressed out of wind with a minimum loss of thickness, it is advisable to mark the work carefully to permit leveling with the least number of cuts. A hold-down block is always used, especially when surfacing thin stock. Very thin material usually requires an auxiliary fence screw fastened to the standard fence, so that it will not slip underneath the standard fence when side pressure is applied during the feed.

Rabbeting on the jointer is done by setting the fence to the width of the cut and cutting on one end of the cutterhead. The front table is set to the required depth. The guard usually must be removed. Some jointers are equipped with both a front and rear guard. This rear guard is useful in the rabbeting operation, since the cutterhead on the opposite side of the fence is the only place where the knives are exposed. Two or more passes can be made if required. In making end rabbets on narrow stock, the work should be followed with a backing block for added support.

Bevels are cut by tilting the fence to the required position. Several passes are usually required to arrive at a full bevel. The jointer fence can usually be tilted in or out as desired. Tilting the fence out at too great an angle sometimes allows the work to slip downward toward the table; careful pressure against the fence should be used to avoid this.

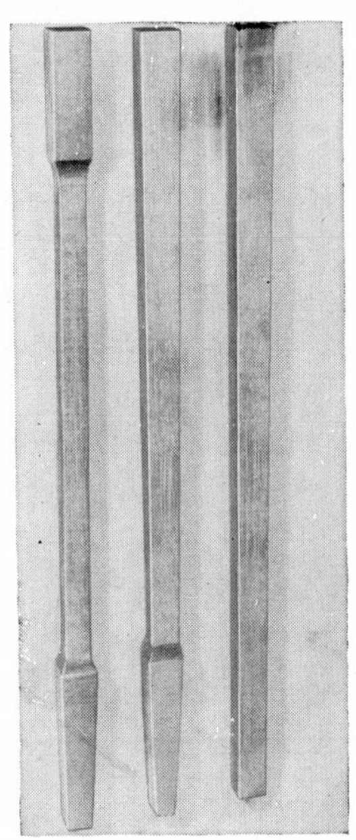

Taper Jointing

Taper jointing is one of the most useful jointer operations and can be used to advantage on a wide variety of work. The furniture legs shown in the illustration above are typical examples.

The simplest kind of tapering involves stock which is shorter in length than the length of the front table. On the 6-inch jointer, this takes in stock up to 14½ inches long. In making the cut, the front table is lowered to the necessary depth of cut. The stock is then placed against the fence. The far end of the board is in such a position that it will land on the rear table at the start of the cut, as shown in illustration 1. From this position the board is moved forward to cut the taper. Work longer than the length of the front table can be handled similarly by making a front-table extension, as shown in illustration 1A.

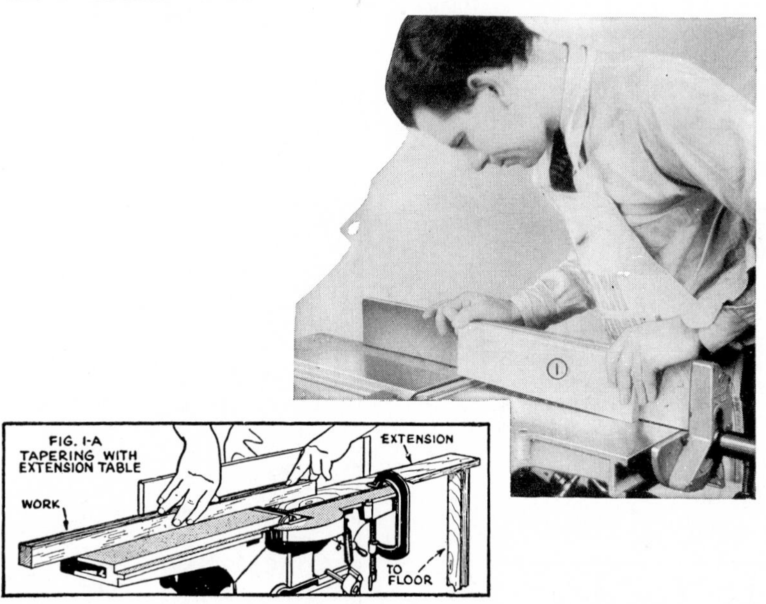

Where long tapers are to be cut without the use of an extension, a slightly different procedure must be followed. The basic rule is that the stock must be divided into a number of equal sections, each slightly shorter than the length of the front table. A 28-inch board, for example, would be divided into two sections. The depth of cut must also be divided into a corresponding number of equal parts, which in this case would be two. For example, a 28-inch board is to be tapered ⅜ inch from end to end. The board is divided into two equal parts. The front table is set to a depth of $\frac{3}{16}$ inch. Two cuts are necessary, the first cut being started by dropping the mark over the knives as shown in illustration 2.

Illustration 3 shows the completion of the first cut. The second cut is started at the far end of the board, as shown in illustration 4. This cut proceeds the full length of the board to complete the full ⅜-inch taper. Any length of board can be handled by using this method. A 36-inch board would be divided into three spaces of 12 inches each. If the taper required was ¾ inch, the front table would be set to one-third of this, or ¼ inch.

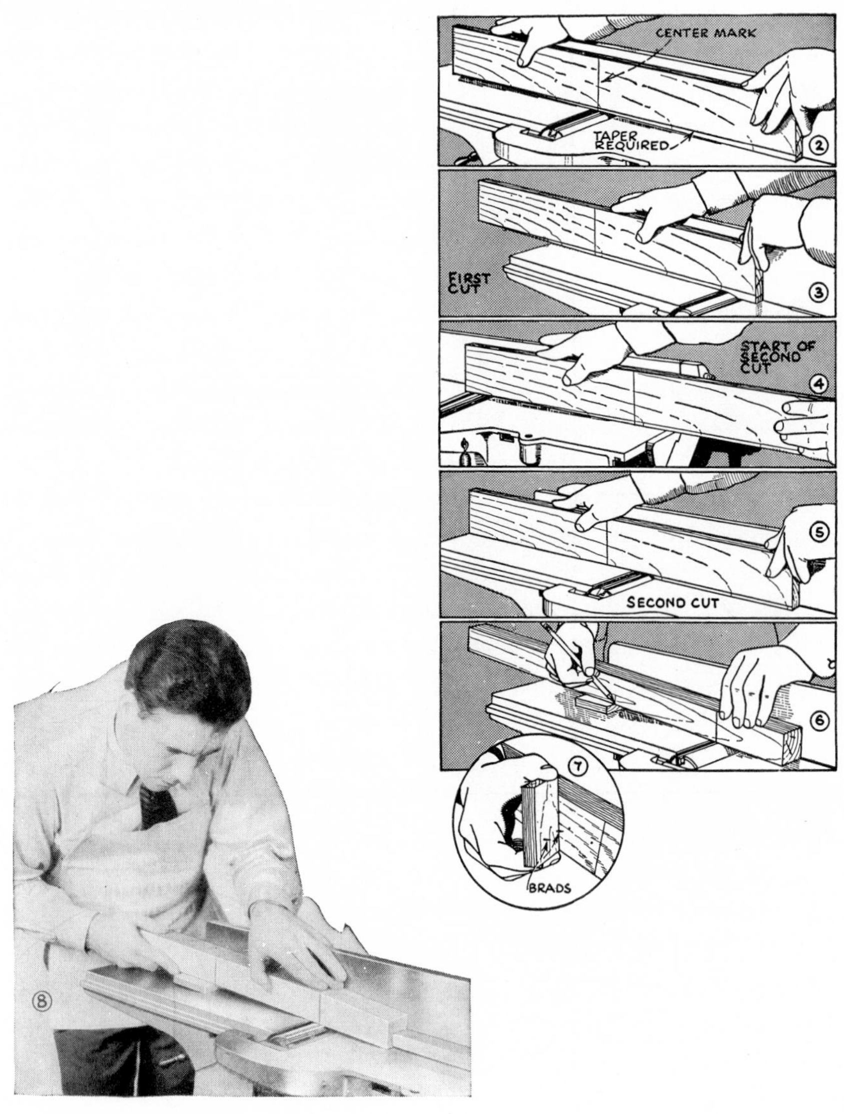

Very short, fast tapers are best cut by pulling the work over the knives, as shown in the illustration. In setting up for the cut, the front table is lowered to the desired depth. The stock is then placed on the table so that the point at which the taper is to start comes over the knives, as shown in illustration 6. The board is pushed down so that the end contacts the front table, and a suitable block is placed under the free end of the stock to maintain this position. The position of the block is marked so that it can be lightly tacked in place, as shown in illustration 7. From the starting position the stock is pulled over the knives to cut the required taper. As a variation of this method, the block can be clamped to the rear table instead of the work, the result being a slightly curved surface throughout the length of the taper. Short tapers demand a stopblock against which the work can rest at the beginning of the cut; otherwise the slight kick of the knives in making contact will pull the work.

Practically the same tapering methods may be used in tapering to hexagon or octagon shapes by mounting the work between two blocks at each end of a special fixture, the blocks being equipped with indexing holes to provide the necessary stops for each flat.

One of the few jointer operations in which both the rear and the front tables must be lowered is stop-chamfering. A stopblock is necessary to avoid kickback, and a stopblock on the rear table is useful in setting the correct length of the chamfer. A slight roughness caused by cutting against the grain at the end of the cut can be easily sanded out, or the cut may be made halfway and then reversed. A true stop-chamfer, with the fence tilted to bevel the work, is made in the same manner as the straight cut previously described.

The jointer is a machine without equal in saving many hours of tiring work with a hand plane and can be used for many other operations otherwise impossible.

Chapter 4. BAND SAW

Description

The band saw is used extensively for sawing all kinds of curved work or combinations of curved and straight work, and to some extent for resawing.

All band saws operate on the same general principle. The saw blade is a flexible band of steel, with teeth cut on one edge. The blade is stretched over two vertical wheels or pulleys, fitted with rubber tires and provided with adjustments for centering the saw upon the rims of the wheels and for giving the saw the correct tension. To prevent the blade from twisting sidewise in the cut, and to give it support when cutting, the band saw is provided with guides, the design of which varies with different makes of saws. There are two sets of guides, one located above and the other located below a table, which is fitted horizontally between the two pulleys. The table is fitted with a hole through which the blade works. Adjustments permit the tilting of the table usually a full 45 degrees to one side, so that bevel cuts can be made. The table ordinarily can be tilted in the opposite direction, but this tilt is commonly limited to about 10 degrees because of interference with the lower pulley.

The size of the band saw is measured in terms of the pulley diameter. The pulley referred to in this case is, of course, the pulley on which the blade runs. Thus the saw with 10-inch-diameter pulleys would be called a 10-inch saw; a saw with 14-inch pulleys would be called a 14-inch saw, etc. Sizes are sometimes also expressed in terms of throat opening, that is, the distance between the two vertical portions of the blade. It can be seen that the throat opening of a 14-inch saw, for example, would be 14 inches minus the thickness taken up by the blade guard on the left, or return, side of the throat. Other important dimensions of the band saw are the table size and the maximum height between the table and the upper guide. The table size is usually proportionate to the pulley size, being about the same in length as the diameter of the pulley, or a little larger on the side. The distance between the table and upper guide is usually 6 inches.

The band saw should preferably have a central location in the shop. A wall position or even a corner location is quite satisfactory

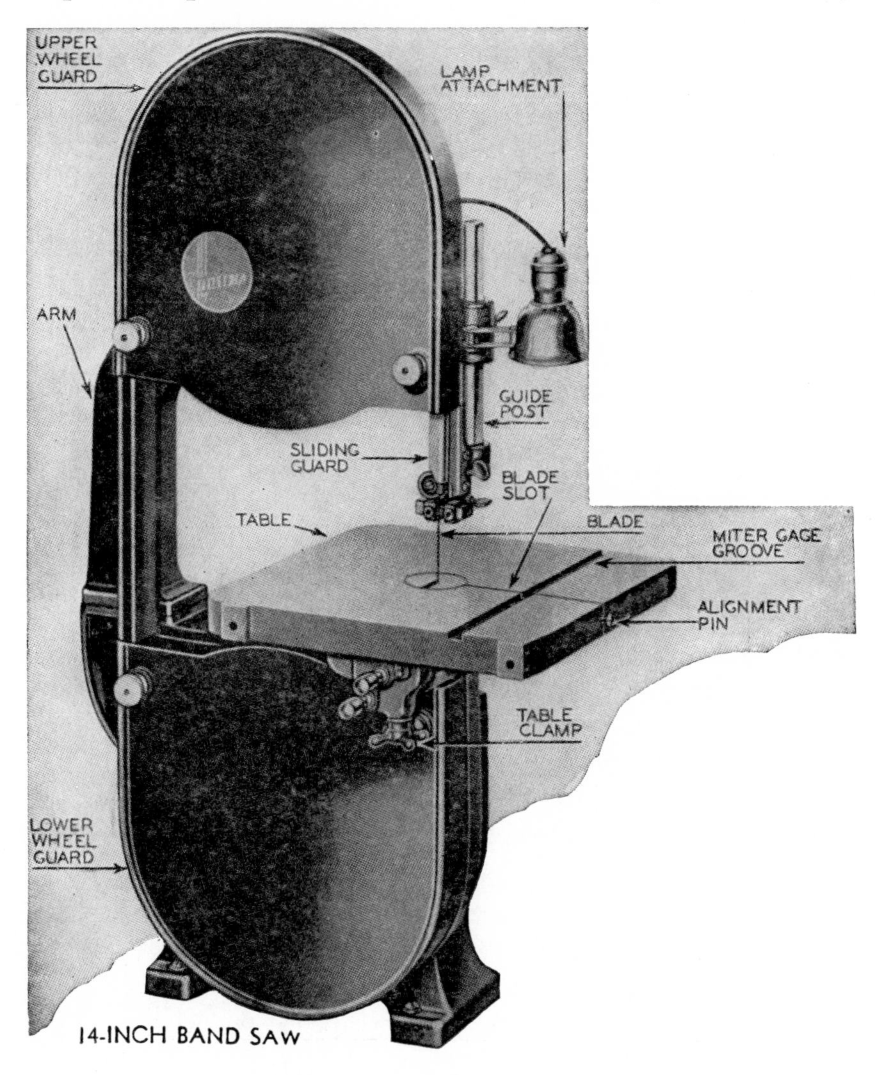

14-INCH BAND SAW

for the average run of small work; however, the machine may have to be moved out from its crowded position for long or bulky work. Since the band saw is used extensively for rough cutting in making small blocks, etc., a position close to the workbench is extremely handy. The mounting for the band saw can be either a steel stand or a suitable wood bench. The band-saw table should be from 42 to 44 inches above the floor, this being the "elbow height" of the average worker.

For most work around the home workshop, a ⅓-horsepower motor will supply ample power. Only a constant-speed 1,725-rpm motor should be used. For average work the band-saw blade should travel at a rate of from 1,500 to 2,200 feet per minute. On a 14-inch band saw, a pulley speed of 600 rpm will give the correct cutting speed of 2,200 feet per minute. Nothing is gained by running the machine faster than this, except where wide blades are used extensively. Narrow blades running at a higher speed will have a shorter cutting life and will show a tendency to clog in the cut unless the blade is in first-class condition.

The most common type of band-saw guide consists of two square pins, one on each side of the blade. There is also a back guide or support, usually a ball-bearing wheel, which supports the blade as

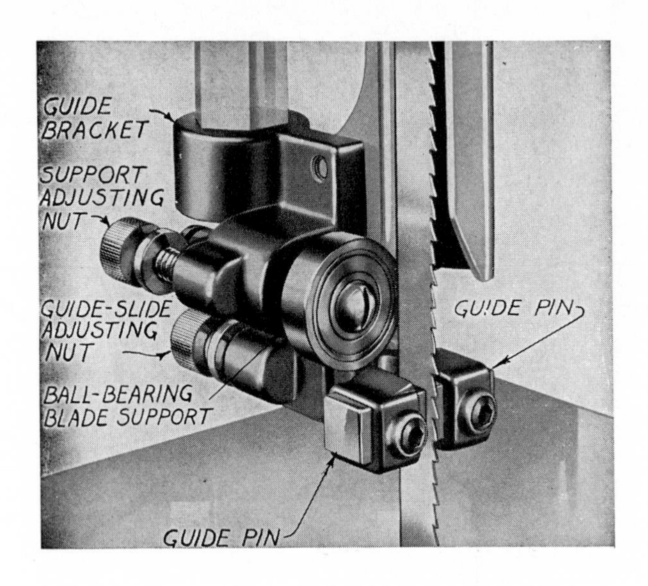

the work is pressed against it. With minor variations in the mounting, the lower guide is identical with the upper guide.

The illustration above shows the upper guide of a typical 14-inch band saw.

The band-saw table is carried on two trunions and is locked in place with star-wheel locking handles. A scale and pointer show the exact degree of tilt at any position. A leveling stop pin is usually provided so that the table can be quickly and accurately returned to the level position. On some band saws the pin can be removed entirely for tilting the table to the left, and it is also adjustable for returning the table to its level setting.

Some band saws are equipped wih special guides permitting the use of narrow sanding belts instead of the usual band-saw blade.

The capacity of the band saw previously described as 6 inches can sometimes be increased by adding an extension block, which increases the length of the upper arm. The addition of a 6-inch extension block increases the maximum cutting capacity to 12 inches. Longer blades are, of course, necessary, as well as an auxiliary blade guard and a longer guide-support bar, both of which are mounted as before.

Table guides on the modern band saw include both the fence and the miter gauge, these units being similar to the equipment used on the circular saw. When a miter gauge is used, the table must be provided with a milled slot for the miter-gauge guide bar. When a rip fence is used, guide bars must be added to the forward and rear edges of the band-saw table.

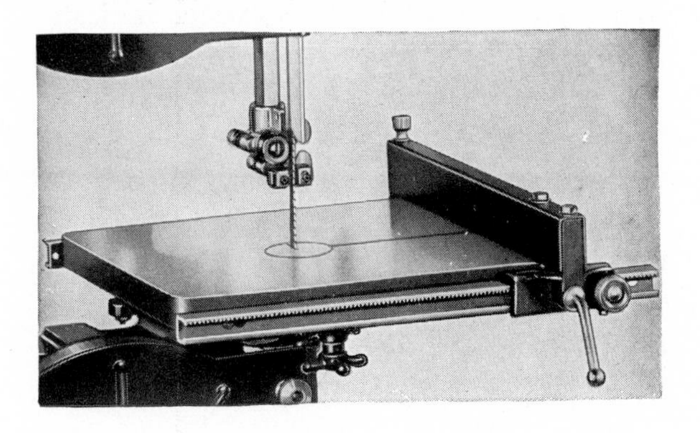

In keeping with the modern safety trend in the construction of small motor-driven tools, the band saw is usually fitted with metal guards completely enclosing the pulleys which carry the band-saw blade and also the motor and drive pulleys. If these guards are not furnished as standard equipment, they can usually be purchased as extras or accessories.

Before a new band-saw blade can be fitted to the machine, it is necessary to remove both the lower and the upper wheel guards by unscrewing the knurled knobs which hold them in place. The table insert and the table-alignment pin are also removed. The tension on the blade already mounted is released by turning the tension handle, after which the blade can be slipped off the wheels and out through the slot in the table. The new blade is fitted to the wheels by reversing this procedure. Before the blade is fitted in place, it is advisable to back off the guide pins and roller support, so that they will not affect the centering of the blade. With the blade in place on the wheels, the upper wheel is raised by means of the tension-adjustment handle until the blade is held tightly. Check the instruction sheets furnished by the manufacturer of the power equipment which you buy for the correct blade tension and any variations in adjustments. The saw is then turned by hand to see that the blade is centered on the rims of the wheels. See illustration above.

If the blade does not center, the upper wheel is tilted in or out as necessary until perfect tracking is secured. After the blade is tracking perfectly, the saw blade is tensioned fully by turning the tension handle, as shown in illustration 2.

Some band saws have a tension scale, which indicates by means of a compression spring the exact strain which should be applied for a given blade. Where the saw is not thus equipped, tensioning is largely a matter of experience. The blade should not be drawn up too tightly. A common method of checking when the blade is not fitted with a tension scale is to place the first and fourth fingers of the hand on one side of the blade with the thumb pressing midway between them on the opposite side. If the blade cannot be slightly flexed by the fingers, it is too tight and should be released slightly. Another test for correct tension allows the blade to flex about 1/8 inch from a true position with a light finger pressure when the upper blade guide is fully raised. These tests can be applied to blades less than ½ inch wide. Wider blades are naturally much stiffer and can

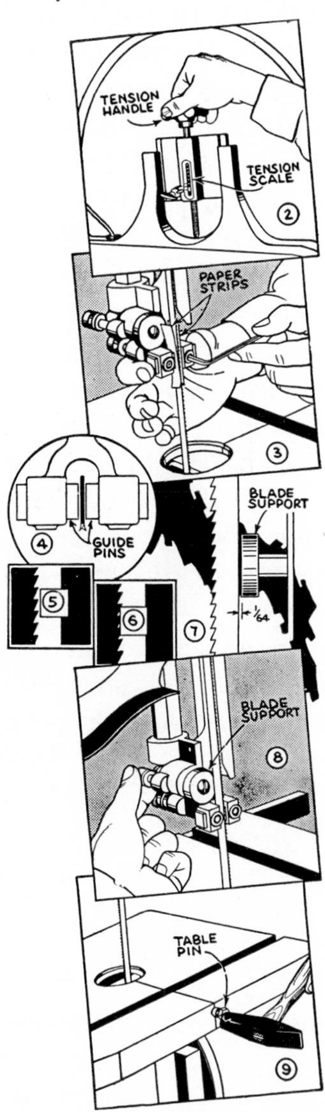

be tightened to a greater degree than narrow ones. If the saw is equipped with a tension gauge, the operator should always set the tension by means of the gauge. It should be pointed out that the spring tensioner registers strain—it has nothing to do with the length of the blade and is just as accurate with rebrazed as with new blades.

With the blade tracking correctly and properly tensioned, the guides can be set. The square guide pins on each side of the blade must be close enough to the blade to prevent it from twisting, yet they should not come in actual contact with the blade. A very accurate method of obtaining the correct clearance is to place strips of paper on either side of the blade while the pins are pressed inward between the thumb and first finger. In doing this it is important that the blade should not be pushed out of a true vertical position. The bracket carrying the guide pins is now brought forward until the front edges of the guide pins are just behind the gullets of the saw-blade teeth. If the pins are too far forward, the teeth of the blade will be worn against the pins; if the pins are too far back, they will not properly support the blade.

The blade support is now brought forward; it should not contact the blade but should be set about 1/64 inch from the back of the blade. The back of the blade rides against this support only when it is actually cutting. If the blade is allowed to run hard against the supports at all times, the back will become casehardened, and this will eventually lead to breakage of the saw blade.

The guide adjustments, as described, are the same for both upper and lower guides. Summarized, the various steps are as follows:

1. Open up guide pins on both upper and lower guides.
2. Run blade support back.
3. Center blade on wheels by tilting upper wheel as required.
4. Set blade to correct tension.
5. Revolve band saw to check blade tracking.
6. Set guide pins inward to thickness of blade, with correct clearance.
7. See that pins do not push blade sideways.
8. Lock guide pins.
9. Set guide-pin bracket so that pins come to bottom of blade teeth.
10. Set blade supports with 1/64-inch clearance.
11. Check settings by revolving saw by hand.

The final step is to replace the table insert, alignment pin, and pulley guards, after which the saw is ready for operation. The alignment pin should be gently tapped into place with a hammer; this should be done cautiously—too vigorous an action could easily crack the table.

The table must be at right angles to the blade when it is in a normal level position. Check should be made with an accurate

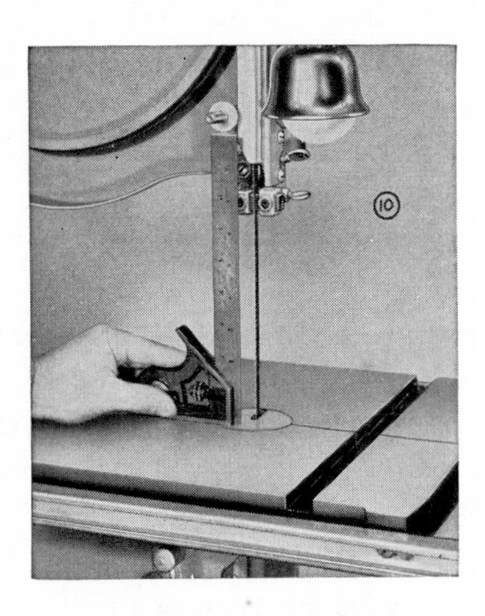

square, as shown in the illustration. Adjustments are made by means of the stop screw under the table, turning this up or down until the table, when it rests against the stop screw, is at right angles to the blade. Recheck by sawing a piece of wood and checking the cut with a square. After the table has been checked level, the pointer on the graduated scale should be set at zero so that it will accurately indicate every degree of tilt.

Smooth band-saw operation is largely dependent on proper adjustment of the guides. The two most common faults in improper adjustment are first, excessive tilt to the upper pulley, and second, improperly aligned upper and lower guides. Excessive tilt is unlikely to occur if the operator first tracks the blade and then sets the blade support. The second fault can be avoided by carefully setting the upper and lower guides so that the blade continues to run in a vertical plane between the two guides.

Band-saw Blades

Common sizes usually supplied include blades from ⅛ to ¾ inch wide, all of which are known collectively as narrow band saws. The thickness of the blade varies somewhat, depending on the quality of steel used, but generally averages about 0.001 inch thick for each inch of diameter of the wheels on which it is run. Thus a 14-inch band saw would take blades 0.014 inch thick. Both thicker and thinner blades, however, can be used successfully. The set of the narrow blade averages about 0.005 inch on a side for ¼-inch blades, this being increased 0.001 inch for each size larger, to give a ¾-inch blade a set of about 0.010 inch. Narrow band saws will run four to seven teeth per inch. A four-tooth saw will give a fairly smooth cut and still have the advantage of fast cutting. Where a smoother cut is desired, a six- or seven-tooth saw will do better work with a slight loss in cutting speed.

Band-saw blades when not in use should be wiped with an oily rag and stored in a dry place. The blade should be wiped free of this oil when the saw is again used. Band-saw blades may be folded and hung on wood pegs for storage. Blades should always be tied with soft metal straps or wire at two points to prevent accidental unfolding.

Band-saw blades are folded in thirds. This is done by grasping the blade at opposite sides and revolving the right hand away from the body while the left hand moves towards the body. The grip on the blade should be maintained. If this is done, the blade will automatically form itself into three loops.

Filing Band-saw Blades

The user of narrow band-saw blades should know something of the filing and setting of the teeth of his blades in order to get the most out of them. Nothing will break a blade more quickly than forcing it to do work after it has become dull. Touching up a blade to keep it sharp is simple and demands no more equipment than a vise and a saw file of the proper size. Slightly more patience is required than for filing a handsaw.

A good-enough emergency vise for the occasional user is made by clamping two boards about 10 inches long in a woodworker's vise, the boards being held high enough to bring the saw to a comfortable height for filing. The boards may be hinged together if desired. The saw is gripped between the upper edges of the boards with the teeth projecting above the upper surface. For those who expect to do a considerable amount of sharpening of their own blades, better types of saw vises are available at the larger hardware dealers.

When touching up a saw, the teeth should be filed straight across and must not be beveled as with a crosscut handsaw. The best guide to follow in checking the shape of the teeth is a new saw blade. The band saw should never be allowed to get into such poor condition that the shape of the teeth is not readily distinguishable. A good shape of tooth for all-round work should provide an angle of 60 degrees between the face of one tooth and the back of the next. The gullets should be round, and the hook, or rake angle, of the tooth should be from 8 to 15 degrees. In filing, an even number of strokes should be made across each of the teeth, in order to keep the saw of equal width throughout its length.

A very important point to observe is that the bottom of the gullet, or valley between the teeth, should always be rounded. This is done automatically on narrower saws by the rounded edge of the file. For widely spaced teeth the gullet should always be carefully rounded out with a rattail file, all sharp corners left by the triangular file being taken out.

Occasional touching up can be done while the blade is mounted in the machine. Best results can be obtained if the blade is turned inside out and remounted so that the teeth point up instead of down. Be sure to reverse the blade again before attempting to cut.

Cracks will sometimes develop at the bottom of a gullet, especially if the gullet has not been properly rounded. The remedy for this is to drill a fine hole at the bottom of the crack, *provided that the crack does not extend across more than one-sixth the width of the blade.* If it is longer than this, it is better to have the saw rebrazed. On very narrow band saws the blade should be broken and rebrazed.

The teeth of the saw blade may be touched up several times before it is necessary to reset them, but eventually setting will become necessary. Setting consists of bending the points of alternate teeth to right and left, so that the teeth will cut a kerf wider than the body of the blade and so provide clearance for it. A number of different machines are made for setting band-saw blades. The occasional home workshop user can also set his blades with an ordinary hand set such as is used for cutting handsaws. The job will consume more time than setting a handsaw.

When setting, do not set the point more than halfway down the tooth; avoid setting so deeply that the body of the tooth is distorted.

The teeth of the band-saw blade should be filed *after* setting. If the teeth are filed square across first and then set, the resulting face of the tooth will be at an angle from the back of the blade. It is obvious that these teeth will scrape instead of cutting cleanly, and, while the saw will operate, it will tend to vibrate in the cut. If the teeth are filed after setting, the front of the tooth will be at right angles to the blade, and the teeth will cut clean and smooth.

Brazing

When the narrow band-saw blade breaks, regardless of the cause, it can be joined together again either by brazing or by silver-soldering. Blades as they come from the manufacturer are often electrically welded, but the repairman is not usually equipped for welding and so either brazes or silver-solders the joint. The occasional saw user should either return his broken blade to the manufacturer for repair or take it to a local saw filer, since it is not worth while for him either to invest in the equipment necessary for brazing or to run the risk of ruining the blade.

Operation

If the operator is right-handed, he will naturally take a position directly behind and slightly to the left side of the band-saw table. He will use his right hand to feed the work to the saw blade, while his left hand will be placed alongside the work to act as a guide. This position is not an absolute "must" but can be varied to suit the work and the operator's natural style. The left hand alongside the work more or less guides the work by means of side pressure. Side pressure against the blade should always be gentle. The feed hand should not jam the work forcibly against the blade but should feed lightly, letting the cutting of the blade itself regulate the feed. The pressure of a single finger on the end of the work will cause the blade to cut; when more pressure than this is required, it is a sign that the blade is dull. The feed hand should not choke the work but should be held at a reasonable distance from the blade. This distance gives better control of the cut and will result in smoother operation than when the work is held close up and fed in a cramped manner. The operator's eyes should be fixed on the line a little ahead of the saw blade.

In cutting, the upper guide should be lowered to a position close to the upper surface of the work being cut. Clearance should be left, so that the operator can clearly see the blade going into the work. The distance of this guide above the work should be roughly 1 inch. If the upper guide is left too high, it will not support the blade but will allow it to twist as the work is turned for a curved cut.

Certain fundamentals of cutting must be thoroughly learned by the operator. The application of these elementary principles should be almost second nature—as much as part of the operator's mental processes as the fact that he should not stick his finger into the moving blade.

If a piece of wood is pushed squarely into the saw blade, it should, under normal conditions, be cut in a straight line at right angles to the blade. Often, however, the blade will pull to one side or the other (commonly known as lead) making it necessary for the operator to adjust the feed accordingly. If the blade leads to the right, it becomes necessary for the operator to move the feed hand to the right in order to follow a straight line. Lead is caused mainly by two things, improper setting of the guides or improper set of the saw blade. If a check does not reveal the first fault, the difficulty can reasonably be laid to the second. Sawing along the side of a nail, riding one side of the blade deep and tight in the guides, or poor filing will result in a saw blade which is dull and poorly set on one side while the opposite side is sharp and fully set. In cutting with such a blade, the sharp side does not cut in a straight line but leads off to one side. Where the lead is slight, it can be remedied by lightly honing the side of the blade with a fine stone. Honing, in this case, is done only on the sharp side of the blade (the side that leads away from the line). The result is to make the set of the teeth equal on both sides of the blade. It can be seen that if the lead is excessive it cannot be remedied by honing, since this simply makes the sharp side as dull as the other. Where the lead is excessive, the blade must be completely reset and sharpened before it will cut properly.

Procedures

Watch the feed direction. Mentally follow the path of the cut before actually cutting the work. Many pieces of work will swing in such a fashion as to bind against the upper arm of the band saw if they are not started properly. When this happens it is often necessary to retrack the blade long distances out of an intricate cut before the work can be finished.

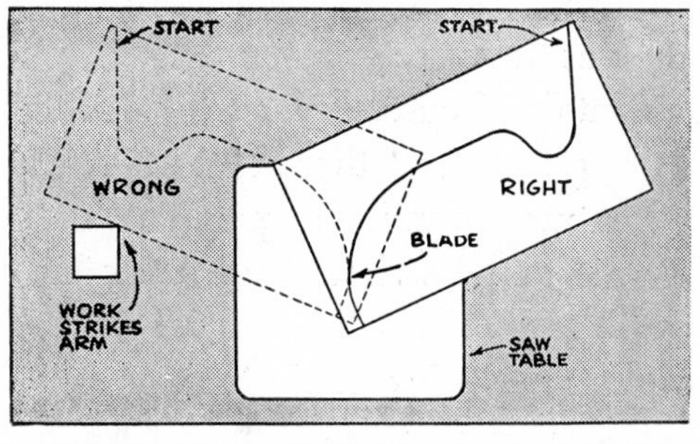

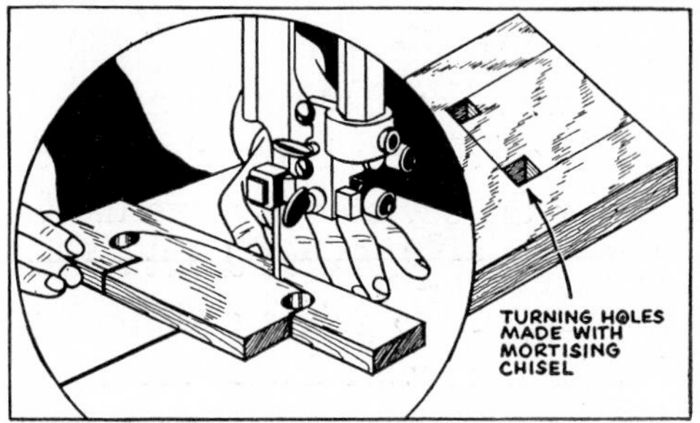

Make use of turning holes. Time can be saved if round turning holes are drilled or square turning holes are mortised into the work before the band-sawing operation is begun. Use this method for short curves with a wide blade.

Always make short cuts first. Where a choice of starting points is offered, always make the shortest cut first. Backing out of a short cut can be done much more quickly and easily than backing out of a long cut.

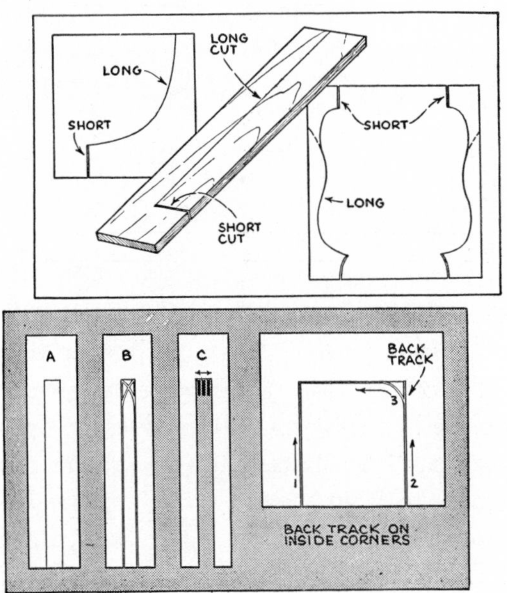

Backtrack on inside corners. Very narrow grooves must be "nibbled" out, as shown at *A, B,* and *C,* in the illustration. On other inside corners, cut to the corner and then backtrack sufficiently to lead the blade over to the second line.

Break up combination cuts. Combination cuts should be broken into a number of smaller cuts. The illustration shows a typical example. Study each piece of work before proceeding, to determine the simplest method of cutting.

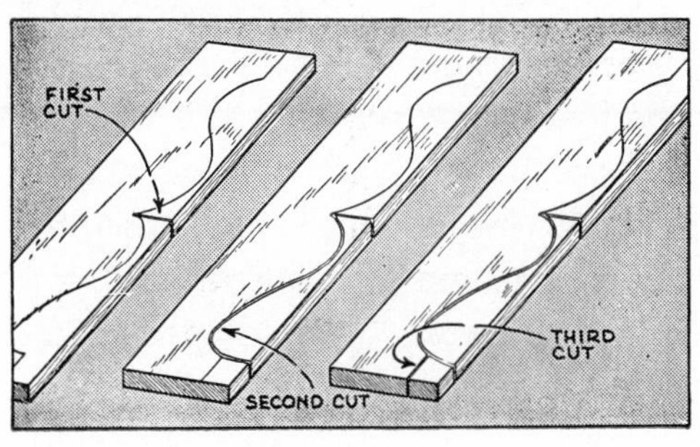

Rough out complex cuts. Where cuts are of a complex nature, start at one end and follow as much of the line as possible on the first cut, then go back over the work and complete the smaller cuts.

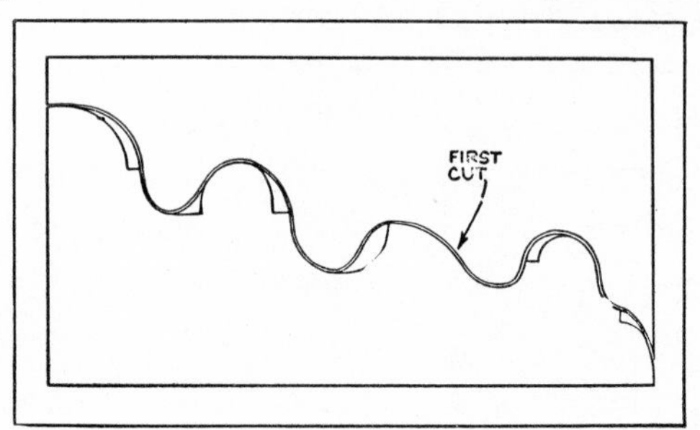

Ripping and Resawing

Ripping and resawing require straight-line cutting. When the stock is worked flat on the table, the work is designated by the term "ripping." When the board is worked on edge, the operation is generally known as "resawing." Cuts of this nature are best made with some form of guide to keep the work in its proper relation to the saw. One of the simplest guides is the pivot block, a narrow block of wood clamped to the saw table and set directly opposite the blade and at the proper distance from it to cut the thickness required. A pencil mark on the work is generally used as an aid in cutting but is not essential. The work is held tight against the pivot block with the left hand, while the right hand feeds the work into the blade. This type of guide is particularly useful when working with a blade which leads slightly, since the work can be shifted as required to follow a straight line.

When the work is to be ripped flat, the same idea of a pivot block can be applied by holding one hand firmly on the table so that the side of the thumb or hand acts as a pivot. The thickness of the cut is controlled by the fixed pivot point (in this case the hand), while a straight line is followed by guiding the work with the feed hand.

A simple form of guide fence, which can be used for either ripping or resawing, is made by clamping a length of straight stock to the table, with a hold-down spring also clamped to the table on the opposite side of the blade. A hold-down spring can be made from wood by making a number of saw kerfs in a piece of hardwood. This is clamped to the table so that it will press the work against the fence.

A regular ripping fence, if the saw can be so equipped, is the logical accessory to use for all ripping and resawing operations. It possesses the obvious advantage of always being ready for use, while permitting accurate settings for ripping to any desired widths. This style of fence requires a blade in proper condition, since nothing can be done to compensate for lead after the cut has been started. In many cases when work is to be resawed, it may first be cut from both sides on the circular saw, after which the finish resawing cut is made on the band saw.

When resawing or ripping lumber, the widest blade available should always be used. It can easily be seen that the wide blade will more readily follow a straight line than a narrow blade. Where extensive resawing is being done, blades specially suited for this work should be used. Ripping blades should have coarse teeth, a generous amount of set, and a hook or rake angle of from 20 to 30 degrees. In ripping pine and other soft woods, a maximum amount of hook is required, while harder woods, such as oak and maple, require less hook.

When the fence is used for bevel cutting, it should be located on the lower side of the table, so that both the work and the fence are below the blade.

Both the fence and the miter gauge can be used for cutting work to exact length, as shown in illustration 1 on the next page.

The gauge presents the work squarely to the blade, while the fence acts as a stop. Unlike the same operation on the circular saw, there is no danger of a kickback caused by the work's binding between the blade and the fence.

Cutting work to length can be done with the use of the stop rod, as shown in illustration 2. The rod should be carried on the outer end of the miter gauge. When required, it can be carried on the side next to the blade, but care must be exercised to prevent the blade from cutting into the stop rod at the end of the cut.

When the saw is fitted with a fence but does not have a miter gauge, cutoff work can be done by using a backing block behind the work. This block should be perfectly square, so that with any side riding against the fence, the adjacent side will be at right angles to the blade. Similar blocks for cutting 45-degree miters and other angle cuts can be made up as required.

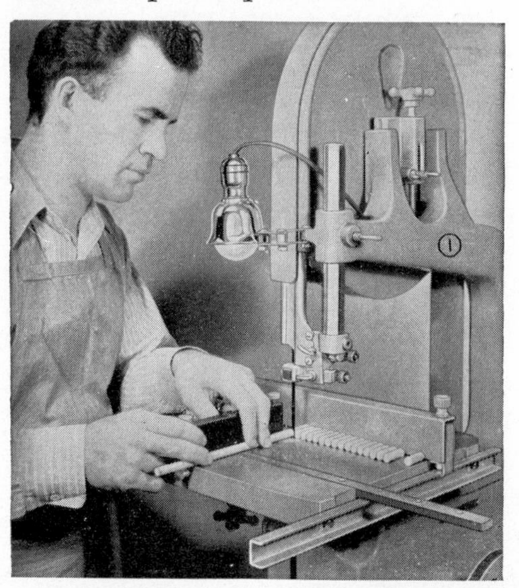

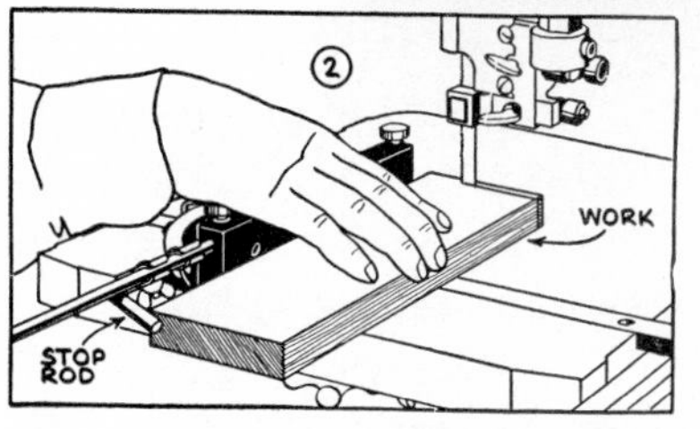

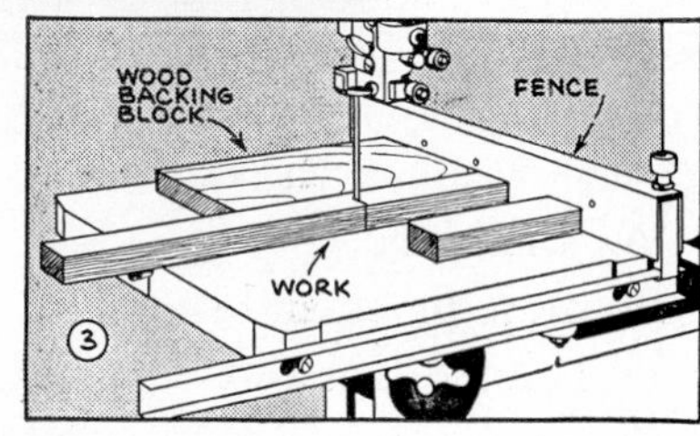

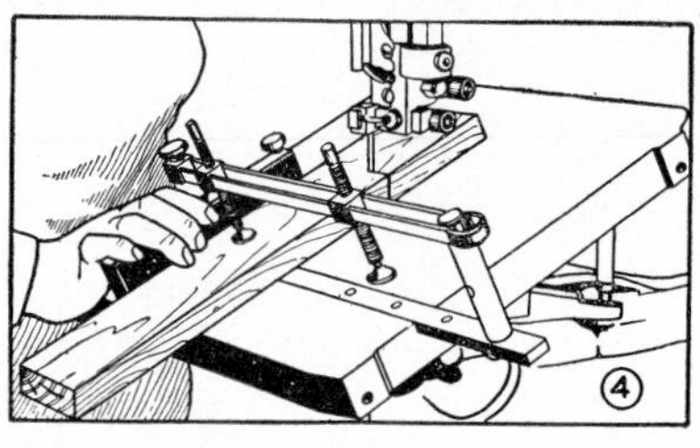

The miter-gauge clamp attachment can be used to advantage in many crosscutting operations and is particularly useful when cutting off with the table tilted. The use of the clamp attachment eliminates the possibility of creeping and greatly simplifies the job of holding short lengths of wood against the miter gauge. The clamp can also be used to advantage for all unusually shaped work which, under ordinary conditions, would be difficult to handle.

The use of the miter gauge in crosscutting wide stock follows the same method as used for similar work on the circular saw. When the work is too wide to be loaded in front of the miter gauge, the gauge is reversed and the work fed from the reverse side, holding it against the miter gauge as it is pushed into the saw blade. Work this large is usually handled on the circular saw, but where the shop is not fully equipped, the band saw is a satisfactory power tool for this and other straightline cutting. The use of an auxiliary wood fence screw-fastened to the miter gauge will make it easier to handle wide boards and will result in more accurate work. Unlike the auxiliary circular-saw fence, the wood fence for the band saw should be kept low (the same height as the gauge), so that it will work under the guides.

Circles can be cut freehand on the band saw in the same manner as any other curved line. More often, however, a pivot jig is used to obtain both speed and accuracy. All circle-cutting jigs for the band saw or the scroll saw feature a pivot point around which the work revolves as it is advanced to the blade. Some home craftsmen fail to realize the importance of the pivot-point position in relation to the blade. In order to get perfect circles, the pivot point must be at an exact right angle (90 degrees) with the blade and on a line with the cutting edge or teeth. A pivot point too far forward will cause the blade to track to the inside of the circle, while a pivot point behind the cutting edge of the blade will result in tracking to the outside.

Bearing this basic rule in mind, any number of jigs can be made to more or less conveniently carry the pivot point. In order for a jig to be practical, this pivot point should be adjustable, so that a wide variety of circle sizes can be cut.

Larger work follows the same basic rule, with the pivot point sometimes entirely apart from the band saw when very large circles are being cut.

An auxiliary wood table, fastened to the regular table, is the commonest of the circle-cutting jigs. A series of pivot holes can be drilled in the auxiliary wood table on a line with the cutting edge of the blade. A variation of the series of holes would be a sliding pivot bar with means for extending and clamping it in different locations at varying distances from the blade.

All the jigs described make a hole in the center of the work at the pivot point. If the pivot jig is an overhead type, this hole may be eliminated by temporarily gluing a small block of wood to the work to take the pivot point.

With the band-saw table tilted to 45 degrees, square stock can be ripped exactly on a diagonal to produce glue blocks or any other work requiring a similar triangular section. The standard rip fence is used with the table to form a V block to support the stock for this cutting operation.

Making Rounded Corners

In cabinetwork it is frequently necessary to run a facing strip around curved work. This can be done without steaming if the facing strip is first ripped to a thin section on the band saw and then applied to a suitable block. The illustration, showing a facing strip being

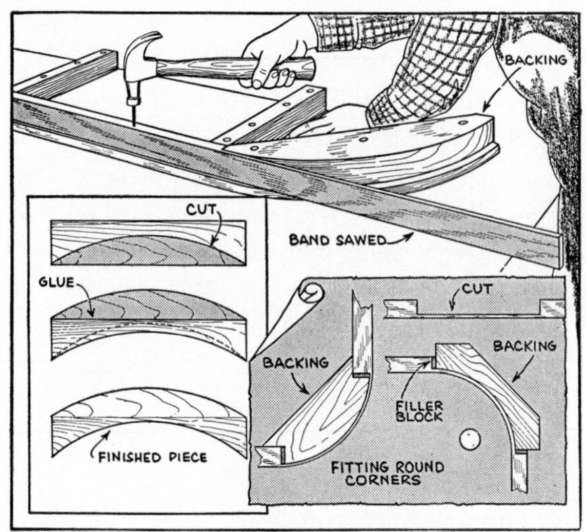

applied to the top part of a mantel, will make the idea clear. The application of a strip of this kind is practical for both inside and outside corners. The distance between the shoulders of the facing strip is made about ½ inch greater than the distance between the shoulders on the backing pieces, so that wedges can be driven between the ends to make a solid joint when glued. For average work, the thinned portion of the facing strip should be about ¼ inch thick; however, it can be made thinner if the curve of the work is of short radius or if the facing strip is wide.

The illustration also shows a stock-saving method of sawing a circular rail or arch. The required curve is cut through any part of original narrow board, the two pieces are glued edge to edge, and the inner radius is then marked off and cut.

For belt-sanding on the band saw, a belt guide is fitted to the guidepost. The belt is tracked on the wheels in the same manner as the band-saw blade. Tension should be just sufficient to prevent slipping. Such guides are available as accessories for some of the band saws on the market. Fast cutting without belt glazing can be done at the standard band-saw speed.

Compound Band-sawing

When work is sawed from two or more sides, the operation is known as compound band-sawing. Cuts of this nature are used in many kinds of work, one of the most common examples being the cabriole leg. The stock for the leg must first be jointed perfectly

square. If the original square of lumber is not true, the band-saw cuts made on the work will not be true. After the stock has been jointed, the leg pattern is laid out on two adjoining sides of the wood. A cardboard pattern is generally used to trace the outline.

The work can then be taken to the band saw, where the two cuts necessary to form one of the complete profile shapes are made.

After this has been done, the waste cuttings are tacked back in place, in order to give the work a base and to restore the pattern markings. The nails used to fasten the waste cuttings should be placed in such a position that they will not mar the leg.

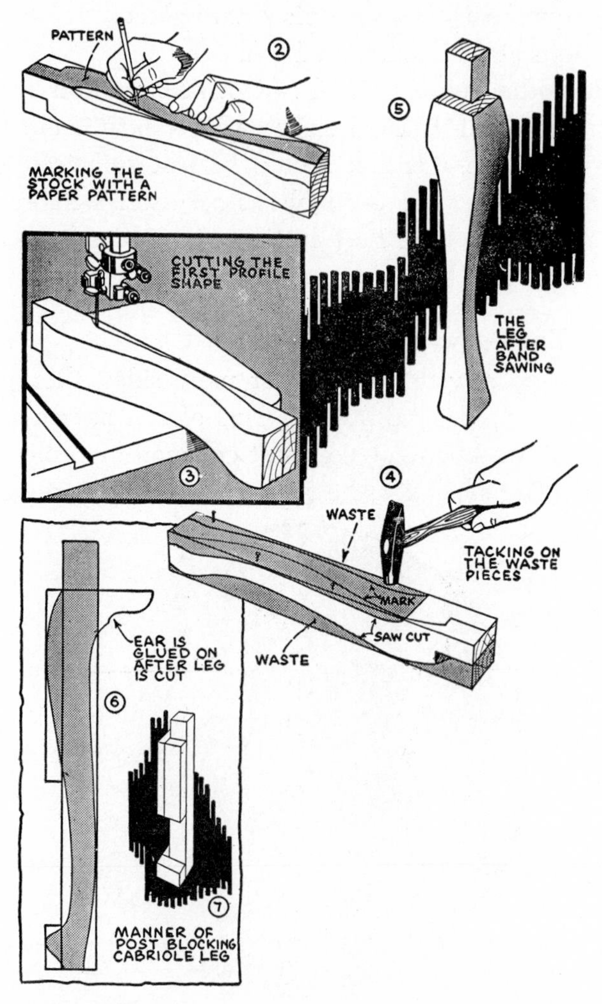

The second profile shape is then cut, after which the leg will appear in its final rough design. From this stage the leg is finished by modeling the front and rear corners. This can be done on the shaper, but the average home craftsman usually does the job with a spoke-shave or other hand tool.

Ears are sometimes added to each side of the leg. While these can be fitted in place and cut at the same time as the leg, the best practice is to cut the leg first and then fit the ears. The ear is first cut to the required profile shape, then glued in place and rounded to the same curve as the facing of the leg.

"Post blocking" is the term applied to the manner in which stock is built up for band-sawing cabriole legs. This method of working is frequently used, since it is often difficult or expensive to secure a piece of fine cabinet wood sufficiently large to take in the full shape of many styles of cabriole legs. Working in this manner, the necessary blocking is first glued in place, taking care that all joints are tight and clean. The pattern is then laid out on the two flat adjacent sides, and the cutting proceeds in the manner previously described. For quality work, the stock glued up for this work should be selected for a good match for both color and grain. If the job is done properly, the post-blocked cabriole leg has the appearance of being cut from a solid piece of stock. In fastening the leg to the framework for which it is intended, any common joint may be used. As in all other forms of cabinetwork, the mortise-and-tenon joint is the strongest; however, equally good results can be obtained with doweled or glued-and-screwed butt joints.

Compound-band-sawed Turnings

Another good use for compound band-sawing is in the preparation of stock for turning. This applies especially to the turning of balls and similar work which must be brought to an exact spherical shape. To start the operation, the required shape is laid out on two adjacent sides of the stock. The stock must be previously prepared by jointing the opposite two sides perfectly square; also, the sides upon which the markings are made must be square and smooth enough to properly take the pencil marks.

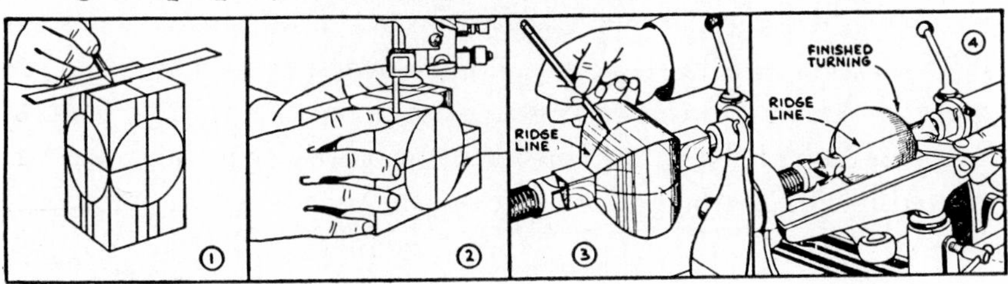

Care must be exercised in laying out the work so that all center lines will match. Sufficient stock must be left at each end of the ball shape to permit mounting in the lathe. Compound sawing is done on the band saw in the same manner as described for the cabriole leg. After being sawed, the work is mounted in the lathe, and the center or ridge lines of the intended ball are marked with pencil. These marks need not be centered but are simply broad pencil marks blackened in on each of the four sides of the work. Turning is then carried on as usual, stopping the work frequently for examination. It is necessary only to watch the ridge lines. When the turning has progressed to the point where the ridge lines are almost removed, the turning will be practically complete, and the ball shape will be just as perfect as the original band-sawed shape. Final trimming of the ball is done in a cup chuck in the manner usually employed for such work. Additional information on lathe work will be found in the chapter covering lathe operations.

A wide variety of compound-sawed ornaments can be made for finials, using the same methods as described for the cabriole leg and ball turning. Thin cardboard patterns are always used to lay out the stock. These ornaments may be lightly sanded and left square, or they may be mounted and turned in the lathe. Sometimes a combination of square-cut and turned work is used on a simple ornament.

Multiple Sawing

As a means of accuracy in cutting duplicate parts for production work, wood parts are frequently sawed in multiple. In general, the method consists of making a pad of the work by stacking layers of lumber on top of one another. Eight or ten designs in ¼-inch plywood can thus be cut in one operation.

Various methods are used to hold the pad securely in place while the cutting is being done. One of the best methods for production work is the box jig. The top and bottom of this jig consist of a previously cut pattern, to which are added two sides and an end. The work is loaded into the box jig, and the band-saw work is done by using the top of the jig as a pattern. Various other methods are employed, including the use of a previously cut wood template which is loaded on top of the work, or the pattern may simply be drawn on the top board of the pad.

For occasional production work the pad may be assembled by nailing, in which case the nails are driven into the waste portions of the design. Another method makes use of a "spring block," the opening in the block being cut to such a size that it can be sprung over the work to hold the mutliple pieces securely. Another method employs the use of straight saw kerfs into which wedges are driven to hold the work securely while the band-saw design is cut. This method is useful when the design has considerable waste in which the wedges can be set.

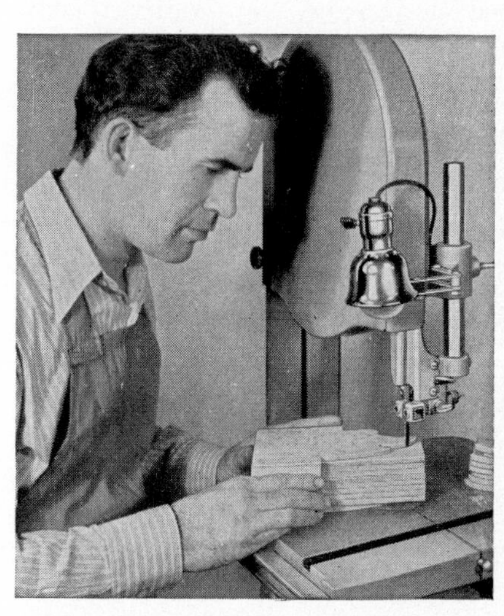

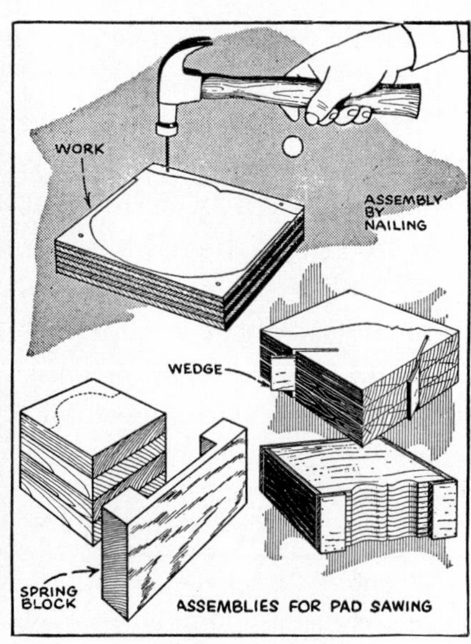

ASSEMBLIES FOR PAD SAWING

A production method closely related to the pad system is to cut the outline of the pattern from a single thickness of heavy stock and then rip the block to form a series of individual pieces of a given thickness. This is just the reverse of pad sawing, the block being first cut to shape and then ripped to thickness, producing a number of thinner duplicate parts. Light sanding is then required in order to bring the band-sawed faces to a smooth surface. The fence may be used for ripping the material to thickness.

Taper ripping can be done on the band saw with the use of jigs similar to those used for the same purpose on the circular saw. Jigs for individual jobs should be laid out full size on paper and then cut from wood. In use, the work is placed against the shoulder of the jig, and the jig is then pushed along the fence. An adjustable jig for cutting any degree of taper can be made by splitting the body of the jig and then hinging one end. The jig can then be spread to the desired angle and locked in this position with a slotted bracket and thumbscrew.

In cutting legs and similar work, where taper is required on all four sides, the jig is first set for the required taper as before. Two adjacent sides of the leg are then tapered. The jig is then opened to twice the required taper to compensate for the two sides already tapered, these sides are placed against the jig, and the remaining two sides are cut.

Turning squares can be conveniently marked on the band saw with the use of a suitable V block. A saw cut is run part way through the center of the V, and the fence is adjusted, allowing the band-saw blade to operate through the opening. Work to be center-marked is placed on the V block and advanced to the blade, making two diagonal cuts, about ⅛ inch deep, diagonally across the ends of the stock and intersecting each corner. The intersecting cuts in the center of the stock mark the center line of the square and also provide accurate locating marks for the spurs of the live center in the headstock of your lathe.

There are many additional forms of jigs and fixtures which can be constructed for miscellaneous band-saw operations. These include jigs for beveling, for cutting circular arcs, for rounding corners, spiral-cutting dowels, etc. Some of these jigs are designed for individual jobs, while others can be applied with variations to many band-saw operations.

Roller Supports

Roller supports, commonly used in circular-saw and jointer work, are frequently used in the handling of long work on the band saw. Adjustments should be provided so that the roller can be extended to a height of 42 or 44 inches, corresponding to the height of the saw table. This is about the highest working table in the shop. A full range of adjustments, down to the low table of the shaper, should be provided for if the roller support is to be used for all machines. A support of this kind is almost a necessity for handling long work in a one-man shop.

Metal Cutting on the Band Saw

Blades for metal cutting have finer teeth than blades for wood cutting. A good selection of metal-cutting blades for the home workshop would be saws with fourteen, eighteen, and twenty-four teeth to the inch. The coarser toothed blades are excellent for the softer metals such as copper, brass, aluminum, etc., while the twenty-four-tooth blade is better for cutting thin sheet stock in any metal. Most metal blades are hardened and tempered, making it impossible to resharpen them with any equipment within the reach of the small shop. The life of such blades, however, is quite long, and they may therefore be discarded after use.

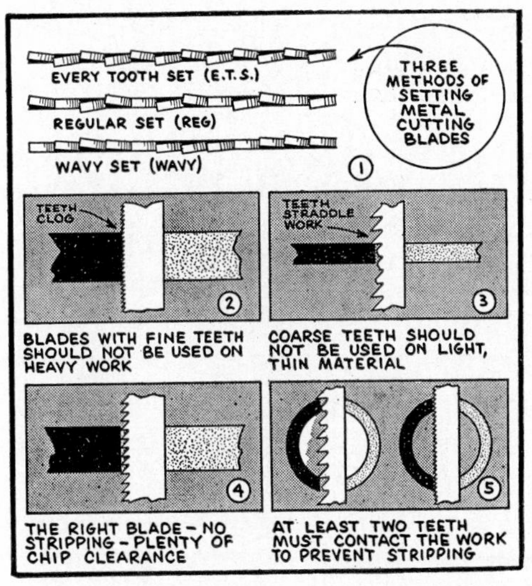

Three different types of set, as shown in the illustration, are commonly used for metal-cutting blades. Blades with every tooth set, alternating left and right, are similar to woodcutting blades. This style of set is used for cutting all the softer metals. Regular-set blades have one unset raker tooth to each pair of set teeth, the purpose of the raker tooth being to keep the cut clean. This type of blade is used for cutting cast iron, cold rolled steel, Monel metal, etc. The wavy-set blade has the teeth set in groups, one set of teeth forming a wave to the right, while the next set forms a wave to the left. This type of blade is extensively used for cutting thin metals, such as pipe, metal tubing, radiator cores, etc. For average work, regular-set blades are recommended. A blade intended for cutting soft metals cannot be used for cutting high-speed steel, although the blade intended for cutting high-speed steel will do very good work in soft metals.

The most important point in blade selection is the number of teeth per inch. A fine-tooth blade will clog and refuse to cut heavy materials. A coarse-tooth blade will straddle thin material, with the result that the teeth will be broken out and the blade ruined in a short time. The blade should have from eight to ten teeth in contact with the work if possible. The coarser the teeth, the faster the cut can be made; however, at least two teeth must contact the work in order to prevent stripping.

Cutting Speeds

While the woodcutting band-saw blade can turn at a speed up to 2,200 feet per minute, the metal blade on the same machine should not be operated at speeds in excess of 330 feet per minute. Operated at high speed, the teeth of the metal-cutting blade are simply burned away through friction with the metal. The necessary slow speed for metal cutting can be obtained by either of two standard methods of speed reduction—back gearing and countershaft. Countershaft units are available and can be fitted to almost any standard band saw. They are arranged so as to retain the required high speed for woodcutting while offering the necessary slow speed of approximately 90 rpm for metal cutting. The back-geared band saw is especially designed for cutting metals and has built-in gearing which permits a range of four slow speeds—125, 175, 250, and 340 feet per minute, while a simple change of belts gives a 2,200-foot-per-minute speed for wood.

Cutting Thin Metal

Despite the use of a fine-tooth blade, thin metals will invariably burr on the underside of the cut, as shown in illustration 1. This is

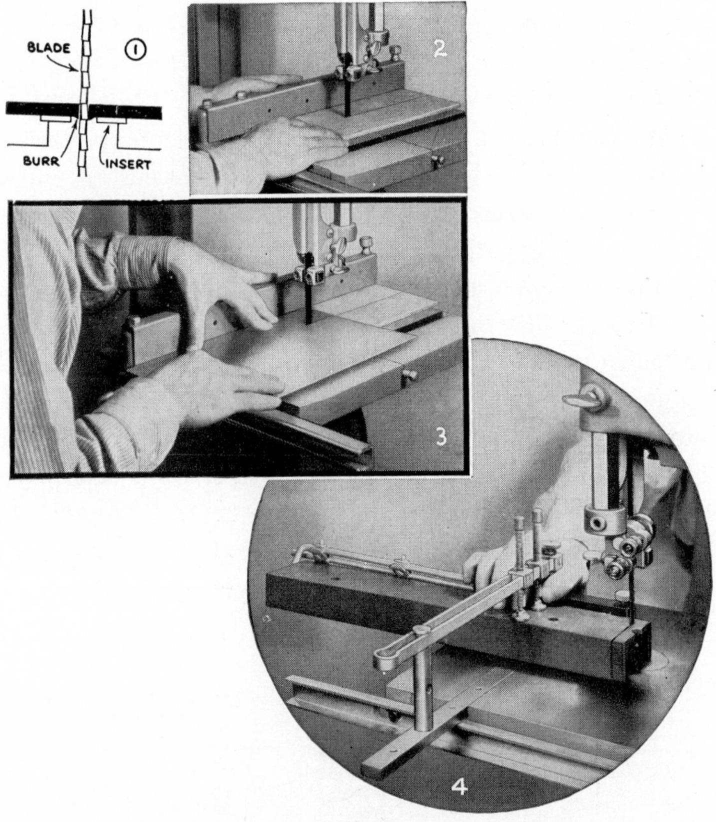

especially noticeable when the softer metals are being cut and is caused by the light body of metal being improperly supported at the cutting point. This burring can be avoided and clean cuts made by the use of an auxiliary wood table, through which a saw cut is run. When the metal is cut on this table, it is fully supported at the point of cutting, and the underside of the work shows a clean edge.

The principle is very much the same as that used in backing up holes in drilling on the drill press. Other methods are employed to obtain the same effect. The sheet of metal can be glued to a wood base or sandwiched between two boards to obtain the necessary support. These methods of backing are impossible when thin-wall tubing is being cut, and it then becomes necessary to plug the tubing with a dowel rod if clean cutting is required. It is sometimes simpler, however, to let the work burr and then clean out the opening with a reamer.

Clamping Methods

Clamping is used extensively in metal-cutting operations. This clamping is sometimes absolutely necessary, as in cutting tubing or pipe, while in other cases clamping is employed only to simplify the work. By comparison with woodcutting operations on the band saw, metal cutting is comparatively slow work, and very often a simple clamping device will eliminate the strain of holding the work for freehand cutting. As in cutting wood, good use can be made of both the ripping fence and the miter gauge, together with the stop rod and miter-gauge clamping attachment. Where an irregular-shaped piece of work must be cut to exact size, this setup is indispensable. The stop rod sets the length, while the use of the clamping attachment relieves all strain on the operator while the cut is being made.

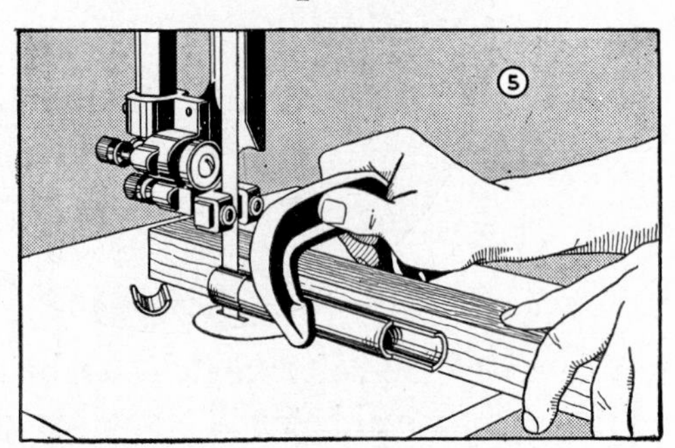

A simple clamping arrangement for sawing a length of pipe can be devised by clamping the pipe to the side of a wood block with an ordinary C clamp. This method not only makes the work easier to handle but also ensures an exact vertical cut.

Round material, both solid and tubular, including plastics, pipe, thin tubing, etc., should always be clamped securely for sawing. This applies especially to tubing, which is almost impossible to hold freehand against the constant drag of the saw. A simple V block, in some form or other, is the most commonly used clamping device. A double V block in wood, with bolts through each end to apply clamping pressure, is often used to hold rod stock in place for sawing operations. Most of these methods are not production-shop setups but simply makeshift setups used in occasional home workshop work.

Metal Sawing in Multiple

Metal pieces can be sawed in multiple by using the same general methods as previously described for woodcutting. In some special cases where these methods are not practical, the various blank pieces can be soldered together either by tacking or by sweating. The assembled pad can then be sawed, drilled, filed, etc., as one unit, after which the pieces can be separated by the application of heat. This method is especially useful for precision work, where a number of exact duplicates must be made.

Band-saw Projects

Many woodworking and metalworking projects can be constructed entirely, or almost entirely, with the use of the band saw alone. One such project is the folding lawn chair shown. In the con-

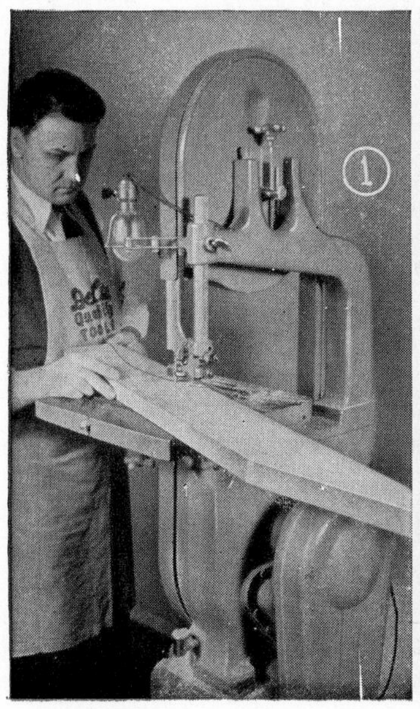

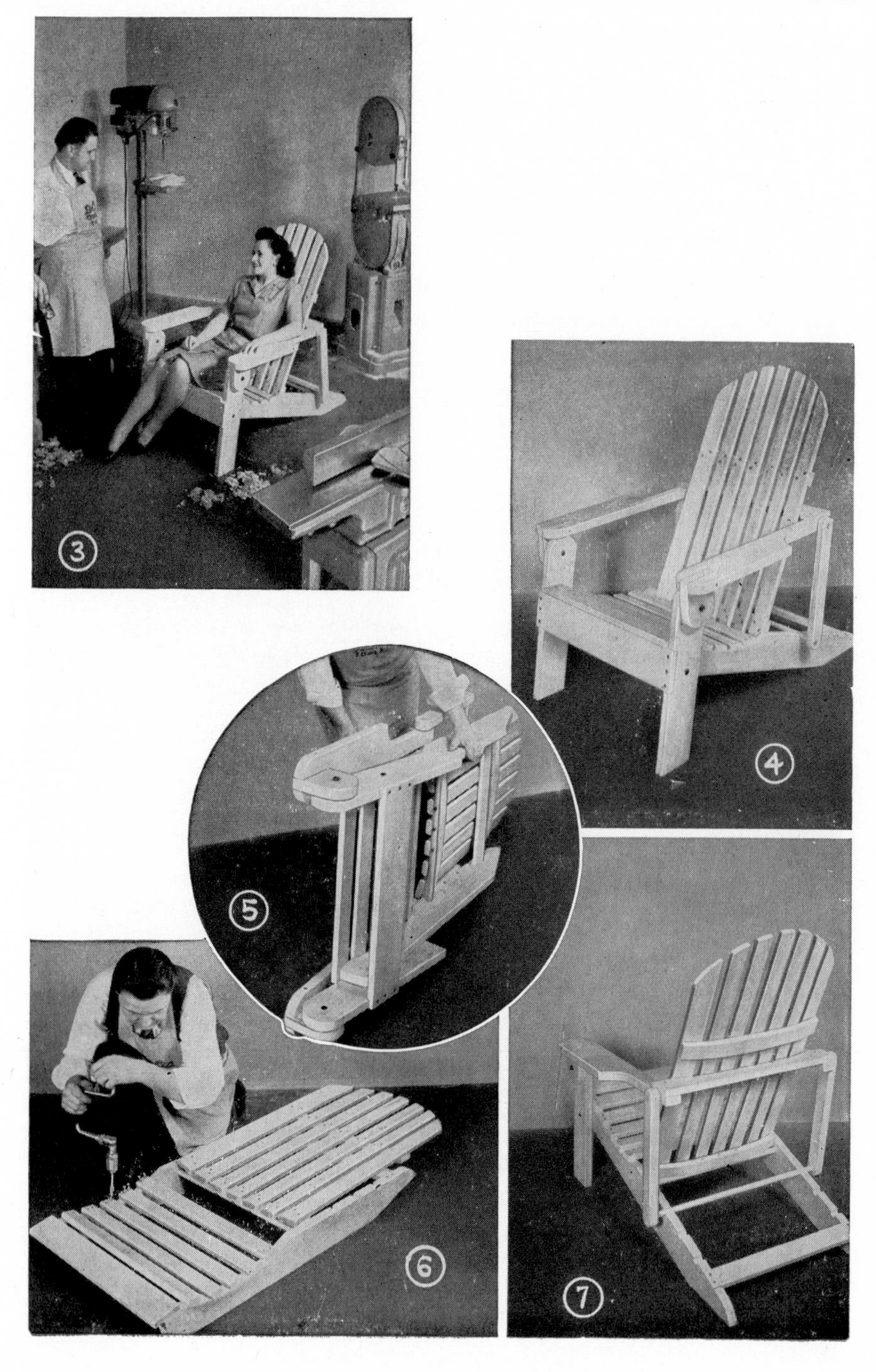
3
4
5
6
7

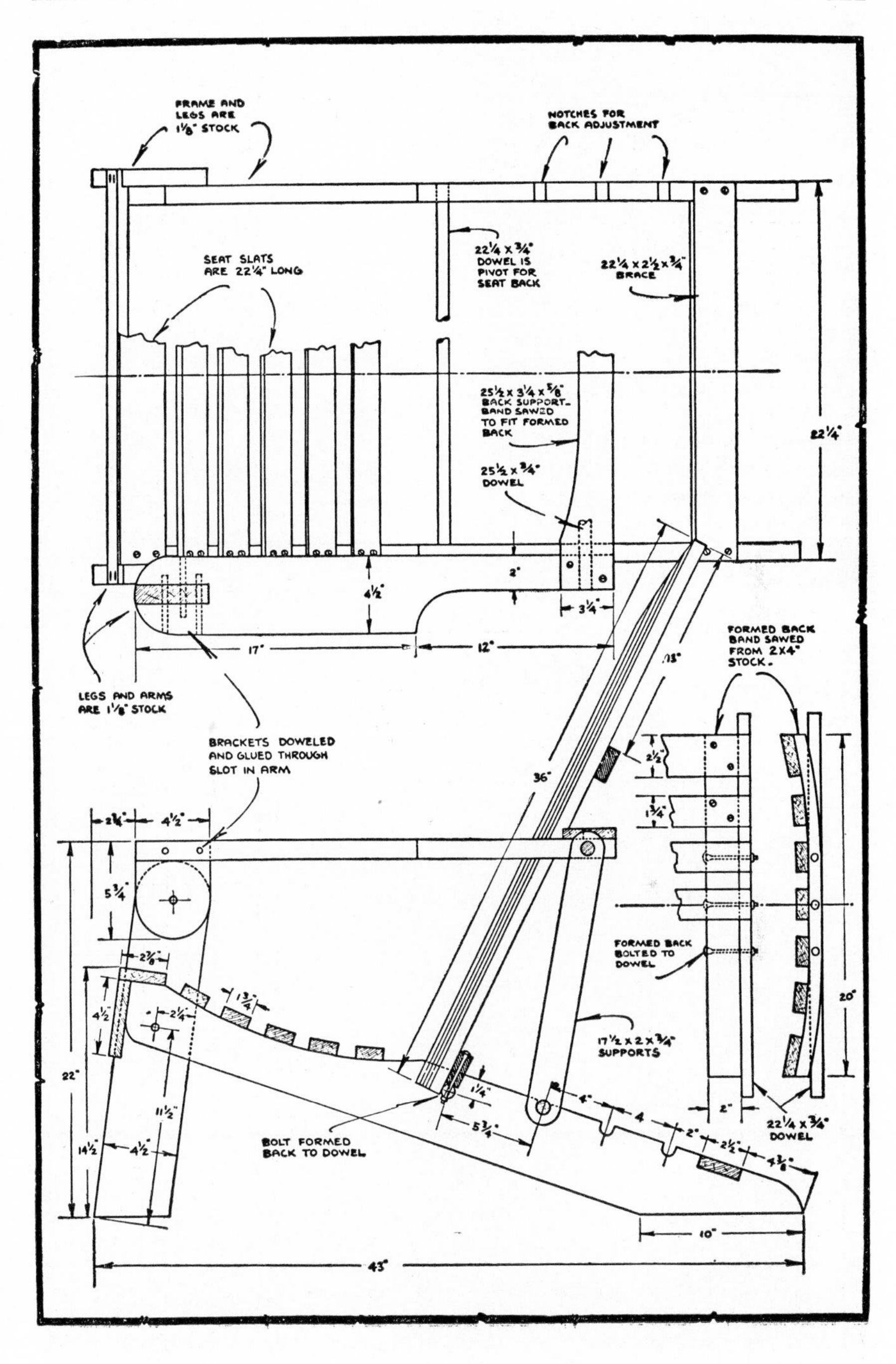
FRAME AND LEGS ARE 1⅛" STOCK
NOTCHES FOR BACK ADJUSTMENT
22¼ x ¾" DOWEL IS PIVOT FOR SEAT BACK
22¼ x 2½ x ¾" BRACE
SEAT SLATS ARE 22¼" LONG
25½ x 3¼ x ⅝" BACK SUPPORT-BAND SAWED TO FIT FORMED BACK
25½ x ¾" DOWEL
22¼"
2"
4½"
3¼"
17"
12"
13"
LEGS AND ARMS ARE 1⅛" STOCK
BRACKETS DOWELED AND GLUED THROUGH SLOT IN ARM
FORMED BACK BAND SAWED FROM 2X4" STOCK.
36"
2½"
1¾"
2¾"
4½"
5¾"
2⅞"
1¾"
2¼"
4½"
22"
11½"
14½"
FORMED BACK BOLTED TO DOWEL
17½ x 2 x ¾" SUPPORTS
20"
1¼"
5¾"
4"
2"
2½"
4⅜"
BOLT FORMED BACK TO DOWEL
22¼ x ¾" DOWEL
10"
43"

struction of the lawn chair, duplicate parts, such as the arm rests, leg frames, supports, etc., may be band-sawed in pairs by temporarily nailing the stock together. The pattern is then laid out on the top piece and the band-saw operations accomplished as described in the section on multiple sawing. Lumber for such projects as lawn equipment should be constructed from stock which will

GUN RACK

☆ **This simple rack for your guns is made from 3/4" pine lumber. The notches which are cut in the side rails for the stock and barrels of the guns must be fitted to the individual guns which you wish to hang. The squared drawing below shows suggested arrangement for the guns shown in the photograph. Finish is oiled, followed by shellac and varnish.**

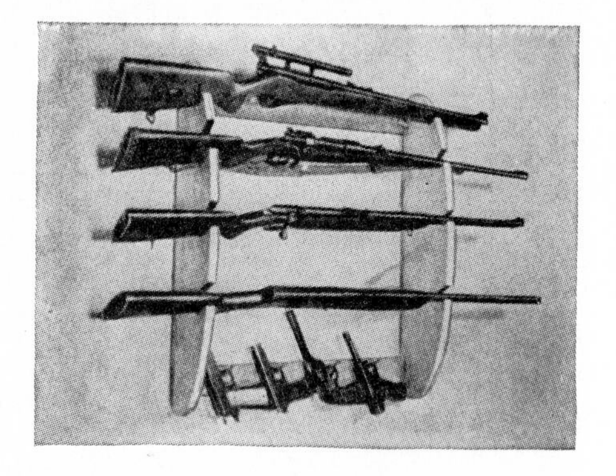

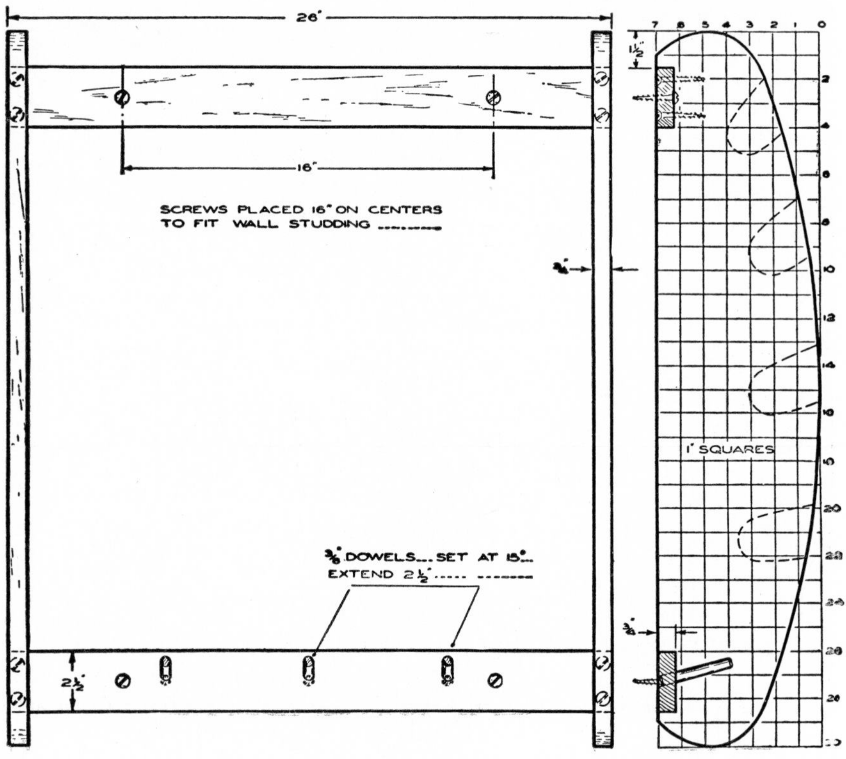

withstand the rigors of outdoor weather conditions, and the pieces must be finished accordingly. Outdoor furniture, as a general rule, should be treated with several coats of boiled oil before outside paint is applied. It is also advisable to use brass screws and similar hardware which will not rust and deteriorate with moisture. The necessary dimensions, and all construction details for the folding lawn chair, are shown in the drawing on page 121.

Additional woodworking projects which can be completed with the band saw include the gun rack shown in the illustration at the bottom of the page opposite.

Chapter 5. SCROLL SAW

Description

The scroll saw is a mechanical device centering around a crankshaft, which converts the circular motion of the pulley or motor into an up-and-down motion. This mechanical part of the scroll saw must be precision-balanced if the power tool is to run at high speed without excessive vibration. Aside from the driving mechanism, the scroll saw consists simply of a blade attached to the vertically moving plunger and a table fitted around the blade, upon which the work can be supported.

The size of the scroll saw, according to which it is named, is generally expressed in terms of the throat opening, that is, the distance between the blade and the support for the upper arm. For example, 24-inch scroll saws measure 24 inches from the blade to the front edge of the upper supporting arm. A machine with a 24-inch throat capacity will cut to the center of a 48-inch circle; although provisions are made on some scroll saws for extension arms which permit the handling of much larger work. Another important measurement in scroll-saw specifications is the cutting capacity in thickness. The thickness of the stock which can be cut on the scroll saw generally averages about 2 inches, which is as heavy as the mechanical structure of the saw can cut successfully.

Very little power is required to operate the scroll saw. A good ¼-horsepower motor is ample for the average cutting, while ⅓ horsepower will give plenty of power for heavy continuous duty. The motor should be the constant-speed type, 1,725 rpm. Properly coupled with cone pulleys, the saw will have four speeds of approximately 650, 1,000, 1,300, and 1,725 rpm.

The scroll-saw guide serves the dual purpose of guiding and supporting the blade during the cutting operation. Since a wide variety of blades and attachments are used on the machine, the guide is generally of the universal type, which permits a wide range of adjustments to accommodate various blade sizes. The scroll-saw guide offers both side adjustment and back support for the blade.

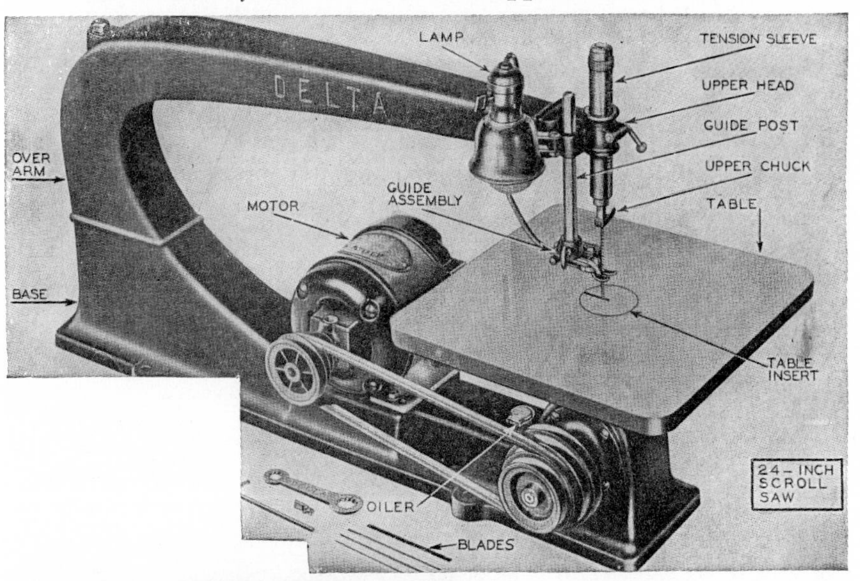

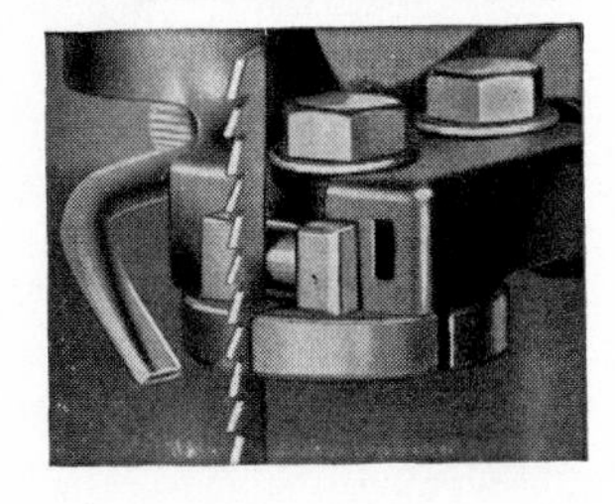

The table of the modern scroll saw has two main adjustments: it can be tilted to permit bevel cutting, and it can be rotated to give clearance space when large work is being handled. The tilting adjustment is the most used. This is usually controlled by a knob or handwheel under the table, which is loosened, permitting the table to swing on trunion mountings. A scale is usually provided, which, after once being set at zero (with the table perfectly square with the blade), will accurately register any degree of tilt up to 45 degrees, either right or left. No arrangement is made for tilting the guide to match the tilt of the table; however, an adjustment is provided for tilting the spring hold-down to follow the table and to contact the work evenly.

The chuck is a small vise which is attached to the plunger, its purpose being to clamp the blade in position. The average machine has two chucks, one on the end of the driven plunger and another on the upper plunger. Some blades are held at either end in both chucks, while others are held by the lower chuck only. In addition to the standard chucks, self-centering chucks for both upper and lower plungers are frequently used where fine blades are used extensively.

While universal guides will successfully handle practically any blade, special guides which are designed to fit one particular blade

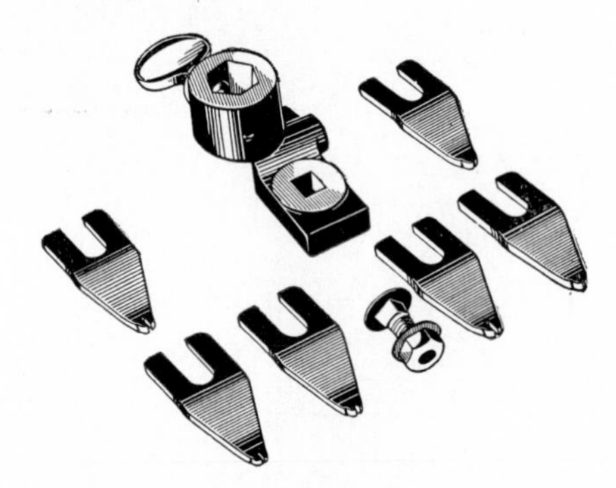

are often useful. Complete sets of these guides are available for most scroll saws and are generally preferred by home workshop owners.

Another special guide, fitted below the saw table, is often used to support saber blades. Used in conjunction with the upper guide, it enables perfect straight-line work to be done, as it eliminates any possibility of spring in the blade.

In some special cases, but only where an extremely stiff blade is used, the lower guide can be used alone as a support for the blade. This is often useful in cutting odd-shaped work which will not fit below the upper guide. The top of the blade, however, will have a tendency to weave in the cut if heavy cutting is attempted. The best use for this method of working is where the cut is thin but the body of the work is heavy, for example, a wood or metal tube. This may be so large that it cannot be worked below the guide, yet the cut can be made around the cylinder with the blade supported by the lower guide only.

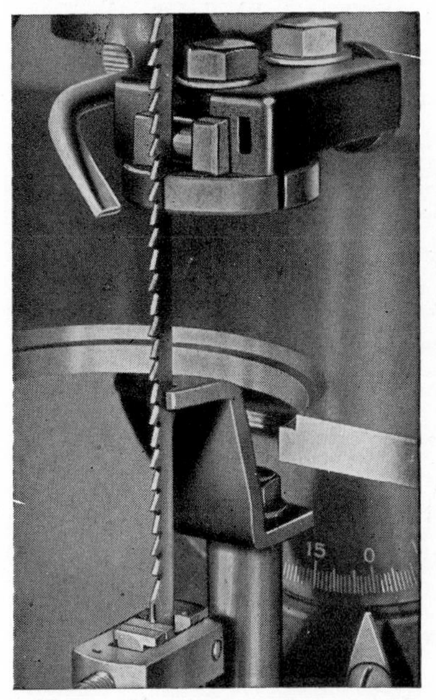

The belt guard is invaluable in accident prevention. The guard shown is a metal casing which completely surrounds the pulleys and belt. The outer casing is hinged at the rear, so that it can be instantly swung out to permit belt changing. Belt guards for all machines, besides adding immeasurably to safety of operation, also give a more finished and modern appearance to the machine.

Many operations in scroll-sawing can be done more conveniently if the operator is seated. Provisions can be made for a separate seat, or one can be built onto the front of the scroll-saw stand. If the operator prefers to build it onto the machine, provision should be made for folding the seat out of the way when it is not in use.

Scroll-saw Blades

Many different sizes and styles of blades are supplied for the scroll saw. All blades, however, are classified in one of two main divisions: first, blades which are gripped by both upper and lower chuck, commonly known as "jewelers' blades"; and second, blades which are held in the lower chuck only, known as "saber blades." Jewelers' blades are useful for all fine work where short curves predominate, while saber blades are fast-cutting blades for heavier materials where curves are not abrupt. Jewelers' blades can, of course, be used successfully in heavy material up to the full capacity of the saw. The larger sizes of jewelers' blades are very near to the same dimensions, in both gauge and width, as the smaller sizes of saber blades.

Because of frequent change of blades, some form of rack to hold the commonly used sizes is a great convenience in scroll operation. These blade holders should, of course, be attached to or located near the scroll saw.

Fitting Scroll-saw Blades

Jewelers' blades are held between the *flat* jaws of the upper and lower chuck; saber blades are held between the V-jaws of the lower chuck only. The exact method of mounting should be apparent from the illustrations on page 129. Note that when saber blades are used, the lower chuck must be turned 90 degrees. This is easily done by loosening the setscrew which holds the chuck, swinging the chuck over, and then retightening. The saber blade will naturally align itself in relation to both table and guide. More care is required to avoid misalignment in mounting jewelers' blades.

The universal guide consists of two parts: a disk which guides the blade and a roller which supports it. The disk has a number of slots around its rim, each being of a different width to fit various blades. The slot selected should be neither too loose nor too tight. The disk is adjusted to bring any slot to the front by loosening the screw which holds it in place and turning the disk to the required position. In regard to the width of the blade, the guide is set so that the forward edge of the disk is just behind the gullets of the blade teeth. The roller support is worked independently and should be moved forward until it just *lightly* touches the back of the blade.

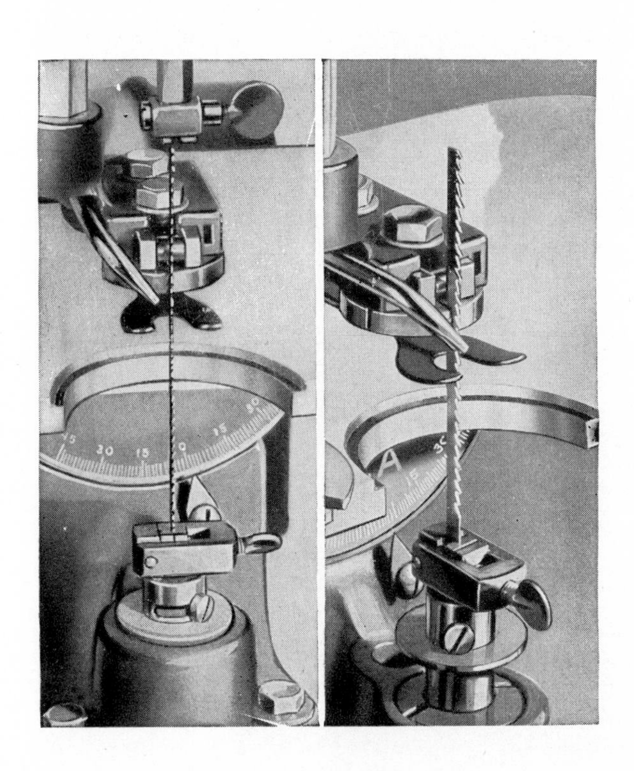

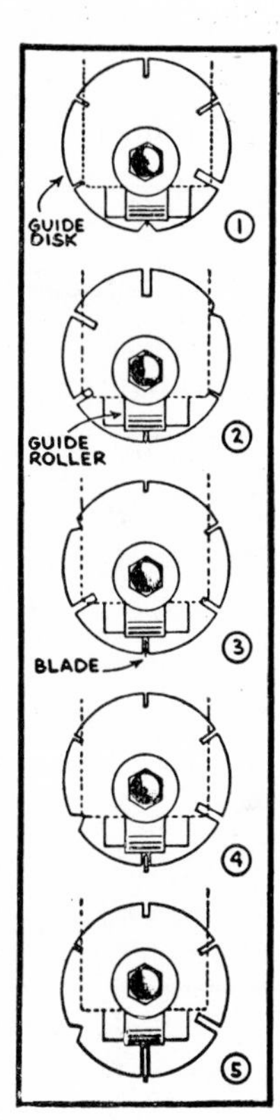

No matter what the thickness or width of the blade, a slot and a roller position can be found that will guide it correctly. Illustrations 1 to 5 make this point clear. The V notch on the rim of the disk is used for very fine blades. Blades of such small size work just as well without a guide, and the guide is often removed entirely, the tension of the blade itself being sufficient to guide it. The V notch, if used, is not really a guide but simply a back support, since the very fine blade is not wide enough to afford any appreciable rudder. Fine blades have a tendency to drift in the cut and must be worked slowly, in regard to both the speed of the machine and the rate of feed.

Operation

For average work, the scroll-saw operator takes a natural position, either standing or sitting at the front of the table, with the blade facing toward him. Where the work is so long that it will strike the upper arm before the cut is completed, cutting from the side is necessary. Side cutting requires that both the upper and the lower chuck be turned around, this being done by simple adjustments on most scroll saws. On some machines the table must be rotated, so that the groove in the table insert will center around the blade. For occasional work the insert maybe laid aside and the table used in its regular position.

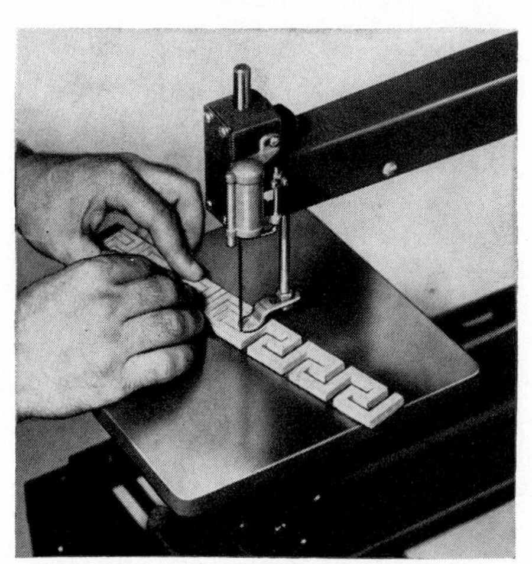

The technique of cutting with scroll-saw blades generally follows the same practice as used on the band saw. Because of the fine blades used, there are a few additional points worth noting. The first of these concerns the cutting of an inside square corner, as shown in the illustration opposite.

In one method of cutting, the fine blade is turned directly at the corner. This gives a very slight round to the corner, the degree of rounding depending on the size of the blade used. Turning in this manner is necessary in some work, and the slight round is usually no detriment to the work. In another method of cutting, the blade

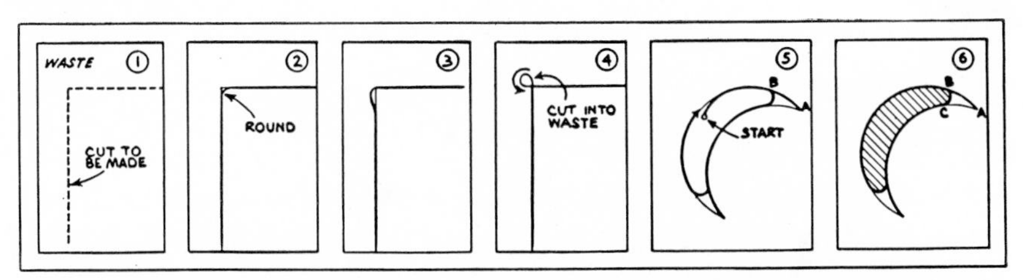

is allowed to swing wide at the corner. This permits a perfectly square corner but has the disadvantage that the bulge must be later smoothed by sanding or filing. In yet another method, the blade is run out into the waste stock and turned completely around so that the blade can enter at right angles to the first cut. All these methods are practical, the selection depending on the nature of the work.

Illustration 5 shows a variation in scroll-saw technique in the cutting of acute corners. The cut is started at any inside point and proceeds to point *A*. The blade is then backtracked to *B* to prevent running over to the other line, this being the same technique as used in band-saw cutting. The difference comes in cleaning out the corners, as shown in illustration 6. Where the band-saw worker would clean the corner by cutting directly from *C* to *A*, the scroll-saw operator often prefers to *back* into the cut from *B* to *A*, until the back of the blade comes to *A*, and then cut from *A* to *C*. This gives a perfectly clean corner, whereas the meeting of two cuts often shows a ragged point.

Saber blades can be used for a large portion of all scroll-saw work, and should be used where possible, because of their faster cutting

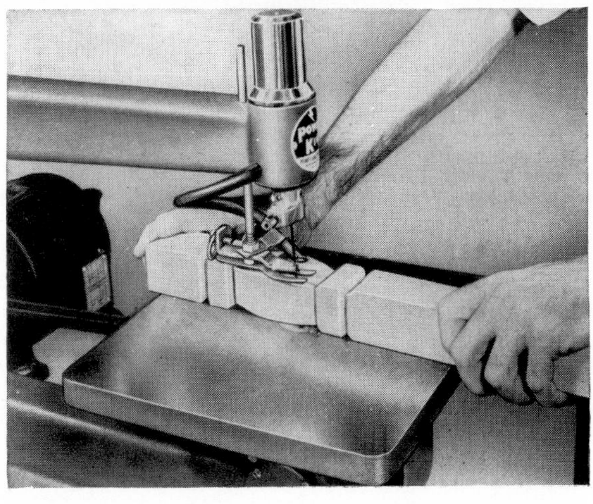

action and simplicity in jumping from one opening to another in pierced work. Where the cut is inside, a starting hole must be drilled. The guide is then lowered and the work cut as required. It should be noted that saber blades are mounted between the V jaws of the lower chuck, not the flat jaws. Wide saber blades and not thin jewelers' blades should be used in cutting heavy stock. The thin blade, even at full tension, will often drift when making the cut. If the jewelers' blade must be used on heavy stock, select a blade of generous body.

While intended primarily for kerf cutting, the scroll saw can be used successfully for ripping when the shop is not fully equipped. If a standard rip fence cannot be mounted on the scroll-saw table, an auxiliary wood fence can be fashioned by clamping a straight length of lumber in the required position to the scroll-saw table.

Laying out Patterns

The first and one of the most important steps in cutting any shape from wood is the job of marking the pattern shape on the wood stock. In any method of working, it is first necessary to make a full-size paper pattern of the work, either by the common method of enlarged squares or by the use of a projector. This paper pattern can sometimes be mounted directly on the wood as a guide. Where this is not practical, the simplest method of transferring is with carbon paper. If the pattern was first drawn on heavy paper or cardboard, it can be cut out with scissors and transferred to the work by tracing the outline. After the first pattern has been cut from wood, the work itself can be used for the pattern.

Miscellaneous Cutting Operations

Paper cutouts can be perfectly cut on the scroll saw by using the pad method of sawing. The entire secret of this work is to clamp the paper sheets tightly between outside boards of ⅛- or ¼-inch plywood. The various sheets of paper thus become equivalent to a solid block and can be cut without the slightest fraying of the edges. This work is frequently useful in making greeting cards, signs, or decorations. The blade used should be narrow enough to make the necessary curves, and the teeth should not be too coarse. On the other hand, a very fine blade will quickly become clogged with paper particles and will burn the work.

Cloth can be cut on the scroll saw in pad form in the same way as paper. Here, again, it is exceedingly important that the cloth pieces be tightly clinched between supporting boards. Cloth demands a somewhat finer blade than paper. For production work on some materials, better results can be obtained by using knives instead of toothed blades.

Metal-cutting blades, both saber and jewelers', can be obtained for most scroll saws. In general, metal cutting on the scroll saw follows the same technique as used on the band saw. Fine teeth are necessary in order to prevent stripping. Special table inserts should be made, with a slot which will take the thickness of the blade with a minimum of clearance. This is necessary in order to support the work directly at the cutting point and thus prevent burring.

Plastics can be cut with either wood or metal blades, under much the same conditions as sawing hardwood plywood. The feed should be somewhat slower, to prevent discoloration or burn.

A wide variety of cutout letters and signs in wood, metal, plastic, and other materials can be cut and sanded on the scroll saw. This kind of work demands a certain degree of skill in laying out the original patterns. Where letters are to be cut from wood, clear stock must be used—knots or other imperfections will cause trouble. Whitewood, white pine, and some of the varieties of 5-ply wood, put up with waterproof glue, are excellent. Where letters are to be cut from metal, the usual procedure in metal cutting is followed.

A number of circle-cutting jigs previously described for the band saw can be used equally well on the scroll saw.

Sanding and Filing

Standard accessories for most scroll saws include a sanding attachment and a variety of machine-file shapes. The sanding attachment has a semicircular body, making it suitable for sanding both curved and flat surfaces. The attachment takes round sleeves of the same size used on the small drill-press drum, the shape being easily altered to fit the semicircular shape of the scroll-saw attachment.

Machine files are available in both ¼- and ⅛-inch shanks and a wide variety of shapes, including square, triangular, round, pillar,

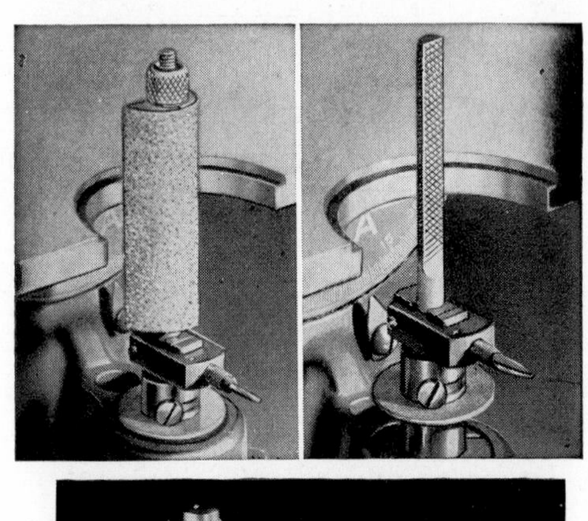

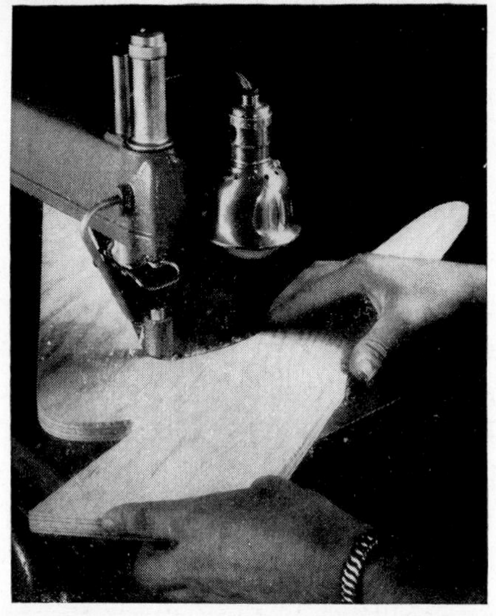

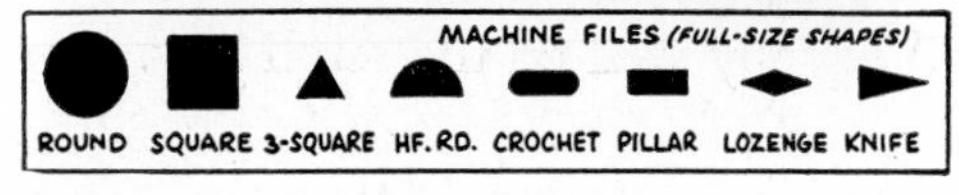

knife, etc., as shown in the illustration. All files, as well as the sanding attachment, are held between the V jaws of the lower chuck. No guides or supports are needed or used. An auxiliary wood table or the use of a special cutout metal insert becomes necessary when working small pieces which might fall through the table opening.

The work is usually fed from the front, but the chuck can be swung over for side feed if desired.

Both sanding and filing should be done at slow feed. If worked too fast, a machine file will simply scrape the work without cutting, while the sanding sleeve will quickly glaze over and be of no further use. The finer the file is cut, or the finer the abrasive particles of the garnet sleeve, the slower the speed should be. Coarser abrasives can be operated faster. Just as cutting with a scroll saw is much slower than cutting with a band saw, so also are sanding and filing slower operations as compared with the speed of machines especially designed for this work. These operations on the scroll saw are useful for fine, delicate work. Nothing is accomplished by speeding up the machine in an effort to get a faster rate of cutting.

It is usually necessary to remove the metal table insert when doing filing or sanding, in order to permit the passage of the abrasive unit being used. This is of no disadvantage on most work, but where the work is small, the supporting area around the file becomes of considerable importance. The required support can be obtained by using an auxiliary wood table into which a hole has been cut to the proper size to admit the file or sanding attachment being used. Blank inserts may be cut away to suit, using this same method. Where a considerable amount of filing or sanding is being done, inserts made up to fit the various units are extremely useful.

Scroll-saw Projects

One of the most frequent operations on the scroll saw, and one which has resulted in an amazing number of sales, is the cutting out of the famous "jigsaw puzzle." The home workshop owner may produce his own puzzles by gluing a suitable calender illustration or picture to ⅛- or ¼-inch plywood and then doing the work of cutting up the puzzle. The work of cutting the puzzle can be as sim-

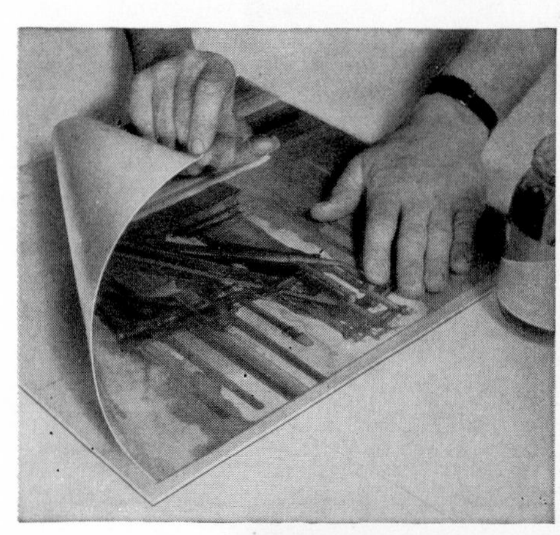

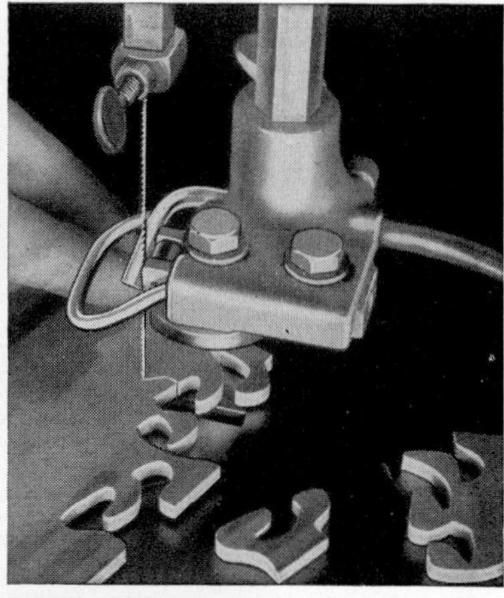

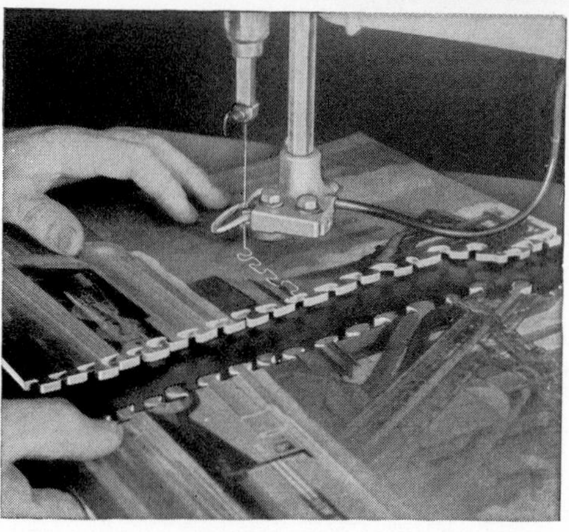

ple or as intricate as the operator wishes. The number and type of interlocking pieces is limited only by the imagination of the crafter.

Another popular scroll-saw project is the corner wall shelf. The design should be enlarged to the full-size pattern and transferred to the work by one of the methods previously described under scroll-saw operations. Holes should be drilled in the pattern in order to start the inside cuts. A suitable jewelers' blade will produce a smooth edge to the design, requiring no sanding. Both halves of the design may be cut at one time by the pad method, allowing the additional width on one of the halves for the corner joint.

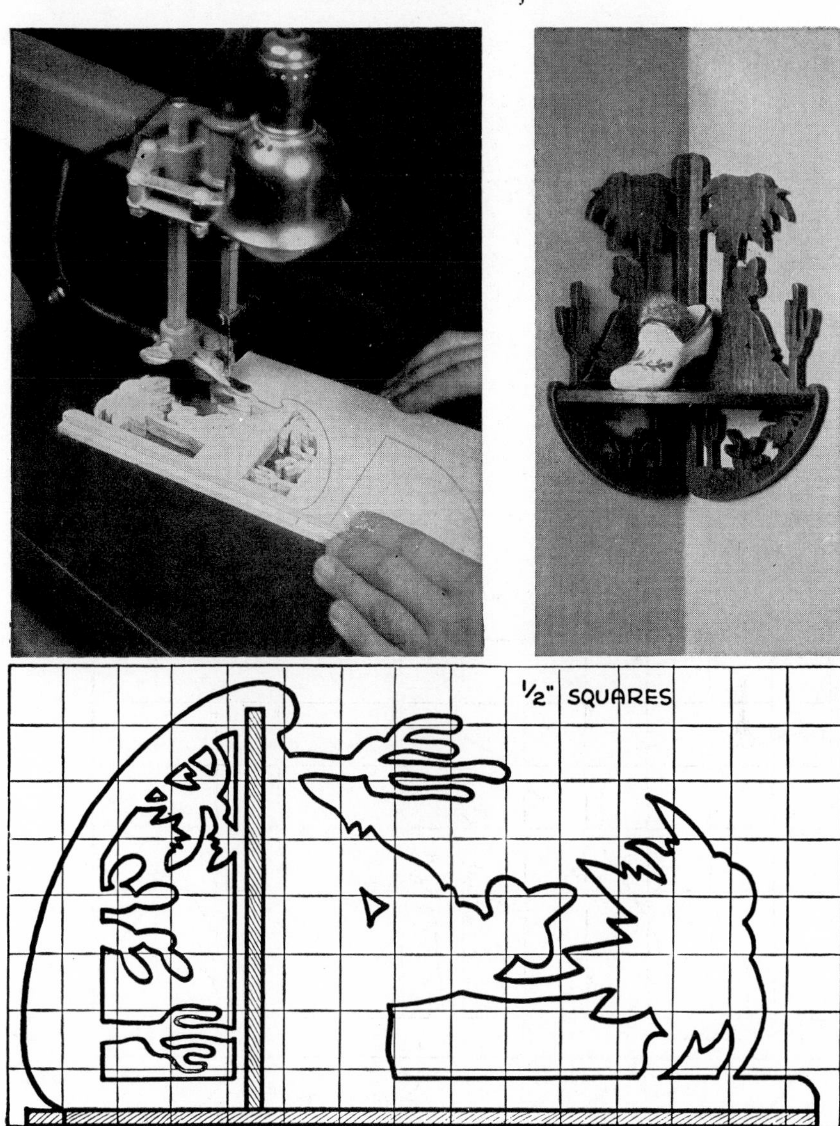

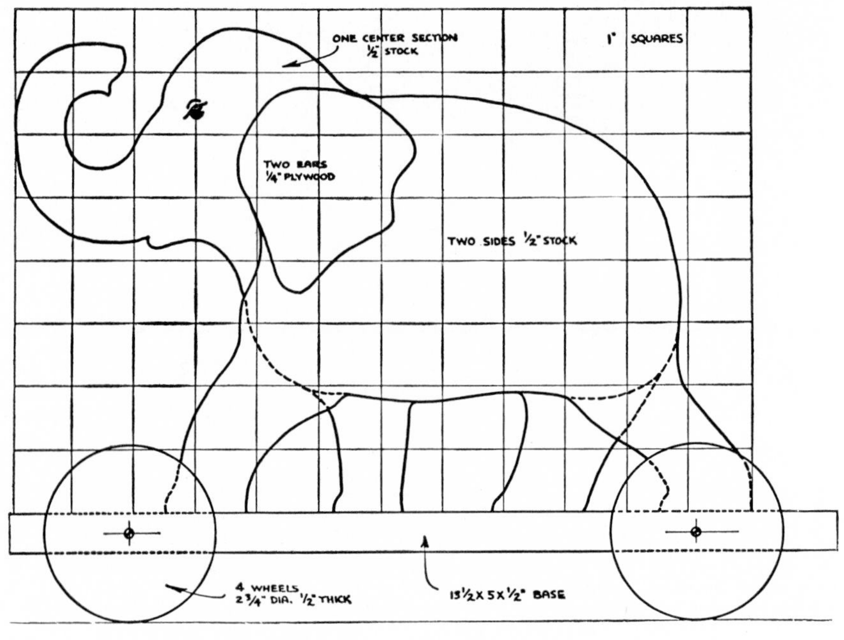
ONE CENTER SECTION
½" STOCK
1" SQUARES
TWO EARS
¼" PLYWOOD
TWO SIDES ½" STOCK
4 WHEELS
2¾" DIA. ½" THICK
13½ X 5 X ½" BASE

Many childrens' toys are popular scroll-saw projects, since they usually require sawing of an intricate nature or inside cutting. Any number of patterns for childrens' toys are available in books and in the current crafts magazines at your local newsstand.

Additional scroll-saw projects include many styles in birdhouse designs, and dollhouses.

Chapter 6. LATHE

Description

The lathe, more than any other power tool in the shop, is a complete unit in itself and is capable of producing finished work. Wood turning is a fascinating hobby, and the operation of the machine is not difficult. Any beginner in wood turning can do an acceptable job of turning on his very first try, by using scraping methods. True wood turning, however, is a cutting operation, and acquiring the necessary skill to fashion turnings quickly and well using this method demands more knowledge and considerable practice.

Wood lathes are designated according to the maximum diameter of the work which can be swung over the bed. A lathe capable of swinging a 10-inch-diameter disk of wood over the bed is called a 10-inch lathe. The terms "wood lathe" or "speed lathe" are usually used to avoid confusion with screw-cutting, metal-turning lathes. A typical 12-inch wood lathe is shown in the illustration.

The essential parts include the lathe bed, the headstock, the tailstock, and the tool rest. The tool rest consists of two main parts, the base and the tool rest, or support. Different types of rests or supports are interchangeable in the same base.

There are two general types of lathe headstocks: the spindle is either hollow or solid. The lathe shown in the illustration has a hollow spindle, internally tapered at both ends, to take No. 2 Morse shanks. Smaller lathes have either a hollow spindle with No. 1 Morse taper or a solid spindle. The spindle of the tailstock is usually made to match the headstock spindle, so that the various attachments can be used in either position. The two main attachments are the spur center, which fits the headstock spindle and is commonly known as the "live center," and the cup center, which fits the tailstock spindle

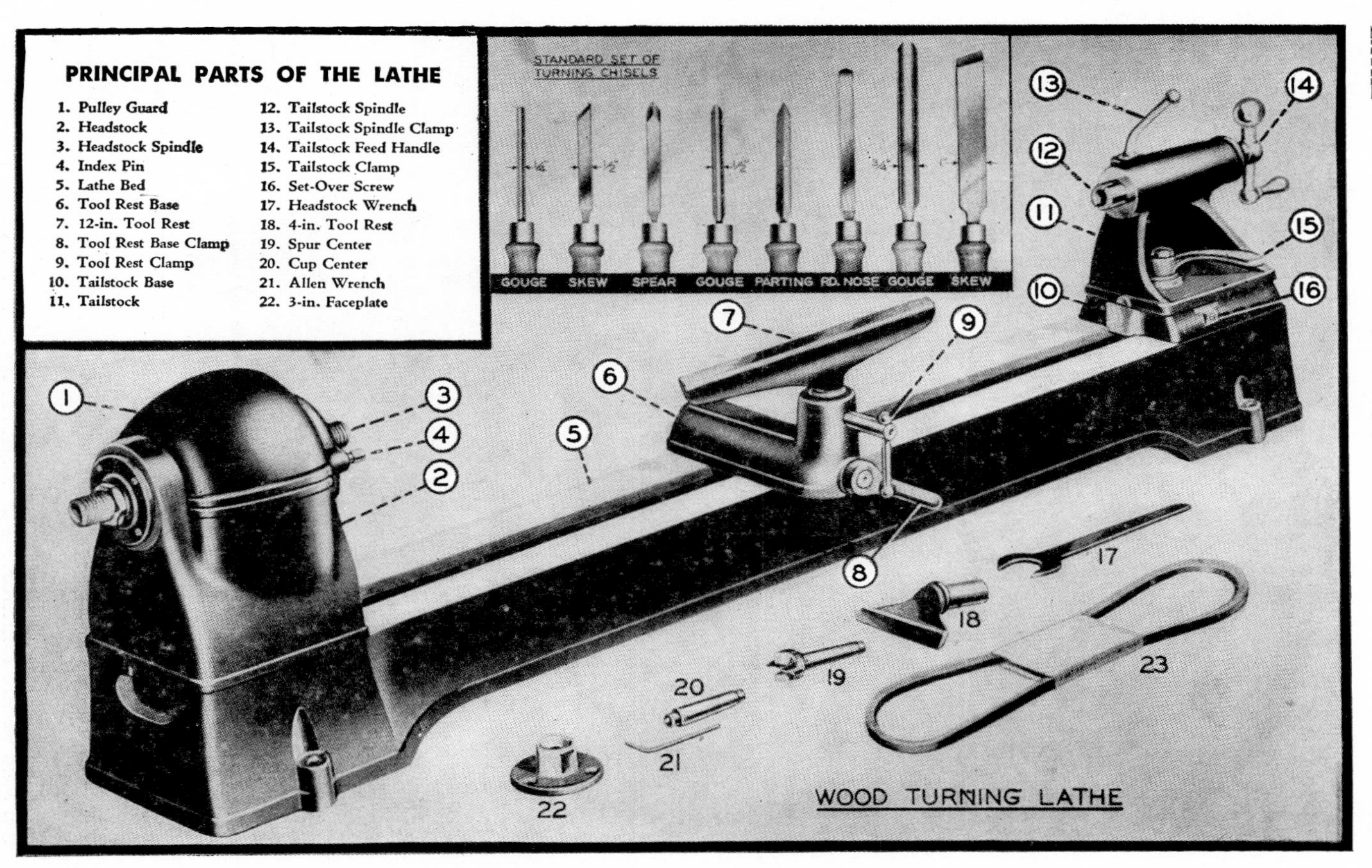
PRINCIPAL PARTS OF THE LATHE
1. Pulley Guard
2. Headstock
3. Headstock Spindle
4. Index Pin
5. Lathe Bed
6. Tool Rest Base
7. 12-in. Tool Rest
8. Tool Rest Base Clamp
9. Tool Rest Clamp
10. Tailstock Base
11. Tailstock
12. Tailstock Spindle
13. Tailstock Spindle Clamp
14. Tailstock Feed Handle
15. Tailstock Clamp
16. Set-Over Screw
17. Headstock Wrench
18. 4-in. Tool Rest
19. Spur Center
20. Cup Center
21. Allen Wrench
22. 3-in. Faceplate
STANDARD SET OF TURNING CHISELS
GOUGE SKEW SPEAR GOUGE PARTING RD. NOSE GOUGE SKEW
WOOD TURNING LATHE

and is known as the "dead center." In operation, the work is mounted between these two centers for turning, the spurs of the live center serving as the driving member.

The tailstock of the lathe has three adjustments. First, it can be moved bodily along the lathe bed and can be clamped at any position by means of the wrench, which fits over the tailstock clamp screw. Second, it can be moved within slight limits across the bed of the lathe by means of setover screws. Third, the spindle can be projected or retracted inside the body of the tailstock by manipulating the feed handle. Any desired position can be fixed by clamping the spindle with the tailstock spindle clamp.

The indexing mechanism consists of two rows of holes around the rim of the drive pulley, as shown in the illustration.

There are sixty holes in the inside row, spaced 6 degrees apart, and eight holes in the outer rows, spaced 45 degrees. The sliding pin on the side of the headstock has a short lever on the end which can be turned to engage any hole in either the inner or outer hole. The indexing mechanism is used for dividing faceplate work and for spacing cuts in fluting and reeding.

Turning Tools

The standard set of tools used in wood turning includes five different shapes. Most important of these is the gouge. The gouge is a round-nose, hollow chisel which is used for roughing cuts, cove cutting, and other operations. Next in importance is the skew chisel. The skew is a double-ground flat chisel, with the end ground to an angle instead of being straight across. This tool is used for smoothing cylinders and for cutting shoulders, beads, V grooves, etc. The spear, or diamond-point, chisel and the round-nose chisel are scraping tools which are used where their shape fits the contour of the work. The parting tool is a double-ground chisel and is used for cutting off and for making incisions or sizing cuts to any required diameter.

Setting up the Lathe

The lathe can be mounted on any workbench or on a special bench with cast-iron or steel legs and wooden top and shelf, as shown in the illustration.

The height of the lathe-spindle center line should be 40 to 44 inches above the floor, or at waist level. The motor can be mounted below or to the rear of the lathe headstock, depending on the method of installation. The motor should be ⅓-horsepower 1,750 rpm, capacitor or repulsion-induction type for average wood-turning operation. A switch rod or electrical off-and-on switch should be installed to bring the power control within convenient reach of the operator.

Lathe Accessories

The illustration pictures various accessories which are commonly used in wood turning. The 24-inch tool support is invaluable when

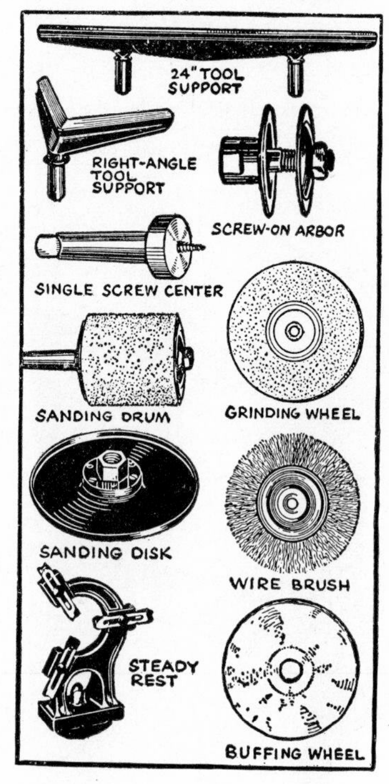

doing turnings which cannot be covered from one end to the other with the shorter tool rest. The right-angle tool support is used for faceplate work and permits operations on both the rim and the face of the turnings. The screw center furnishes a quick and practical method of mounting small faceplate turnings. The screw-on arbor is valuable as a means of mounting a grinding wheel, wire brush, or buffing wheel. This type of arbor is usually available in both right- and left-hand thread so that it will fit either end of the headstock spindle. Sanding accessories are worth-while aids, the most common types being the sanding drum and the sanding disk. The steady rest is used as a support for long, slender turnings or as an end support for shorter work. Accessories for any specific model of lathe may vary slightly in construction to suit the mechanics of the lathe for which they are made.

Layout Tools

Lathe work demands certain measuring tools, the most important being the rule and calipers. The rule is used for taking dimensions and marking various sections along the turning. A variety of calipers

are used in measuring diameters. The most used variety is the spring type, since calipers are often applied directly to the revolving stock and must be depended on to hold a set dimension when in this position. The dividers are used mainly in faceplate work, where they are useful in setting off diameters.

Safety Rules

The lathe is a safe power tool. The most important safety rule has to do with clothing. Never let a necktie dangle, and never work with unbuttoned, frayed, or dangling sleeves. Always mount the work securely, using the standard prescribed methods. Cultivate the habit of spinning the work by hand before turning on the switch —you will learn to do this automatically, if you fit a handwheel on the outboard end of the spindle. By doing this, you will always be sure, before power is applied, that the work does not strike the tool rest or interfere with any other part of the lathe. Always keep your turning chisels sharp for easy cutting. Run all work at a comfortable, yet practical, high spindle speed.

Plain Turning

Any turning which is worked between lathe centers is called a "spindle turning." This is the principal type of wood turning, as typified by chair and table legs, lamp stems, etc. Spindle turning can be done with either a scraping or a cutting technique. For good work, the cutting technique is more practical, removes wood faster, and produces a cleaner surface.

Wood stock for any spindle turning should be approximately square, and the ends should be at right angles with the sides. There are several common methods of determining the center on the ends of turning stock. One method is to set the combination square for a distance of a little more or less than one-half the width of the stock. Using the square against each face of the stock, lay out a mark across the center section of the work. A small square thus set off in the center can be used in marking the true center. The diagonal method consists of drawing lines from corner to corner, the intersection marking the center of the work.

After marking each end, the true center should be definitely marked with a punch, or, if the stock is hardwood, the center should be drilled to a depth of about ⅛ inch. The spur, or live, center is then placed against one end of the work and seated by striking it with a mallet. After setting the spur center, it is best to hold the spur and work together and fit immediately to the headstock spindle. The end of the work at the tailstock center should be oiled, placing the lubricant on the wood either before or after it is put in the lathe. Many craftsmen use beeswax, tallow, or a wax-and-oil mixture as a lubricant. The ideal method is to use a spinning or ball-bearing center, which eliminates lubricating entirely. If the work is to be removed from the lathe before completion, an index mark should be made as a guide for recentering.

The work is mounted by moving the tailstock up to a position about 1 inch from the end of the stock and locking it in this position. Advance the tailstock center by turning the feed handle until the center makes contact with the work. Continue to advance the center while the work is rotated slowly by hand. After it becomes difficult to turn the work, release the feed handle about one quarter turn and lock the tailstock spindle.

The next step is to mount the tool rest in place, about ⅛ inch away from the work (at its widest point) and ⅛ inch above the center line. This position may be varied to suit the work and the operator. With a little experience, the setting of the tool rest will become almost second nature.

Roughing Cuts

The large gouge is used in the first turning operation or roughing cut. This operation removes the sharp corners of the work. Run the lathe at a slow speed, and hold the gouge in the manner shown in illustration 1. The cut starts about 2 inches from the tailstock end and continues from this point toward and off the tailstock end. A second bite is then taken about 2 or 3 inches to the left of the first

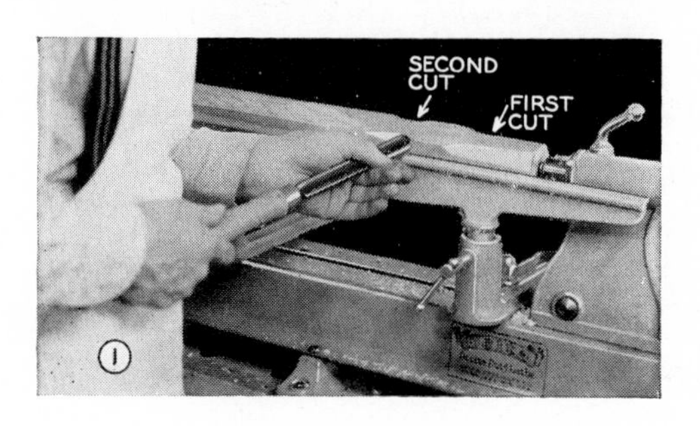

cut, advancing again toward the tailstock until the second cut merges with the cut previously made. This procedure continues until a point about 2 inches from the live center is reached; at this point the gouge is rolled in the opposite direction to carry the final cut off the live-center end of the work. The roughing cut should not be carried out with one continuous movement, as shown in illustration 3, as this tends to tear long slivers from the corners of the work. The cut should not be started directly at the end of the stock for the

same reason. The cut can be safely carried from the center of the stock toward and off either end, once the first roughing cut has been made.

The position of the gouge in relation to the work involves two or three important points. First, the tool may be advanced along the work either from right to left or from left to right. From left to right (from headstock toward tailstock) is preferable, since this throws the chips clear of the operator. The gouge is rolled slightly in the

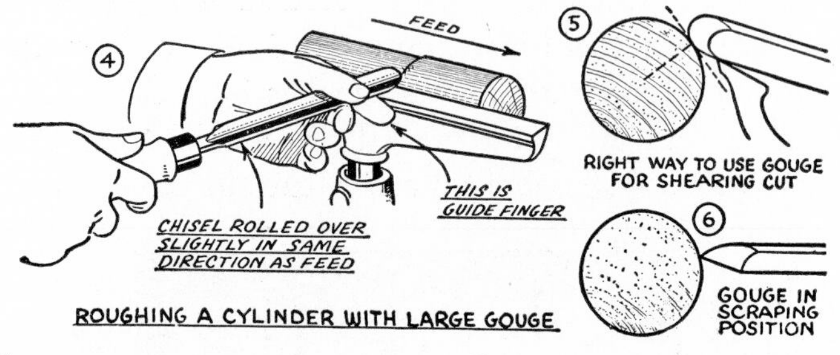

same direction as it is advancing. The tool is held well up on the work, with the bevel or grind tangent to the revolving surface. In this position it will make a clean, shearing cut. When pushed straight into the work, the gouge has a scraping action, which is normally poor practice in spindle turning. The roughing cut is continued until the work approaches ⅛ inch of the required diameter. The speed is stepped up to from 1,400 to 2,400 rpm once a roughly cylindrical form has been obtained.

In all tool handling, the handle hand takes a natural position, nearer to or farther from the end of the chisel, depending on the amount of leverage required. The position of the tool-rest hand is more a matter of preference rather than of any set, or proper, position. A palm-up grip, as illustrated with the gouge, is generally considered the best practice. In this position, the first finger acts as a guide, sliding along the tool rest as the cut is made. The alternate position is a palm-down grip, which is shown in the next illustration.

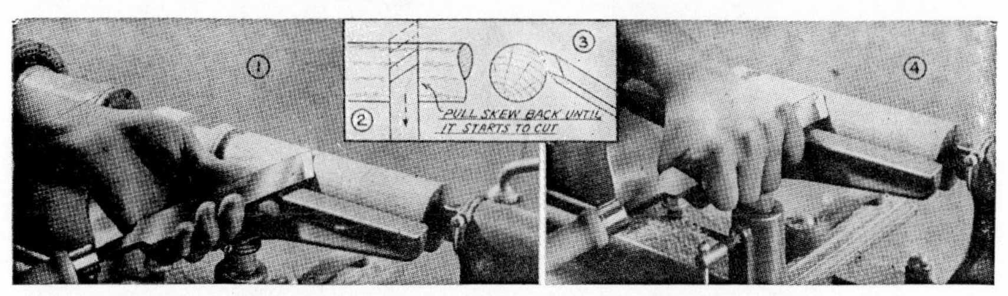

In this position, the heel of the hand or the little finger serves as a guide. The palm-down position is solid and positive, excellent for roughing and heavy cutting. Most beginners start with the palm-down grip and switch later to the palm-up position for better manipulation and control of the chisel.

Finishing Cuts

The finishing or smoothing cut on a cylinder is done with the large skew chisel. It demands a little practice and should be mastered thoroughly, since it is one of the most important cuts in turning. In this operation, the point at which the cutting takes place is nearer the center of the chisel edge and high on the work. The chisel must be supported by the tool rest at all times; in striving for a certain position in relation to the work, the beginner often overlooks this important point. Beginners often use the method shown in illustration 2 to locate the proper tool position. To do this, place the skew well over the work and riding flat against it. Pulling back slowly on the chisel will eventually put it into position, where it will bite into the wood. Raising the handle increases the depth of cut; lowering the handle makes the cut less. As with the gouge, the skew can be advanced in either direction. The part of the skew which does the actual cutting is the center portion toward the heel. It is worth while to stop a test cut in progress and note just how the skew cuts. You will note that the back portion of the grind or bevel supports the tool, and the handle hand controls the depth of cut by rocking the chisel on this pivot point. For this reason it is important that the skew bevel be a perfectly flat one, not a double bevel or a rounded one.

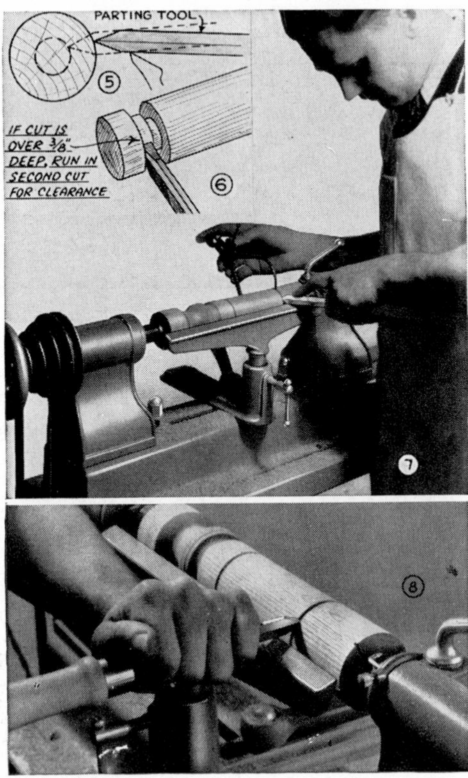

Other Cuts

The parting tool is perhaps the easiest turning chisel to handle. It is a scraping tool and is simply pushed into the work, as shown in the illustration. A somewhat better cutting action is obtained if the handle is held low and raised gradually as the work diameter decreases. The tool is frequently used with one hand, the other hand holding the calipers in the groove being cut.

When parting-tool cuts are deep, a clearance cut should be made alongside the first cut, to prevent burning the tool point.

The operation of squaring an end can be done with the parting tool. The parting tool, however, is a rough cutter, so that ultimately the skew must be used in cleaning the cut. The whole operation can be done with the skew, and this technique is shown in the illustration. The first operation is the nicking cut with the toe of the skew.

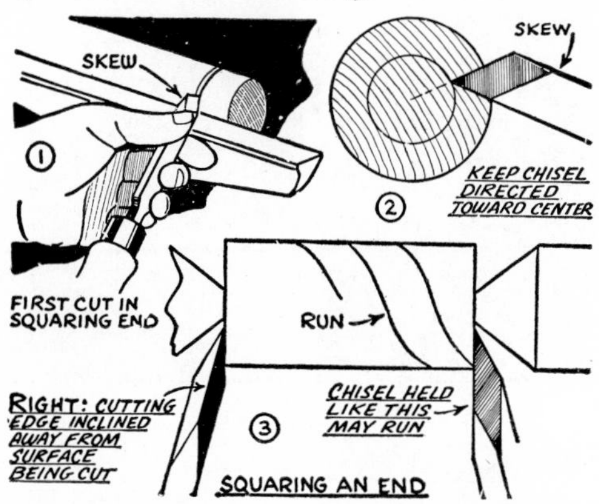

This cut cannot be made very deep without danger of burning the chisel, so a clearance cut is made by inclining the skew away from the first cut and again pushing the tool into the work. This procedure of side cut and clearance cut is repeated as often as needed. The important point to note is that while the skew can be pushed into the wood in any direction, the cutting edge itself must be inclined a little away from this plane. It will be noted that if the full cutting edge of the skew bears against the cut surface, the tool will have a tendency to run. In making the cut properly, the chisel is pushed straight into the work, but the cutting edge is inclined away from the cut surface—only the extreme toe does the cutting. This is the most important principle in handling the skew, and you will run into it repeatedly in making shoulders, beads, and V cuts.

In cutting a shoulder, the parting tool is first used to reduce the wood to within $\frac{1}{16}$ inch of the required shoulder and diameter, as in the next illustration. The waste stock is cleaned out with the gouge. Actual cutting of the shoulder is done with the skew. This operation is a duplication of squaring an end. The horizontal cut is also made with the skew, but in a little different manner from that used in doing plain cylinder work. If the shoulder is long, the ordinary skew position can be used for the outer portion of the cut. At the angle between the horizontal and vertical cuts, the heel of the chisel moves into a position tangent between the skew and the cylinder, as shown in illustrations 2 and 6.

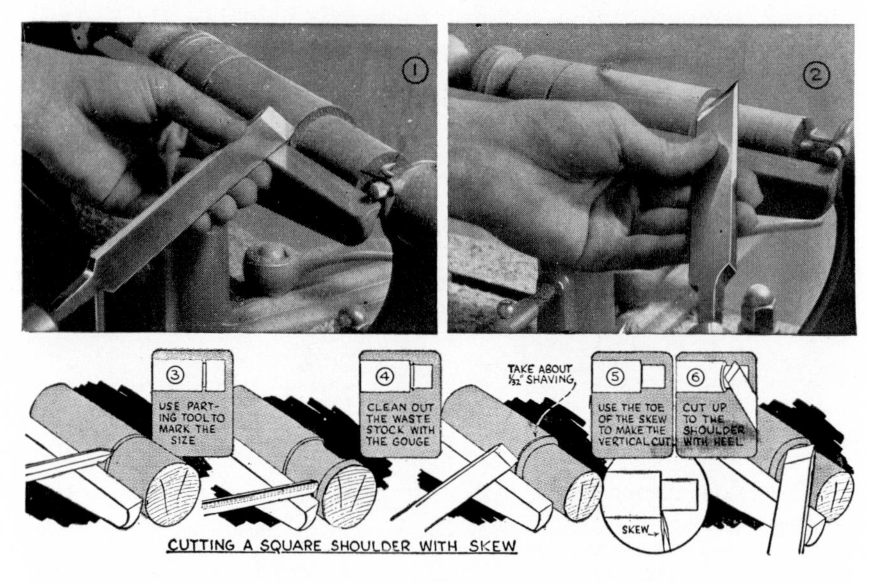

CUTTING A SQUARE SHOULDER WITH SKEW

In this position, the handle of the chisel is raised slightly to allow it to cut as the tool moves along the rest. A very light cut should be taken in order to produce smooth work. The heel of the skew can be used for making the entire cut, if desired, but the cut, whether in this or any other position, should not be started directly at the end of the stock. It is evident that any horizontal cut started directly from the end of the work will have a tendency to bite into the work and will often ruin the entire piece. Always run *off* the end and not *into* it. Where a very short shoulder makes this impossible, it is best to use the skew flat in a scraping position. If the cutting technique is used, engage only the heel of the skew in a very light cut.

In the cutting of small beads, the operation can be done by either the scraping or the cutting method. The easy method of scraping is done with the spear chisel and works to best advantage on beads which have been separated by parting-tool cuts. Scraping is slower and does not produce the clean work which results when cutting methods are employed. Scraping has the compensating advantage of perfect safety.

Cutting beads quickly and accurately with the small skew is one of the most difficult lathe operations. Various working methods can be used, the usual system being illustrated in numbers 2 to 4 of the next illustration. The first cut is a vertical incision at the point where the two curved surfaces will eventually come together. This cut can be made with either the heel or the toe of the skew. Next the

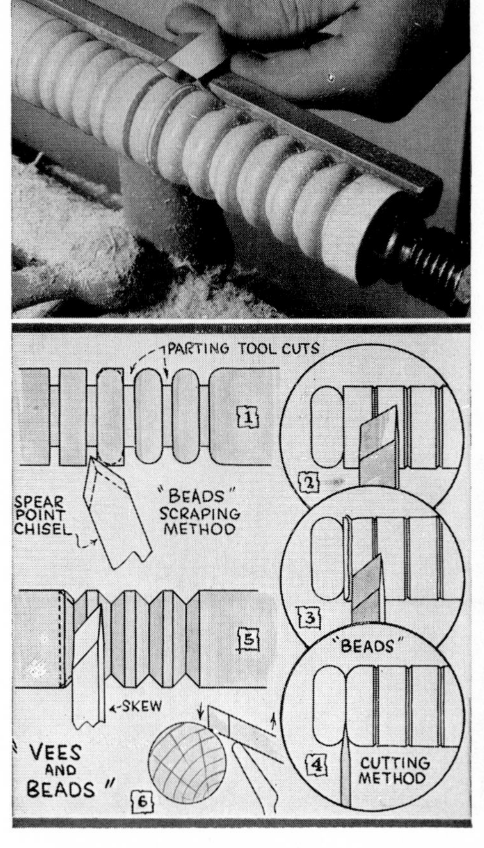

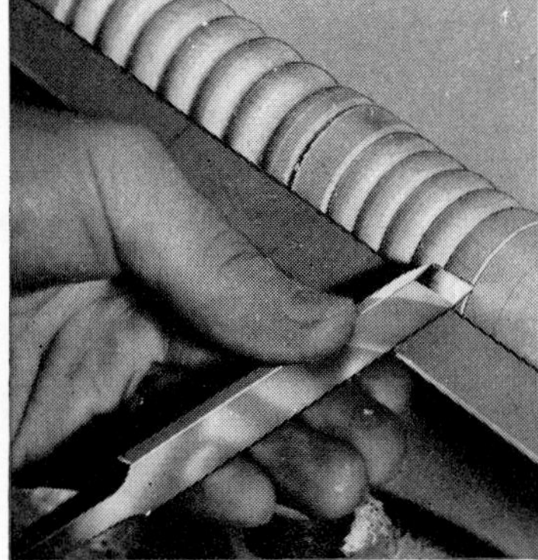

skew is placed at right angles to the work and well up on the cylinder. With the skew flat on its side, it is then evenly rotated through the successive stages of the cut, at the same time being pulled backward to maintain a cutting point. The entire cut is made with the heel of the chisel. The opposite side of the bead is cut in the same manner, one cut serving to produce the full shape in each instance. Beads cut in this manner are beautifully smooth and polished, and the technique is well worth the time and effort of mastering it.

Cutting V grooves demands much the same technique as cutting beads, except that the skew is swiveled straight into the work without rotation. Only one half of the V is made at a time, and two or more cuts may be needed on each side to obtain the desired shape. As in all cutting with the skew, the bevel next to the cut must be used as a fulcrum, without allowing the full edge of the chisel to catch and cause a run. V grooves can also be made with the toe of the skew, in the manner already described for squaring an end.

Long cuts are usually either convex or straight tapered surfaces. With a convex surface, the following method is used: The gouge is turned on the tool rest so that it will be inclined considerably in the direction in which it is about to move. The grind is tangent to the work, and the center point of the cutting edge is the contact point with the wood. As the cut progresses toward and around the end of the curve, the handle is gradually raised and swung to the right in order to maintain the tangency between the grind and the surface being cut.

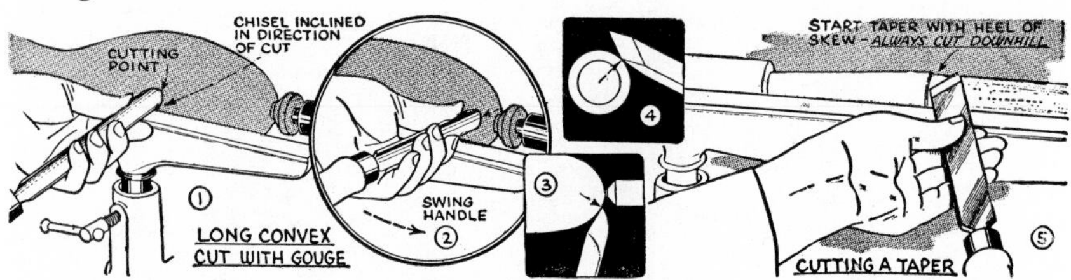

The skew is used in cutting a long taper. The operation differs from smoothing a cylinder only in regard to the cut. The starting cut should be made with the heel, to prevent the tool from digging into the work. As the tool runs down the work, the chisel can be pulled back to allow the center point of the cutting edge to cut. The full taper can be made with the heel of the chisel. There is a tendency to cut too deeply at the center of the taper, which should be guarded against. The direction of cutting on a taper is always downhill, or from the larger to the smaller diameter.

The next most difficult cutting operation to master is the forming of cove or concave cuts. These cuts are made with the gouge, the size of the chisel depending on the size of the cut. The size of the intended cove is first laid out, and the gouge is pushed directly into the work to remove the surplus stock. The cove cut can then be made.

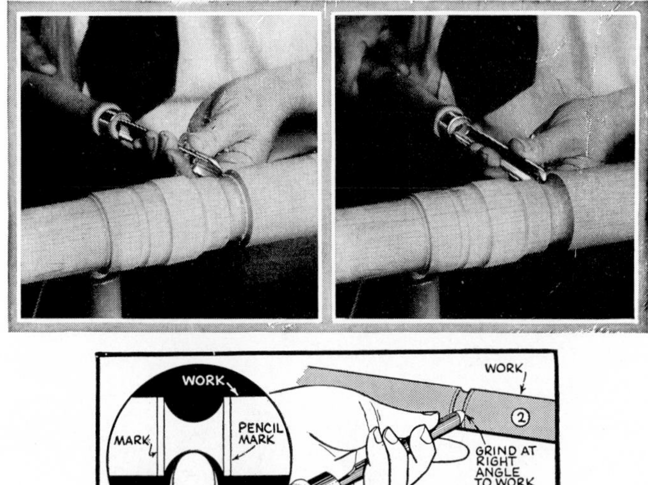

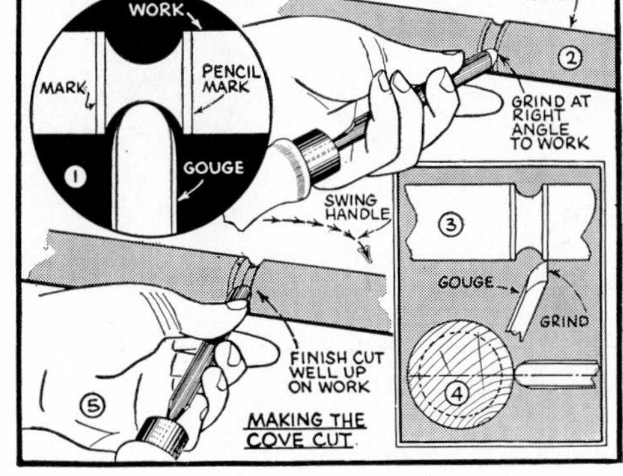

The gouge is placed on edge on the tool rest in such a position that the grind on the chisel forms an approximate right angle with the work. The chisel contacts the work at the center of the cutting edge, the tool being held so that the center line of the gouge is pointing directly toward the center of the revolving stock. This starting position is important—in any other position the gouge will have a tendency to run along the surface of the work.

From the starting position, the gouge is pushed into the revolving stock, and the tool is rolled on the rest. A triple action takes place here: first, the chisel is rolled to follow the shape of the cut; second, the handle is dropped slightly so that the portion already cut will force the lip of the chisel sidewise; third, the chisel is pushed forward so that at the end of the cut, it will be well up on the work and tangent with the cut surface. Only one half of the cut is made at a time, and the chisel is then reversed to cut the other half. An occasional lathe operator may prefer to make cove cuts with a scraping technique, using either the small gouge or the round-nose chisel.

When a lathe turning has a section which is to be left square, the stock should be jointed before turning. For this work, good centering is essential, since any error will show at the shoulder where the round meets the square. Turning of the shoulder can be done in various ways, one method being pictured in the illustration. If the

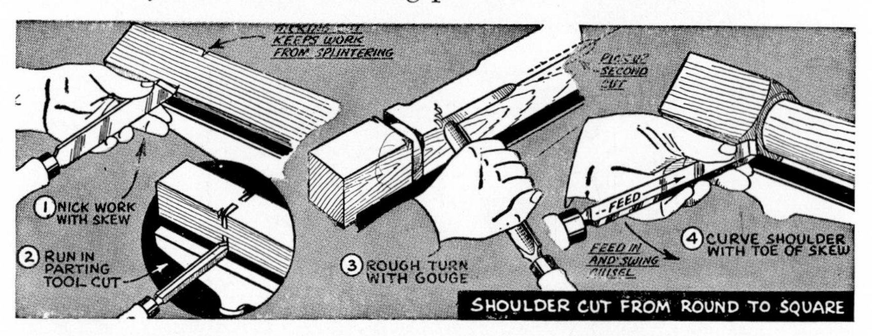

SHOULDER CUT FROM ROUND TO SQUARE

parting tool is sharp, the nicking cut with the skew can be omitted. The final trimming operation can be done with either the skew or the spear chisel. This is a scraping operation. While the shoulder can be cut with the same technique used for cutting a bead, the simpler scraping technique does clean work and is considerably easier.

Making a Lathe Turning

Any spindle turning is simply a combination of the individual cuts which have been described. The roughing work is done with the gouge to a maximum-size cylinder and is then given one running cut with the skew to make it smooth enough to take pencil marks. The required dimensions along the turning are then set off with ruler and pencil. If the pencil marks are made about ½ inch long, they will be visible when the work is turning in the lathe. Marking can also be done while the work is rotating, using either rule and pencil, or some kind of marker.

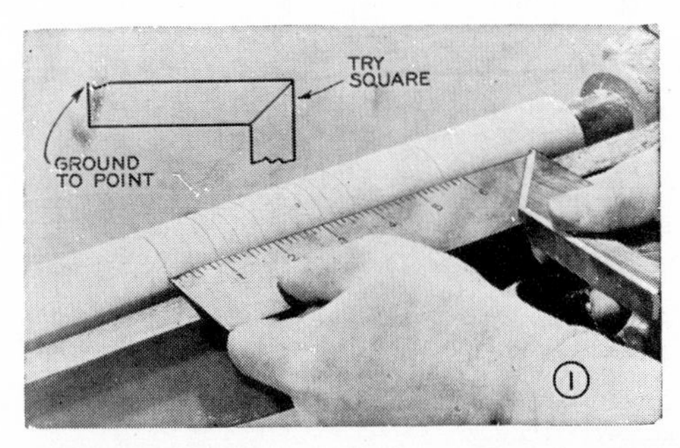

A half-section pattern of the work (template) is useful when more than one turning is to be made. Another device used for production is the marking board, which is fitted with sharp brad points to mark all needed layout lines in one operation.

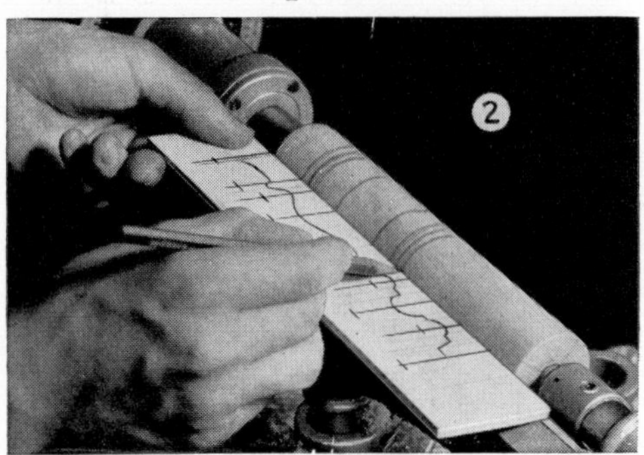

When the turning is first roughed with the parting tool and gouge to the main diameters, these sizing cuts should be a little wide of the action mark to allow for a finishing cut. The use of a pattern or template for long curves is recommended. The template can be made of sheet metal or cardboard, in which case it is used only as a template to check the work after turning. Some workers make use of a plywood pattern and manipulate the chisel over the pattern to produce the required shape.

In all spindle turning requiring two or more duplicate spindles, the turning which is first completed automatically becomes the master spindle and is used as a reference in forming the remainder. It is helpful to mount this turning directly behind the lathe, so that it can

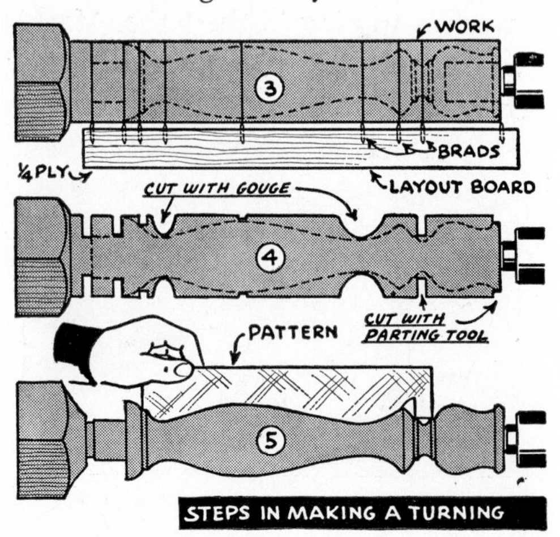

STEPS IN MAKING A TURNING

be seen while the additional turnings are being made. Calipers are the greatest single aid in determining diameters—time can be saved if several pairs set for different diameters are used.

Faceplate and Chuck Turning

Work which cannot be turned between centers must be mounted on a faceplate or other holding device. Most turning of this type is done with the faceplate mounting. There are, however, a number of jobs which require special chucks. All cutting in faceplate work is done by the scraping method. Any attempt to use a cutting technique on the edge grain of large work will result in gouging cuts which may tear the chisel out of the operator's hands. All work should be roughly band-sawed slightly larger than the pattern to eliminate heavy roughing cuts in the turning operation.

Faceplate work is usually mounted by fastening the stock to the faceplate with wood screws. Faceplates consist of the small single screw center, the 3-inch faceplate, and the 6-inch faceplate. Because of ease in mounting, faceplates should be used whenever the work permits. When normal screw fastenings interfere, the work can often be mounted on a backing block, and the backing block screwed to the faceplate. When screws are not permissible at all, the work is glued to the backing block by fitting a sheet of paper at the joint to allow a later separation without damaging the wood. Work with a diameter of less than 3 inches can be mounted on the single screw center.

All turning is done by scraping, with the tool rest in a position putting the cutting edge of the chisel on the center line of the work. The handle end of the chisel is usually dropped slightly to give a better cutting angle. Any chisel can be used which fits the surface of

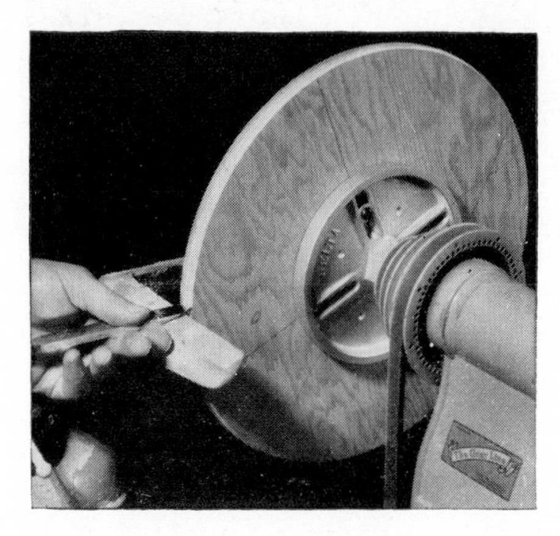

the pattern being cut, and most cuts can be made in a number of different ways. Cutting the mounted work to diameter is generally the first operation. This is usually done with a square-nose or spear-point chisel. The gouge and skew can also be used, both in a level scraping position. The preferable chisel is usually the spear-point, picking up the bite at the edge of the work and moving across the surface.

Facing the work can be done with the square, spear, skew, or gouge chisels. A surfacing cut with the spear chisel is generally taken by starting at the center of the work, cutting toward and off the rim. Roughing cuts in facing work should be done with the gouge, since its cutting action is faster than that of the other chisels.

Large turnings which cannot be swung over the lathe bed are mounted on the 6-inch faceplate and turned on the outboard end of the spindle. A floor stand is needed to hold the tool rest for this operation.

Deep boring is required for bowls, boxes, and similar faceplate work. This work is slow but not particularly difficult. Whenever it is practical, it is faster to rough out the recess by drilling a series of holes to the required depth on your drill press. If this is not done, at least a central starting hole should be drilled. The chisels used for deep boring are the skew, round-nose, and spear-point. The skew is useful for trimming down the edge of the hole. Cuts on the bottom only are best worked with the round-nose chisel, starting at the center, with overlapping short strokes directed toward the center. The tool rest should be positioned at an angle into the hole to provide maximum support to the chisel. Final finishing cuts down the side are made with the skew.

Methods of Chucking

Practically the entire technique of faceplate and chuck work has to do with the various methods of chucking or holding the work. The actual turning employs standard methods. In general, the technique calls for a wood chuck or holding device of some kind, so that the work itself can be reversed for turning on both sides. The first method is the spindle chuck, so called because it is a spindle in itself and fits inside the work. It is used for all work having a straight central opening. The turning of the central opening, which is done first, is called the "first chucking," while the chucking on the spindle chuck is labeled "second chucking" or "rechucking."

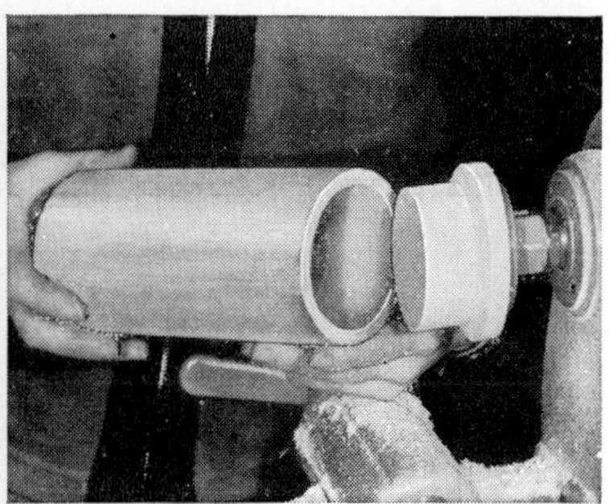

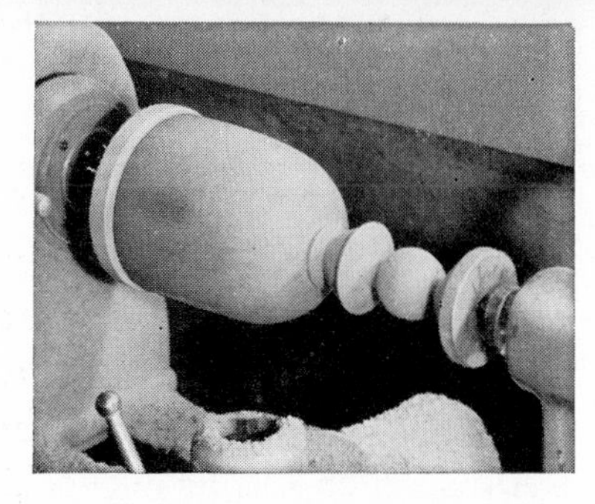

The work is first mounted on a faceplate or screw center to permit internal turning of one end. A spindle chuck is then made, over which the work is pressure-fitted. The opposite end of the work can be turned or bored straight through as desired.

Plug-chucking methods are usually second chuckings after the plug or tenon has been turned. In this type of chucking, a plug, or tenon, is first turned on one end of the work. This plug is then gripped by or driven into some form of chuck.

The first illustration on page 162 shows a homemade ring chuck. The next shows a threaded sleeve fitted to the spindle nose; the work is a drive fit. The work in the third illustration is gripped by a collet chuck.

One method of turning a ring makes use of a recessed chuck. This type of chuck is used for bowls, rings, and other types of work which

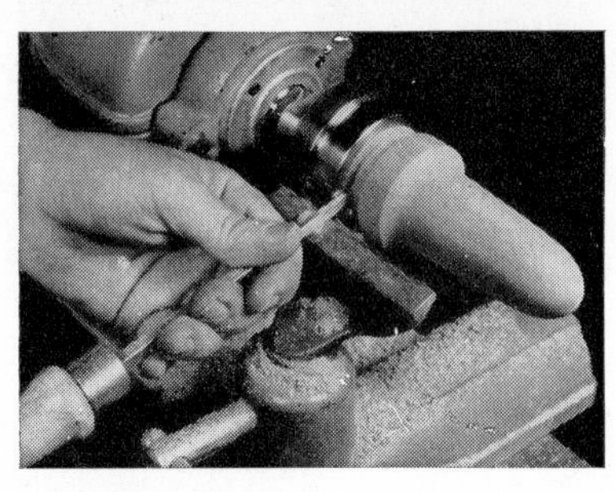

can only be gripped from the outside. Time is saved in making the recessed chuck if the rim portion is band-sawed and nailed to the body. Another similar method is to nail four pieces of wood around the face of the chuck. In both cases, of course, the applied wood is trued up by turning. All wood chucks for rechucking must be accurate, with a firm pressure fit. This is particularly true when the holding surface is small. The recessed wood chuck in the illustration below is just the opposite of a spindle chuck. The outside and the face of the work are first turned to net size, and the recessed chuck is then made for a firm pressure fit. With the work mounted in the recessed

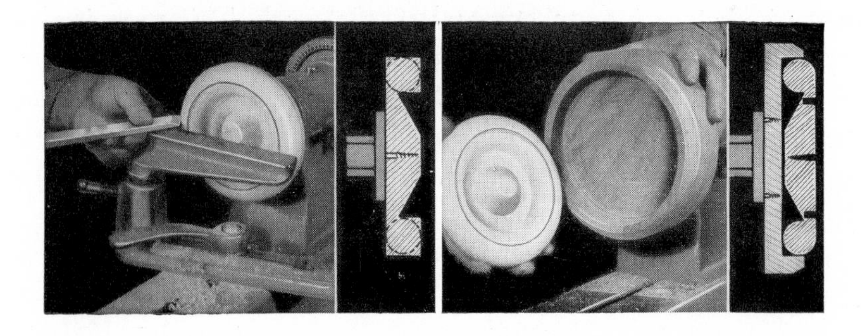

chuck, the center of the ring is cut out, after which the second face and internal cuts are made.

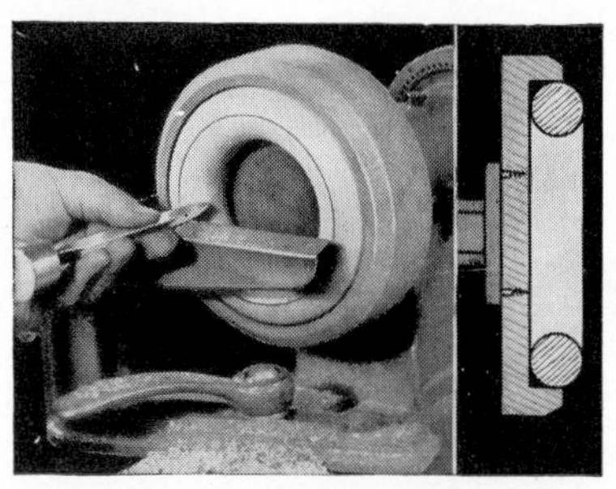

The rabbeted picture frame is a job of spindle chucking. The work is first mounted on a 3-inch faceplate and the rabbet is turned. The surplus wood at the center of the frame is sawed out with the jig saw. A spindle chuck is then made up to take the rabbeted frame. Mounted on the spindle chuck, the face of the frame is then turned to shape.

Turning a Ball

Wooden balls of any size can be worked as spindle turnings, by mounting the work between centers. Care must be used in maintaining the length the same as the diameter. Frequent checking with a template is recommended. The turning operation itself is best done with a scraping technique; however, if you have had enough practice, you can roll a finished cut with the skew. After the ball has been roughed as accurately as possible, one end can be turned down to a stub tenon for rechecking in a plug or cup chuck.

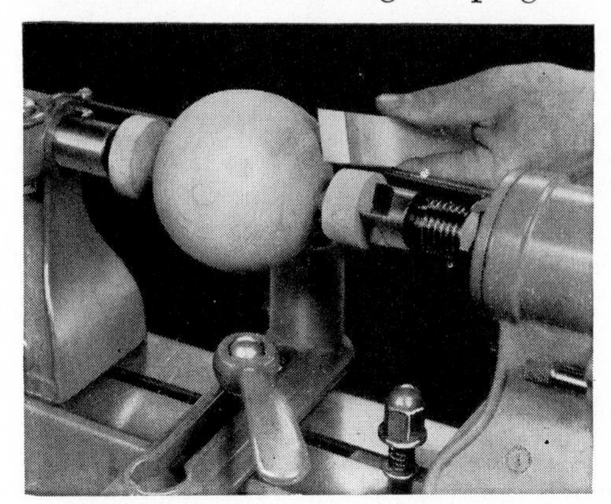

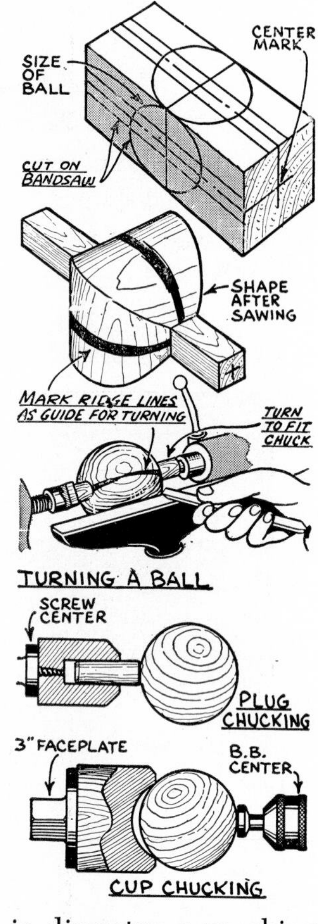

If the ball to be turned is over 2 inches in diameter, a roughing operation with the band saw can be used. This is done by marking the ball shape on two adjacent sides of the square turning stock, extending the center lines to the ends of the work. Work a little oversize to allow for trimming. Band-saw to shape, nailing the pieces from the first cut back in position to allow the second cut to be made. This is the same method as described in the chapter on band-saw operations. Blacken the ridge lines as shown, and then center carefully in the lathe. If the work is turned exactly to the ridge line, it will be a perfect ball shape as true as your band-sawing operation will allow.

The final finish is done in plug or cup chucks, using one or both as desired. If you use the plug chuck, the work is rounded by work-

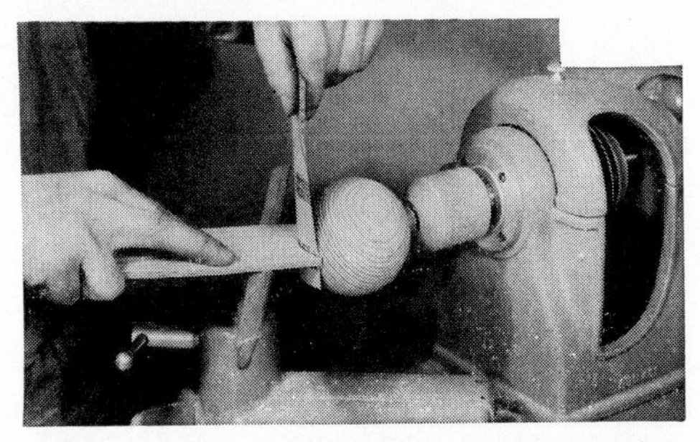

ing over the entire surface, using a plywood template and sandpaper. If you use the cup chuck, turning and sanding is done on the major diameter only, the work being rotated as needed to present new surfaces. The cup chuck is especially suitable for smoothing, since it allows working of the entire surface.

Where a number of similar balls are required, they should be worked in a string, allowing a parting-tool cut between each for cleaning up. After careful sanding with a template, the balls are cut

apart on the band saw and can then be finished in one chucking with the use of a cup chuck. Balls less than 1 inch in diameter are often turned with a special chisel ground to the required shape.

Turning Boxes

Turned boxes can be made with the grain either vertical or horizontal. The vertical grain is preferable, since this construction is somewhat more stable. The general working procedure consists of turning the inside of the lid and the body as separate faceplate turnings and then combining the two parts to permit the turning of the outside shape.

Most faceplate turnings consist of light wood sections of fairly large diameter. It is important, therefore, that the work be perfectly seasoned, so that it will retain its turned shape without warping. Proper conditioning is automatically obtained by storing normally seasoned wood for two or three months in the same location as the finished turning will occupy. Some crafters go even farther by first rough-turning the job and then giving it six weeks' seasoning. In this way the wood is allowed unrestrained warp—any twisting which is going to happen will be done before the work is turned to its final shape.

Special Spindle Turnings

Several types of spindle turning have special features which set them apart from the usual run of work. Included in this division are post-blocked turnings, off-center work, spirals, combination turnings, split turnings, etc.

A spindle turning with a square section which is smaller than the diameter of the largest round section is described as having a reduced square. In preparing the stock for turnings with reduced squares, two distinct methods can be used. The first of these methods consists of using stock large enough to accommodate the largest diameter of the turning; the reduced squares at either end or along any part of the turning are cut to the required size on the band saw. The second method of working is known as "post blocking," and with careful workmanship and good glue joints, the finished product has the appearance of a solid turning with less expense. The first operation in post blocking consists of joining the main body of the turning to a perfectly square section. Next, blocks of the same wood of sufficient size are glued to two sides of the square stock at the proper position. A slight projection is allowed, so that the wood can be sanded or jointed to a perfectly flush surface. The two remaining blocks are then glued in place, bringing all four sides of the enlarged portion to the same thickness.

The block post is turned using the same methods as for any other spindle. The work should be well centered to avoid an unbalanced condition.

Oval Turnings

Oval turnings can be made on the lathe by off-centering the piece to be turned. The stock from which the turning is to be made can be either square or a suitable rectangular shape. The true center is located in the usual manner, after which the required off-center points can be located by experiment. A compass is used in marking the end of the stock, the compass curve showing exactly how the finished work will shape up. A typical example of this type of turning is the handle of a hammer.

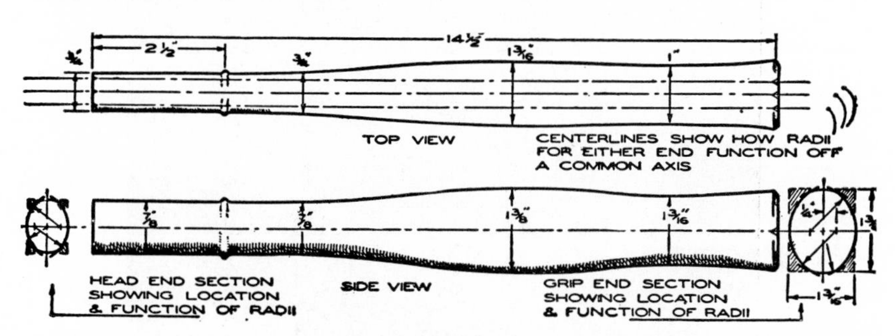

In making the turning, centering holes are drilled at the two off-centers and at the true center at each end. The work is then placed in the lathe, using two corresponding off-centers as centers. Turn the lathe by hand to see that the revolving stock will not strike the tool rest. Use slow speed for the roughing cut and a faster speed to finish. The lathe should be stopped frequently to allow inspection of the progress of the work. Cutting should continue until one side of the stock is rounded to the ridge line of the center on the high sides of the oval. The work is then removed from the lathe and re-

DELTA
MILWAUKEE
1
DELTA
MILWAUKEE
2
DELTA
3

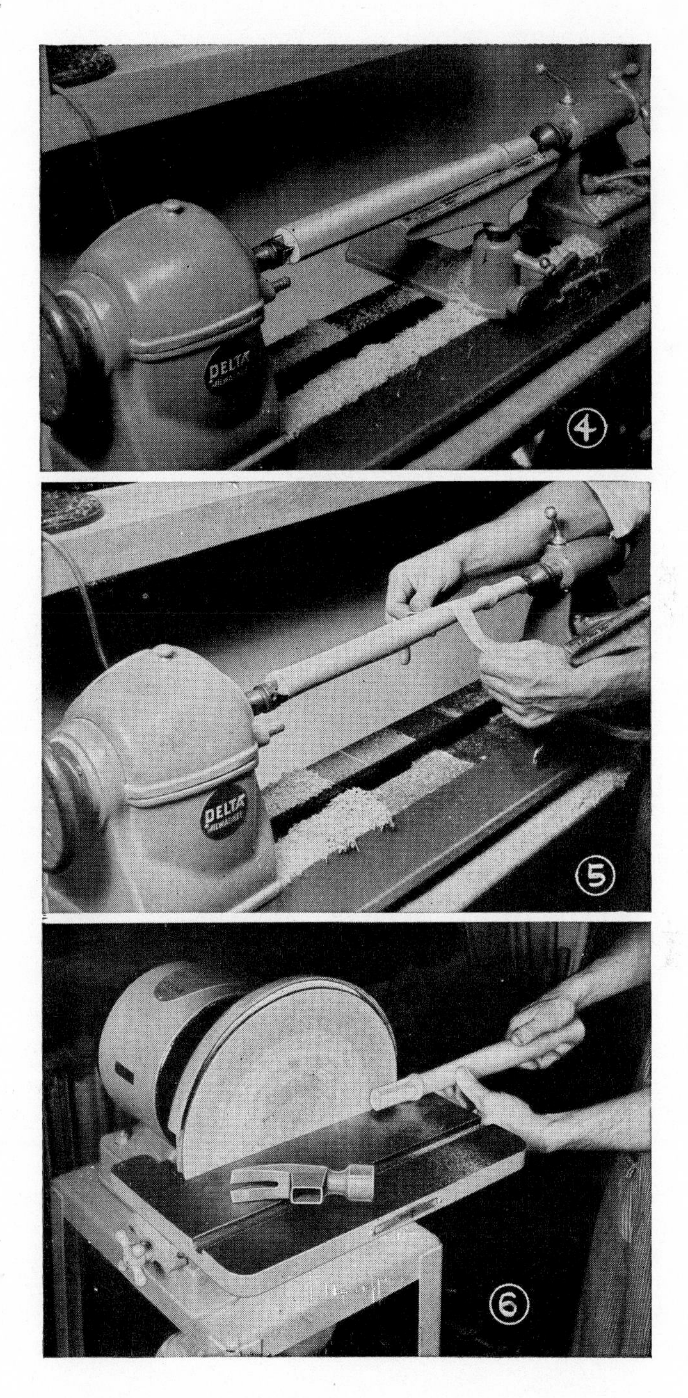
DELTA
DELTA
4
5
6

mounted, using the opposite side of the off-centers. Duplicating the same procedure as before, the work is turned down to the ridge line. The stock is finally mounted on the two centers and the sharp points cut away. A further approximation of a true ellipse is obtained by sanding while the lathe is running with the stock on true centers. A slow speed is used for this operation. The hammer handle is completed by fitting it to the head on the disk sander.

Turning a Club Foot

This style of turning is started by making a paper pattern, which is used to mark the shape on two adjacent sides of the work. The

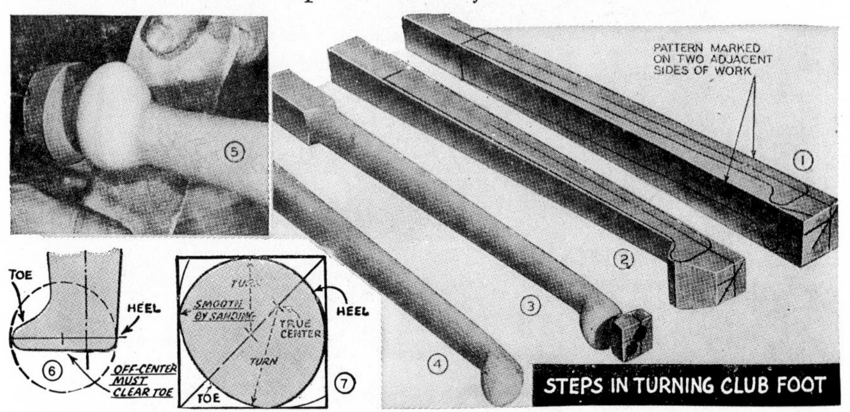

STEPS IN TURNING CLUB FOOT

true center is marked on each end of the work. Off-centering is done at the tailstock end only, as shown in the illustration. As in oval turning, experimenting with a compass will show the centers needed for any desired shape. The toe of the work must be in the clear when the work is in the off-center position. The waste wood is removed by compound band-sawing. This saves a lot of rough wood turning. The leg is then mounted on true centers and turned to shape, which includes the full length and covers the front or toe portion of the club foot. The work is now off-centered at the tailstock end only, and the heel portion of the club foot is turned, stopping the lathe frequently to inspect the work. Next-to-the-slowest speed should be used for this operation. When the turning is complete, there will be sharp ridge lines where the two circular arcs meet. These can be softened with a few file strokes, after which the work can be run at low speed and sanded smooth.

Turned Cabriole Leg

Turning the foot of the cabriole, or Queen Anne, leg has the advantage of uniformity, which is not easily obtained by hand-carving methods. The work is similar to the club foot previously described, except that off-centering is optional.

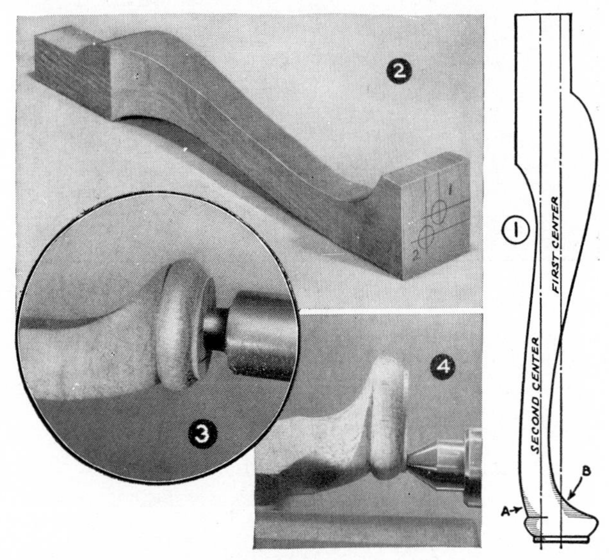

The foot itself is circular and is generally referred to as a "pad foot," especially if the extremity is a circular pad, as shown in the illustration. In making the leg, the pattern is laid out on two adjacent sides of the work. The center of the foot is marked across both ends of the wood, as is the first center. A second center line is marked at the exteme heel of the fillet at the bottom of the foot. The work is compound-band-sawed, as described under band-saw operations.

The work is mounted in the lathe on the first center line. The fillet and toe portion are then turned, running the cut a short distance along the internal corner, as shown at *A*. The crafter should watch the cut closely, as it is very easy to remove too much wood. Illustration 3 shows the work at this stage, with the pad foot fully formed. If desired, turning can be discontinued at this point. If mounted on the second center, it is possible to clean up the external toe, as shown at *B*. The work must be stopped frequently for inspection to avoid overcutting. Final modeling of the leg is a matter of handwork with a cabinet rasp and other files. The lathe serves as a convenient holding device but is not in operation. To lock the lathe in a convenient position, use the indexing head.

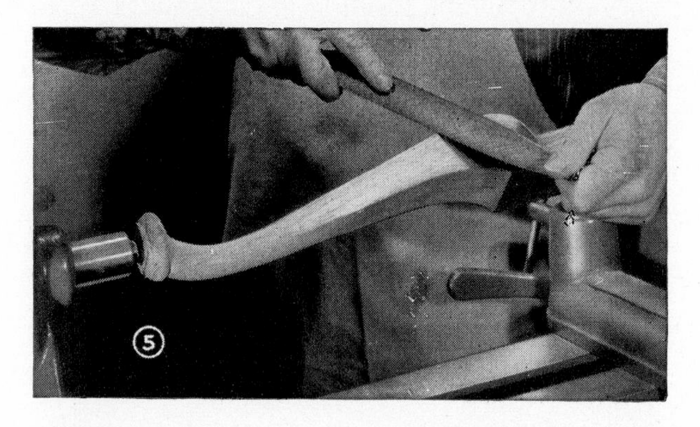

Spiral Turnings

Spiral turnings are not actually turned on the lathe. The lathe serves to hold the work while the spiral portion of the turning is carved by hand. The most common type is the single twist or single spiral. Like any screw thread, the pitch of the spiral is the distance from center to center of consecutive ridges. The lead is the distance advanced in one revolution. In the single spiral, the pitch and the lead are equal. A double spiral has two ridges advancing along the cylinder. The pitch is the same as in the single spiral, but the lead, or distance traveled, is twice as great. In a triple spiral, three ridges wind around the cylinder, and the lead is three times as great as the pitch.

To lay out a single spiral, the first step is to turn the stock to a cylinder of the required size. Next, mark the extremities of the intended spiral, as illustrated opposite. Select a suitable pitch. This is most pleasing if it is about the same as, or a little less than, the diameter of the work. The exact dimension is decided partly by the length of the spiral, since the length must be divided into a number of equal spaces, each space representing the pitch of the spiral. Each of these main divisions is again divided into four equal parts. Next, the dividing head is set to quarter the stock, and four horizontal lines are drawn on the work, using the edge of the tool rest as a guide. The ridge of the spiral can then be sketched in by drawing a line diagonally across each of the spaces. The distance between threads or ridges (pitch) is the same as the distance that the thread or ridge advances in one revolution (lead).

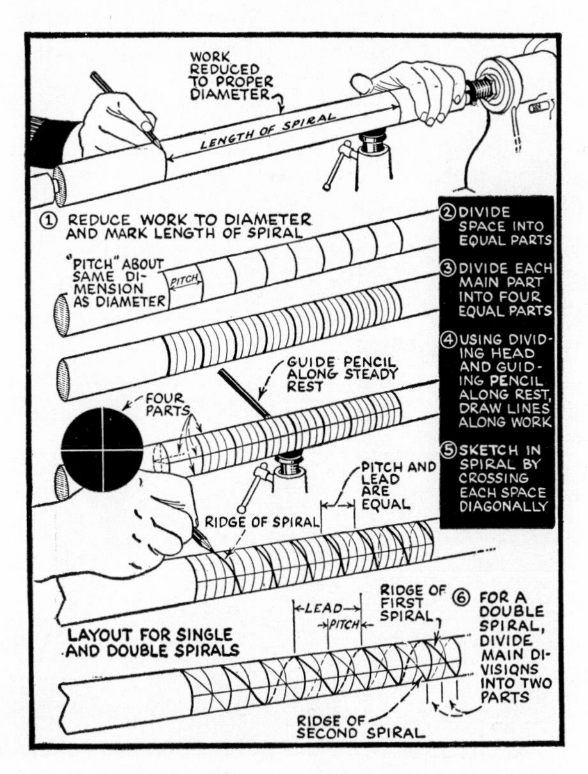

In laying out a double spiral, each main division is divided into two parts instead of four parts. A diagonal line is then drawn as before to produce one ridge of the double spiral. The second spiral is started directly opposite the first. The distance between ridges remains the same, but the distance each ridge travels in one revolution is twice the pitch.

Besides the ridge line, other lines can be drawn, preferably in colored pencil, to mark the bottom of the groove, the limits of the true groove portion, etc. The same result can be obtained in a simpler manner by wrapping a strip of paper spirally around the turning, as shown on the next page, marking between the edges of the strip to locate the ridge line. A double spiral laid out in this manner would require two strips of paper.

The actual work of turning is started by sawing a spiral cut accurately between the ridge lines, using a stopblock clamped to the saw to limit the depth of cut. After the saw cut has been made, a wood rasp is used to rough out the hollow of the spiral, the saw cut serving as a guide and depth indicator. The lathe, of course, is not under

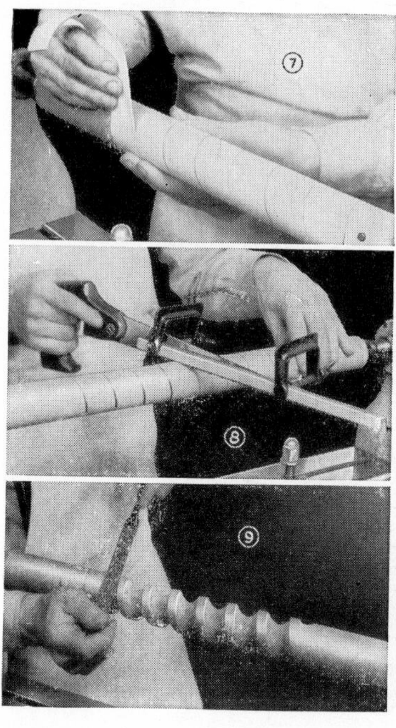

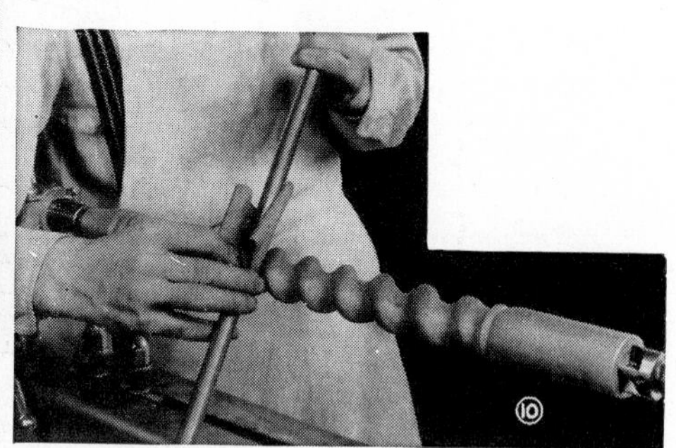

power. After a uniform groove is formed, the edges are rounded over to the ridge line. The lathe can then be run at its lowest speed, following along the spiral with sandpaper, as shown in the illustration.

Hollow spirals are made with double, triple, and quadruple twists. It is not practical to use a single twist, because the work would not be symmetrical. The double twist is the simplest as well as the most attractive form. The work is laid out in the usual manner, setting off the lead and dividing into four equal parts or setting off the pitch and dividing into two parts. The ridge and a line between the ridge lines are marked on the turned piece of work. The in-between line, which normally represents the bottom of the groove, is used as a drilling line. A V block must be used in this operation in order to produce accurate work. A series of overlapping holes are drilled through the turning, roughly forming the hollow center and double-spiral strips of wood.

Finishing work on the piece is done with an assortment of files and sandpaper. Again, the lathe is not in operation, but is used merely as a holding device. Needless to say, a generous amount of patience and skill are required for neat work. The wood used should be tough, hard, and free from splintering, as mahogany, walnut, maple, beech, lemonwood, etc.

Making Split Turnings

Split turnings are made by turning up a full-round spindle and then splitting it into half or quarter sections. The half or two-piece split is the most common and is usually worked by screwing or gluing two pieces of wood together, as shown in the illustration. If glue is used, a glazed or slick paper should be used at the joint; this will hold for the turning but will allow the work to be split apart easily after the turning is complete. Sometimes the two-piece assembly is

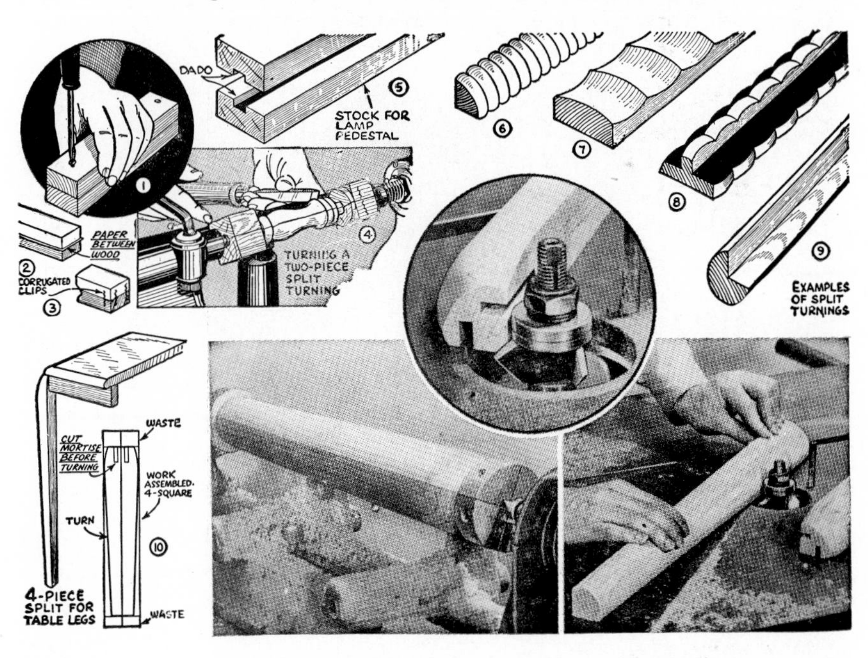

used for permanent work, such as the stem of a lamp, where the split construction is necessary to permit running in the wiring groove.

Attractive moldings can be made by using the split-turning method. The quarter-round molding is usually assembled by using four square strips turned as a unit. Other examples are worked in solid stock and then sawed apart to the desired shape.

Making Combination Turnings

Legs for stools, chairs, and other pieces of furniture often have one end turned while the opposite end is a curved square section. A method of doing this is shown in the illustration.

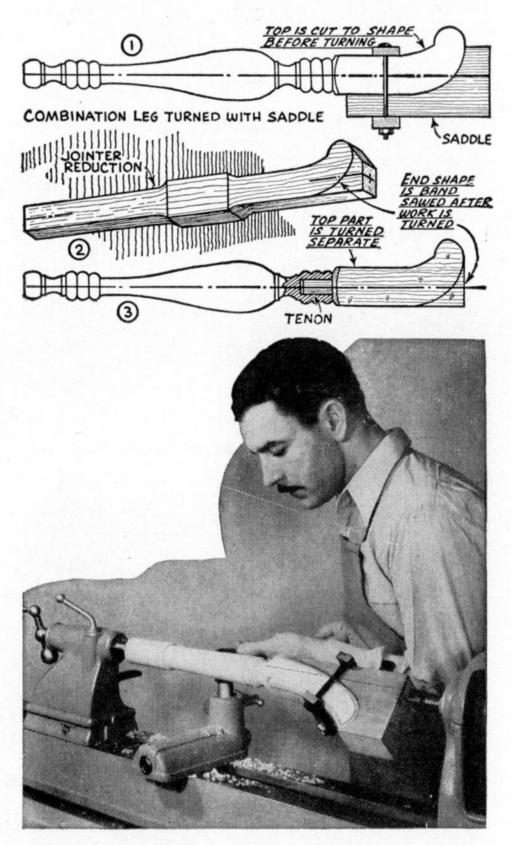

A second method is to leave one end partly formed previous to the turning operation.

A third method is to treat the work as two separate turnings, making an assembly by means of a tenon turned on one end of one of the members.

Thread Chasing

Sometimes it is necessary to cut a thread on a wood spindle. Work of this kind is best done on a regular screw-cutting lathe with a suitable tool or with the use of hand-screw boxes and taps.

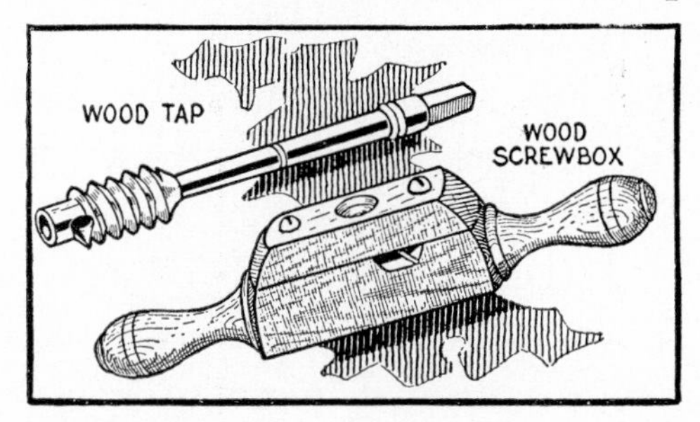

The job can also be done by hand chasing on the lathe, a method formerly used for practically all commercial brass work. The general idea is to move the tool along the work at a uniform rate while the work is turning at slow speed. Offhand this might appear to be a difficult, if not impossible, job, but it is actually quite simple. The tool movement is simplified by the fact that when it is moving at the proper rate, the work seems to stand still. The job starts with a light spiral cut, which is gradually deepened to produce the full thread shape. Once the cut is tracking properly, it is simple to engage the chasing tool in the grooves and extend the thread.

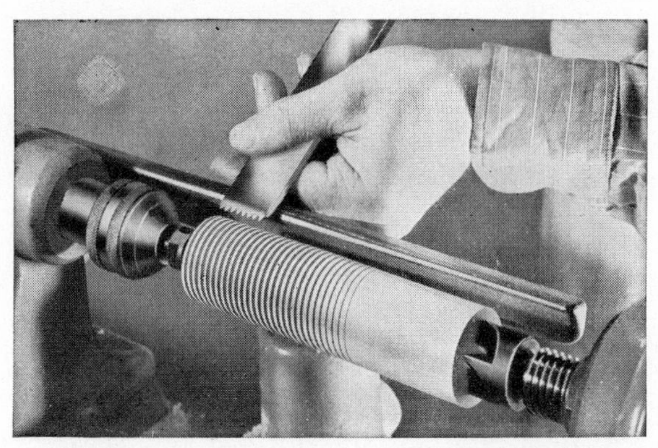

Chasing tools consist of two types, one for external threads and the other for internal threads. The material for the tools should be good tool steel, 3/16 to 1/4 inch thick. A front clearance angle of about 30 degrees is satisfactory for hardwood or soft metals. Both tools

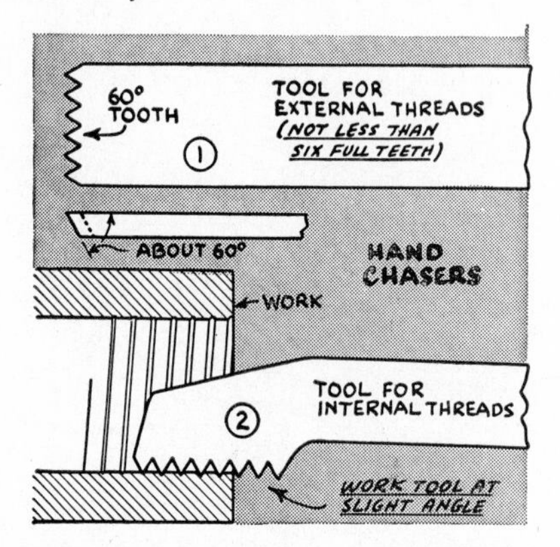

should have at least 10 degrees side clearance on the leading edge of each tooth. Smoothest cutting is obtained if the tool is presented to the work with a fair amount of negative rake; that is, the tool handle should be held high. Thread chasing is impractical in softwoods and should be attempted only on plastics, soft metals, and hardwoods, the latter preferably close grained, as rock maple. One pitch of threading tool can be used on any diameter of work. Eight threads per inch is satisfactory for most jobs.

Making Built-up Turnings

Built-up turnings consist of lathe projects fashioned from several pieces of wood glued together to form a definite pattern. There are three general classes of work: laminated, post-blocked, and segments. Work of this kind demands perfectly seasoned wood and perfect glue joints. A good piece of built-up work will last a lifetime, while poor work will open at the joints after a few seasons of climatic changes. Examples of this type of work are shown in the illustrations opposite.

The first two show laminated, side stack; laminated, sandwich; the next two, segments, solid form; segments, hollow ring; and the last two, post-blocked, four-square; and post-blocked, eight-square.

Wood should be selected for color and hardness. The table below lists several typical woods graded in order from lightest to darkest. Two-color pattern effects are based on a white wood, such as holly

WOODS FOR BUILT-UP TURNINGS

	Wood	Color	Hardness	Stability
Light	Holly	Very white	Medium	Good
	Maple	White	Hard	Good
	Prima vera	Cream	Soft	Good
	Birch	White to pink	Medium	Good
Medium	Red Gum	Red-brown	Soft	Fair
	Butternut	Amber brown	Soft	Excellent
	Cherry	Red	Medium	Good
	Mahogany	Red-brown	Medium	Excellent
Dark	Walnut	Brown	Medium	Excellent
	Paduak	Red	Hard	Good
	Purpleheart	Purple	Hard	Good
	Rosewood (E.I.)	Dark purple	Hard	Good

or maple, combined with a dark wood like mahogany or walnut. The woods used should be of approximately the same hardness; at any rate, extremes of hard and soft woods should be avoided, because such combinations will often turn out of round or develop flats when sanded. Stability or freedom from warping is worth consideration, although any wood seasoned to 7 or 8 per cent moisture content will be stable if kept indoors.

Lamination

This is the simplest type of built-up work and consists of several layers of wood glued surface to surface. If the finished project shows the various layers one over the other, the combination is called "sandwich," or "bread-and-butter" construction. If the layers are side by side, the construction is a "side stack." The assembly of the work is simple and requires only that the adjoining surfaces be perfectly flat. It is usually desirable in sandwich construction to alternate the grain, placing the grain of each layer at right angles to the piece below it. Much roughing work is saved if the various rings are rough-band-sawed to shape before gluing. It is not practical to alternate the grain in a side stack, but a similar protection against warpage is obtained by alternating the heart side of the lumber.

Post Blocking

Built-up turnings made by post blocking represent an artistic form of conventional post blocking, differing from regular work only in that more pieces are used and the wood is selected for contrast rather than for match. A typical project is the lamp stem shown on the next page; it is apparent how the different side blocks shape up into a form of imitation inlay when the work is turned. The preparation of the core is the first step. This can be a solid block, or, if through drilling is required and drills are not available, it can be glued up from two pieces previously grooved and glued up as described for split turnings. Grooves should be stopped a short distance from the ends to provide a solid surface for lathe centering. It is easy to drill into the groove after the work is complete.

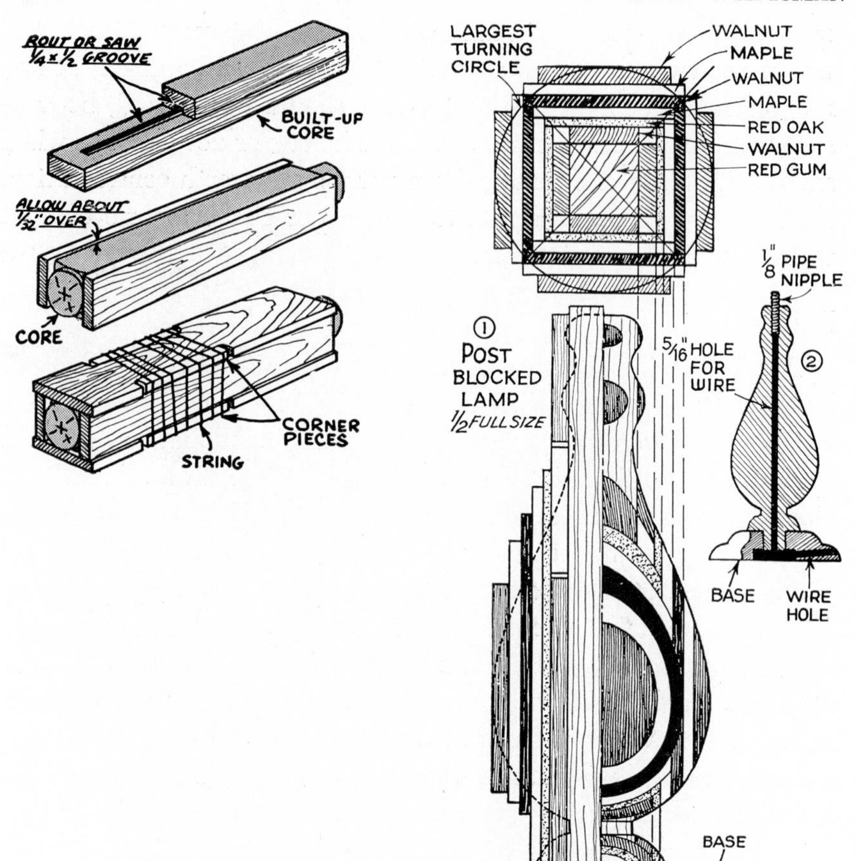

The core should be carefully centered in the lathe, after which a test cut should be run with the parting tool at either end. If the work shows out of center, the heavy sides should be dressed down—the finished piece will show a faulty, out-of-balance design if the core is not perfectly centered. A check mark should be used on the driven end of the work, so that it can be returned to the same position on spur center for each of the various turning operations.

The first pair of blocks are applied; they should overhang the core slightly to permit exact flush dressing. Any kind of glue can be used. A sufficient number of clamps should be used to assure good contact. After the glue has dried, the clamps are removed, and the overhangs are dressed flush with the core. The second pair of blocks are applied, and in this particular design, these blocks are inletted to take the small squares of maple which make the corner diamond figure.

The maple squares can be tied in with string at the same time as the second pair of blocks are applied. It is important that the inner edges of the small squares come exactly flush with the edge of the core. The build-up proceeds in successive layers. On all central layers, only one set of blocks can be applied at a time; no attempt should be made to rush the work. The overlapping joints at corners are preferably broken all one way. The outer layers, which do not overlap, can be glued face to face at any time, and the double blocks can be fitted to all four faces in one clamping setup. Throughout the build-up, small nails can be used to anchor the wood against slippage when clamping pressure is applied. Needless to say, the nails must be well inside the turning surface.

Overhangs must always be dressed carefully. The shaper or circular saw can be used for this operation. If the circular saw is used, a planer blade is recommended for smooth cutting. As further assurance of perfect fitting, the work should be rubbed on a sheet of 80-grit sandpaper over a level surface. Perfect joints and perfect balance are the two most important points to remember if you want good post-blocked work.

Designing your own built-up post-blocked work is not difficult. An essential is that the work must have a predominating bulge at either top or bottom in order to reveal the pattern of the successive layers.

Segments

Segments are a form of checkerboard pattern consisting of a variety of wedges or segments. Although this appears complicated, it is simply a matter of ripping wedges accurately to a predetermined angle. Tables can be figured out giving data on the size of wedges required for any particular figure or pattern. After finding the dimensions of the pieces required, the wedges are ripped or crosscut, using the circular-saw settings determined by the pattern itself.

A sharp planer blade must be used in order to obtain smooth work ready for gluing. The assembly can be made with any kind of glue. A dry assembly should always be made first to check the joints. Most work of this kind can be clamped after gluing with improvised column clamps or merely twine or rubber strips wrapped around the assembly.

A great variety of color in built-up turnings is unnecessary; in fact, too much color may spoil an otherwise good design. Maple and walnut comprise a good pair for light and dark, while cherry, gum, or oak goes well for a third color.

Jigs and Attachments

Various jigs and attachments add to the convenience and scope of operations accomplished on the lathe. Certain attachments, such as sanding drums and steady rest, are indeed almost indispensable. A vast number of special-purpose jigs can be worked out for the lathe as the need arises.

Sanding drums can be obtained in various sizes, usually mounted on Morse taper shanks. In order to keep these drums securely mounted, it is always best to bring up the tailstock with a plain or ball-bearing center riding against the end of the drum. The sanding table or sanding disk alone is used for a wide variety of finishing work on the lathe. If your lathe does not have a sanding table, it is easy to make a table of wood. A good sanding disk can be made from a disk of wood permanently mounted on an extra 3-inch faceplate.

A surfacing cut across the wooden disk after it is mounted will ensure a perfectly flat base for the sanding disk. Arbors are available for holding grinding wheels, buffing disks, and circular wire wheels for use on the lathe.

The Steady Rest

The steady rest, or center rest, has two important uses in lathe operations. First, it is used as a support when making long turnings of long diameter. Second, it forms a bearing for the free end of the turning when end boring or similar operations are being performed. In the first of these operations, the work is turned down to a cylinder somewhere near the center of the stock. The lathe is then stopped, and the steady rest is mounted over this section. The three supporting arms are adjusted to hold the turning firmly, but the pressure should not be so great as to cause excessive heating. All three arms are reversible. The curve at one end of each arm is greater than at the other end, and the use is determined by the size of the turning.

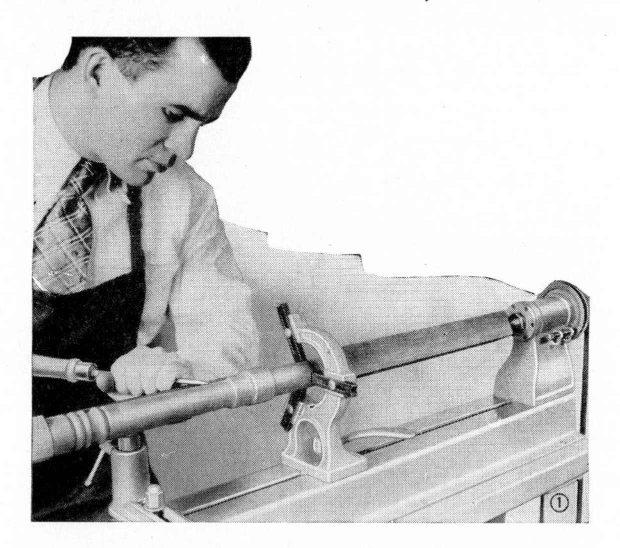

In operation, that portion of the turning between the steady rest and dead center is usually turned first. The live-center end is then turned, and the steady rest is removed. Finishing cuts at or near the point occupied by the steady rest can be run in by making light cuts, supporting the back of the turning with the left hand while using the chisel with the right. In most cases the rest can be shifted a little to permit access to all parts of the turning. You will find that the supporting arms burn the work to a slight extent. Friction can be avoided by using beeswax as a lubricant.

The steady rest is often used to support the free end of the turning for end boring. The same general procedure applies, the rest being properly adjusted before the tailstock is set free from the turning. If possible, the steady rest should contact a shoulder or similar cut, so that it will not only center the work but will also keep it pressed against the live center. This is not strictly essential for end boring, since the drill itself will exert enough end pressure, but it is a necessity when doing end turning.

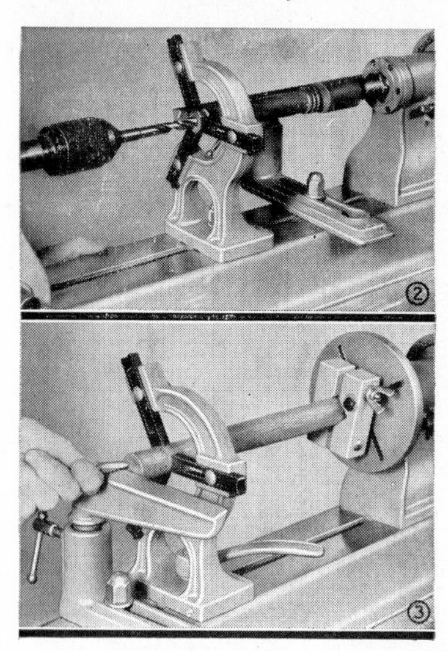

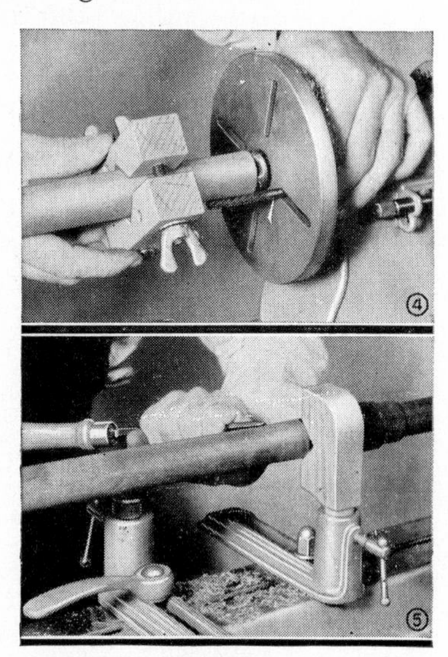

One method of holding the work to the live center when there is no shoulder on the turning against which the steady rest can press is shown in illustrations 3 and 4. It consists of two V blocks which bolt around the work, the blocks in turn being bolted through the slots in the 6-inch faceplate. A simple back rest can be formed with a V block mounted in an extra tool-rest support base. This is a variation of the steady rest and is useful as a support for long turnings.

Finishing Work in the Lathe

Many finishes, such as wax, frictional polish, oil finish, French polishing, and shellac work, can be applied and actually polished while the work remains mounted in the lathe. Of these finishes, French polishing is the most popular. Best results can be obtained on a maple-turning with boiled linseed oil or paraffin oil as a first coat. The polish is made of pure white shellac, boiled linseed oil, and denatured alcohol. These are not mixed in one bottle but are kept in three separate containers. A soft rag (no lint) or absorbent cotton completes the equipment. Both are sometimes used, in the form of a pad of cotton wrapped in cheesecloth. The pad should be about ½ inch thick by 2 inches in diameter. Place the pad over the mouth of the shellac bottle and tip the bottle to fairly well saturate the rag. Then place the pad to the mouth of the alcohol bottle and put on about half as much alcohol as shellac. Add two or three drops of oil. Run the lathe at low speed and apply the pad to the spindle. Hold the pad lightly at first, increasing the pressure until the cloth is almost dry, then add a little more shellac and an equal amount of alcohol and apply again until the pad is almost dry. The operation is repeated until the entire surface of the work is evenly coated. After the first coat has hardened (twenty-four to forty-eight hours), apply a second coat. The second coat is usually more difficult than the first coat. While the first coat was put on with a fairly wet pad, the second and all later coats require a pad just damp with the necessary mix. Gradually increase the proportion of shellac, using just enough alcohol and oil to prevent rings from forming on the work as the shellac piles up. A pure water or alcohol rub is necessary as a final operation to completely remove any oil film.

Metal-working Equipment

Many standard metal-turning operations can be done on the larger wood lathes when they are equipped with low-speed counter-shafts and the necessary tools. Since this partial conversion to metalworking does not include a lead screw, it is impossible to cut threads; however, all other operations, including straight and taper turning, boring, knurling, drilling, and tapping can be done. The general setup for many of these operations is also practical for wood and plastic turning where the precision of a mechanical feed is required.

Compound Slide Rest

This is the name given to the entire unit which slides along the bed of the lathe. It is supported by a base casting and is guided by a machined projection which rides in the central opening of the lathe bed. The slide rest can be clamped at any position along the lathe bed. Above the base is the cross slide, or lower slide, which is used to feed the cutting tool across the work. The lower slide supports the compound rest swivel, which in turn carries the longitudinal, or upper, slide. At the very top is the tool post, with its clamping screw, washer, and rocker.

Standard accessories include the straight tool holder, which has an inclined square hole through one end which is used for mounting any style of ¼-inch-square tool bit used for external turning. The boring-bar holder is used for mounting small boring bars up to ¼ inch in diameter, and it will also take ¼-inch-square tools. Sixty-degree centers, faceplate, and lathe dog are used when work is mounted between centers. The center drill cuts a 60-degree cone-shaped hole and is used to bore the holes for the 60-degree centers.

Lathe Chucks

When the work is not mounted between plain centers, it is generally held and driven by one of two kinds of lathe chuck. One is known as a "universal chuck," having three jaws which move in or out simultaneously through the use of one key. This chuck automatically centers all round stock without further adjustment other than tightening the jaws. The inside and outside jaws are interchangeable to accommodate a wide range of work. The second type of chuck is an "independent four-jaw chuck," so called because its four jaws move in or out independent of one another. The jaws can

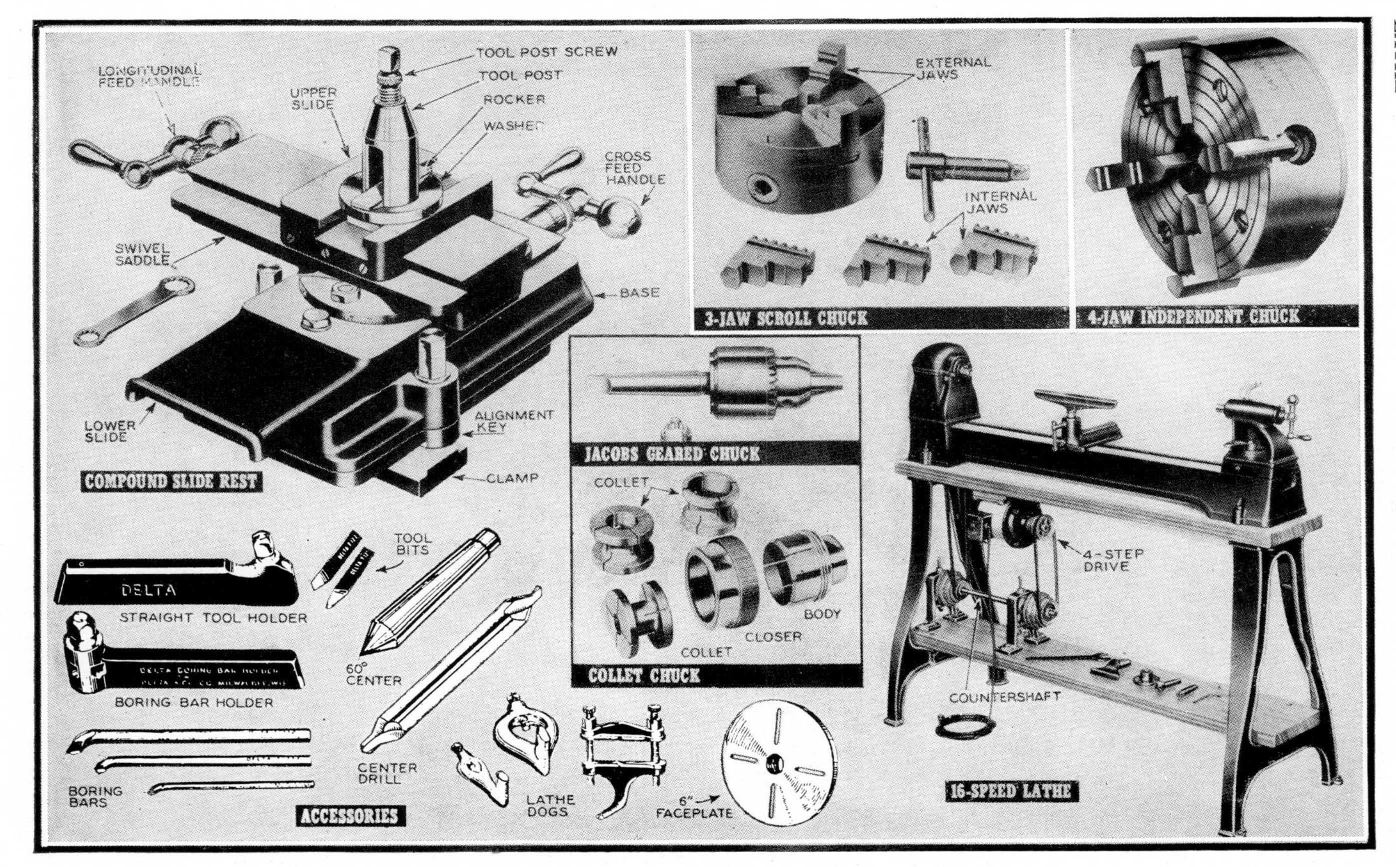
LONGITUDINAL FEED HANDLE
UPPER SLIDE
TOOL POST SCREW
TOOL POST
ROCKER
WASHER
CROSS FEED HANDLE
SWIVEL SADDLE
BASE
LOWER SLIDE
ALIGNMENT KEY
CLAMP
COMPOUND SLIDE REST
EXTERNAL JAWS
INTERNAL JAWS
3-JAW SCROLL CHUCK
4-JAW INDEPENDENT CHUCK
JACOBS GEARED CHUCK
COLLET
BODY
CLOSER
COLLET
COLLET CHUCK
4-STEP DRIVE
COUNTERSHAFT
16-SPEED LATHE
TOOL BITS
DELTA
STRAIGHT TOOL HOLDER
BORING BAR HOLDER
60° CENTER
CENTER DRILL
BORING BARS
ACCESSORIES
LATHE DOGS
6" FACEPLATE

be adjusted to center round stock, while irregular stock can also be centered by the use of the independent adjustment.

Collet Chucks

The collet chuck is useful for holding round work of specific diameters. The body of the chuck shown in the illustration is slotted to take a 2-inch collet. When the internally beveled closer is screwed in place, it squeezes the sections of the slotted body to hold the work securely. Interchangeable collets are mounted inside the body, each collet being bored from both ends to accommodate two sizes—½ and ⅝ inch, ¾ and 1 inch, 1¼ and 1½ inch. For best results the diameter of the work should be net or not more than 0.010 inch undersize.

Drill Chuck

The drill chuck can be used as a work-holding device, but it is intended primarily for holding such tools as drills and reamers. The recommended type is the geared chuck with key. This chuck offers a more positive grip than any type of hand-operated chuck. The drill chuck has a No. 2 Morse shank and can be used in either the headstock or the tailstock as desired.

Speed

The typical wood lathe is a high-speed machine and does not normally offer the low speed required for metal-turning operations. Low speeds as well as the high speeds needed for wood turning are obtained by the use of a countershaft. With the lathe so equipped, the operator has a total selection of sixteen different speeds, ranging from 240 to 3,400 rpm. The power required to drive a wood lathe fitted with a countershaft is more than that for a plain wood lathe and ranges from ⅓ to ¾ horsepower, depending on the nature of the work to be done. For average home workshop use, ⅓ or ½ horsepower can be used, the heavier motor being recommended. The type of motor should be either capacitor or repulsion-induction. A split-phase motor will eventually burn out in starting a load as heavy as this.

Tailstock Adjustments

A setover tailstock is a necessary part of the metal-turning lathe, not only to put the centers in perfect alignment, but to permit the machining of long tapers. This type of tailstock differs from the fixed type in that it can be moved crosswise with the lathe bed as well as lengthwise. The adjustment is made by means of two screws, one on each side of the tailstock. These usually work against a fixed block, and by loosening one screw and tightening the other, the tailstock may be adjusted in either direction from the center line.

In order to check the alignment of the headstock and tailstock, fit 60-degree centers to each spindle, and advance the tailstock until the two centers are touching. If the points are not in perfect alignment, loosen the tailstock clamp and make the required correction with the setover screws. When the centers are aligned, scribe a mark across the joint between the tailstock body and tailstock base to indicate zero. Some lathes have a small pad at one end of the tailstock, with index markings already located. If it is already marked the setting should be checked and re-marked if the original markings are not in line.

Slide-rest Adjustment

The slide rest must be adjusted first so that the base is parallel with the lathe bed. Align the base first by eye approximately square across the lathe bed, and tighten the clamp screws. Advance the tool bit to touch the faceplate mounted on the headstock spindle, and then use the cross-feed to run the tool bit across the surface of the faceplate. The tool bit should maintain its contact, just touching the faceplate all the way from the rim to the center. If it is not in perfect alignment, loosen the bed clamp screws and adjust as needed until correct. After perfect contact is obtained, tighten the setscrews on the underside which hold the alignment key. The cross-feed is now accurately across the lathe and will stay that way regardless of how often the slide rest is removed and remounted on the lathe. The upper slide must now be set so that it will make a parallel cut. To do this, set the slide as nearly as possible by eye or square. Then mount a length of work between centers and turn two collars. Make the first of these cuts at the extreme end of the longitudinal feed toward the faceplate. Make the second cut about 4 inches from the first. Use calipers, and make sure that both collars are *exactly* the same diameter. Now stop the lathe and run the tool bit in until it lightly jams against one of the collars. Mark the reading on the micrometer sleeve, for example, 65. Back off and run the tool up to the second collar. Advance the tool to the collar until it jams lightly as before. Take the reading on the sleeve. It will probably not be the same as the first collar but, for example, 95. This represents a difference of 30 between the two readings. Jam the tool bit against the collar with the higher reading, and then back off half the difference, or to 80. Loosen the adjusting screws and swing the rest until the bit again jams against the work. Tighten the screws. Both collars should now read 80, and the rest is now set to turn parallel. Recheck, and when the final adjustment is made, scribe a mark with a fine, sharp point on the top surface of the cross slide exactly opposite the zero mark on the compound swivel. *Make this adjustment carefully—it is important.*

Metal-turning Operations

In metal turning with a slide rest, the basic idea is to use as high a spindle speed as possible. High spindle speed permits smooth work despite the erratic movement of hand feeding, and the feed itself can be fairly rapid. Use standard tables to find surface speed per minute and revolutions per minute for different materials and diameters of work. The maximum depth of cut in steel is about 1/16 inch, reducing the diameter 1/8 inch in one pass. The feed can be fairly rapid—from ten to thirty complete turns of the feed handle per minute.

Center Drilling

Most lathe work is center-drilled by holding the work in the three-jaw universal chuck while the center drill is advanced by the tailstock. A wide variety of spindle work is done by chucking the work and supporting the center-drilled free end with a 60-degree center.

Since even a good three-jaw chuck may be as much as 0.010 inch off center, work done in this manner must be completed in one chucking. It cannot be rechucked with any degree of accuracy.

Mounting Work between Centers

The usual manner of driving spindle work is the between-centers mounting. The recommended clamp dog is the adjustable style, which fits both round and square stock in a wide range of sizes. The dog is clamped to the work, and the tail of the dog fits into the faceplate slot.

After the work is drilled and mounted between centers, use firm pressure in running up the tailstock center, and then back off slightly to prevent binding. Always oil the tailstock center. Mount a turning tool on the slide rest, and feed from the tailstock end to approximately the center of the work. On the final cut, do not disturb the infeed, but simply stop the lathe and run the tool back to the tailstock end. Now reverse the work, placing the dog on the part already turned. Since the second end is turned at the same tool setting, the work will be of the same diameter throughout, provided that the slide rest is accurately adjusted to turn parallel.

Turning Tools

Lathe tools have a ¼-inch-square body and fit into a square hole in the tool holder. This hole is inclined 15 degrees, so that the point of the tool slants upward or has a positive rake. All tools must be mounted with the point on a level with the work center line. This setting is usually obtained by adjusting the tool to touch the tip of the tailstock center.

A variety of terms are used in describing lathe tools. Front and side clearance are absolutely essential in any tool shape; without clearance, the tool would simply rub against the work and would not cut. The rake angles, back and side, are intended to give the tool the proper "bite" into the work. Back rake is automatically obtained by the position of the tool in the holder, while side rake is ground on the tool itself.

Tool angles vary for different materials. The general idea is that steel takes a heavy positive rake; cast iron, a little less; brass, zero; and aluminum, very heavy positive back rake. In all materials, the front and side clearance angles should run about 10 degrees. Side rake is simply a way of increasing the back rake—if the tool needs heavy back rake, give it some side rake. Beginners are advised to use ready-ground tool bits and in this way gradually pick up a knowledge of tool shapes and why they cut.

Common Operations

Four of the most common operations in metal turning are turning to diameter, facing operations, cutting off, and filing and polishing. In turning work to diameter, after the rough turning is done the

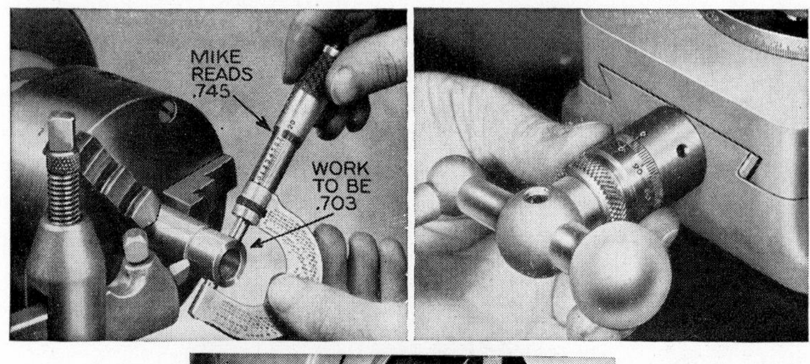

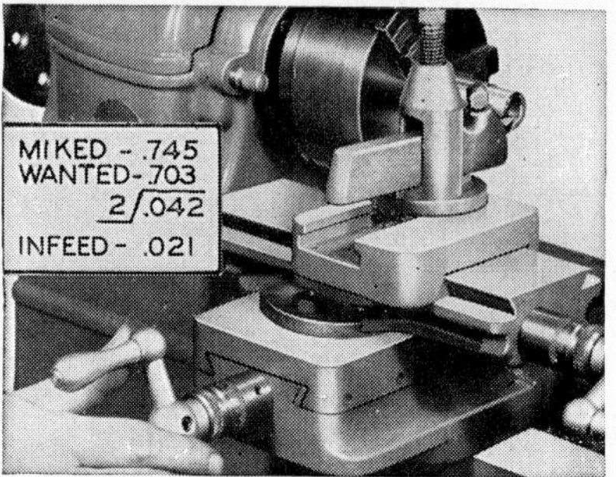

work is miked. The difference between miked size and desired size is divided by two to give the amount of infeed required, which can be made in one or more bits. The tension-fit micrometer sleeve can be rotated (always clockwise) to zero, as shown in the second illustration, to provide a zero for measuring the amount of infeed.

The first illustration shows the operation of squaring an end, using a left corner bit and feeding from inside to outside. When squaring the end of work supported by the tailstock center, it is necessary to use a tool sharpened to about 50 degrees, as shown in the second illustration. Facing on large work is best done with a carbide turning tool, as shown in the third illustration on the right.

Cutting off should be done at low speed and as near the chuck as possible. The work can be supported by the tailstock center until it is reduced to about ¼-inch diameter, after which the tailstock must be pushed out of the way. The use of cutting oil is helpful but not essential. Always use a firm and positive feed—pick up a fair chip and feed fast enough to hold it.

Use long, even strokes when filing, always pointing the file slightly away from the chuck. Do not drag the file backward. Use a file card or brush and keep the file clean. For finishing, 100-grit

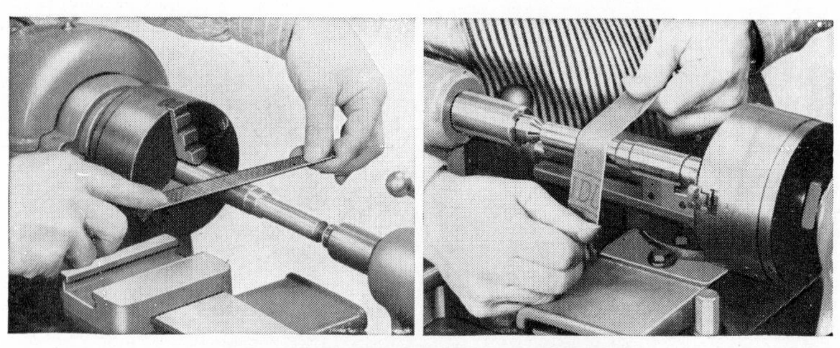

aluminum oxide cloth-backed abrasive is excellent, especially when used with oil. Considerable pressure should be used and is best applied with the abrasive cloth tacked to a board.

Knurling

Knurling is used on metal turnings for both ornamentation and traction. This job is done with a knurling tool, several styles of which are available at your machinery dealer. In use, the knurling tool should be centered with the work, although a certain degree of deviation from a true position is automatically corrected by a pivoting action in the head of the knurling tool.

The secret of good knurling is the application of a fair amount of pressure before the lathe is set in motion. If you are knurling steel, the cross-feed should be jammed in with a heavy turn of the feed handle. Softer metals require less pressure. In any case, the knurling wheels must bite into the metal. For most work, the wheels should be square with the work. A slight angular setting is sometimes useful for picking up the starting bite on hard metals. After the knurling tool is tracking properly, feed the tool slowly along the work. Stop the lathe when the desired area has been knurled, and pick up a second bite with the infeed handle. Feed the tool back to the starting position. Two bites or passes will usually produce a full knurl. Any poor starts will iron out.

Using Drills and Taps

Drilling in the lathe is a practical and essential operation in wood and metal turning. Threading with the use of taps is an allied operation, since the hole for the tap must first be drilled. Since the woodworking lathe has no lead-screw mechanism, taps and dies provide the only method of doing threaded work.

Two general methods are used for drilling. The first and main method requires that the drill be held stationary in a chuck mounted in the tailstock, while the work mounted on the headstock spindle revolves. The feed is usually made with the tailstock feed handle. Specific depths can be set by making a chalk mark on the drill or on the tailstock spindle or by wrapping a piece of tape around the drill. In the second method of working, the drill revolves while the work is held stationary. The feed can be made by pushing on the tailstock or by using the feed handle on the tailstock spindle.

A type of miniature drill table is mounted in the tailstock when the lathe is used as a substitute for the drill press. The pad center, used for all flat work, is combined with a wood facing if the drilling operation is in wood. When the drilling is to be done through the round or side section of circular work, a V block is fastened to the pad to aid in holding the work accurately for drilling.

Reaming provides the best method of producing a smooth and accurate hole, as required for bushings and other precision fits. In general, the operation is carried out in the same way as a drilling operation, except that the lathe speed should be reduced to about two-thirds of the speed which would be required for the same size drill. Holes for reaming should be drilled or board to within 1/64 inch of the required size, leaving just enough stock for the reamer to make a finishing cut.

A common tapping job is done in the lathe by holding the tap in the tailstock, advancing by hand pressure against the tailstock while the tap wrench is used for rotation. The lathe is not under power. The indexing head on the lathe provides a positive stop for the work while the thread is being cut. Always use plenty of cutting oil when doing tap work. The tap most often used is a plug tap having a normal chamfer at the end. The bottoming tap has a full thread almost to the end and must be used if a blind hole is to be threaded all the way to the bottom. The taper tap is commonly used for hand tapping without a guide; its long taper provides accurate entry into the drilled hole.

Turning Plastics

Most plastics are easy to turn, producing conditions midway between wood and the soft metals in general machinability. The two most common varieties of plastics are first, cast resins or phenolics, as represented by Catalin, Bakelite, Cast Resinoid, Trafford, Marblette, Gemstone, and Opalon; second, methyl methacrylate or acrylics, which are sold under the trade names of Plexiglas and Lucite. Other varieties sometimes encountered are the laminates consisting of resin and cloth or paper laminated, represented by such products as Formica, Insurok, and Micarta, and the molded phenolics, incorporating a filler, such as Bakelite, Textolite, Durex, and Durite. Laminates and filled plastics are usually very abrasive and are best turned with carbide tools. The most common cast resins and acrylics are readily turned with ordinary wood-turning chisels.

Practically all plastics should be turned with a tool having negative rake. This means that if you wish to use chisels held in the hand, the handle end is held a little higher than the cutting point. The speed of the work should be about 500 surface feet per minute. The area of tool contact must be held to a minimum. If a wide, flat-nose chisel is held in full contact with the work, it will result in difficult cutting and chatter. The evidence of such a cut is a powdery or sandy chip. When plastic is properly turned, the chip is always like a thin ribbon; if you don't get this ribbon chip, stop the lathe and figure out what is wrong.

The correct way to work a flat-nose chisel is to angle it slightly facing the direction of feed. The round-nose chisel is best for general work. The spear-point chisel is also useful but should be slightly angled to reduce the cutting area to approximately $\frac{1}{8}$ inch. Carbide chisels are almost a necessity for laminates and molded phenolics, both of which are so abrasive as to turn the edge of a standard wood-turning chisel in less than two minutes. Carbide-tipped chisels are also useful for some of the harder cast resins.

Plastic rods are mounted in the same manner as similar metal work. They are mounted between centers or held in a chuck. Lacking a chuck, cylinders are usually mounted on a solid wooden mandrel tapered about $\frac{3}{16}$ inch per foot. The plastic cylinder itself has a slight inside taper, due to the methods used in casting, and the large end should be fitted to the mandrel at the headstock end (the same as the mandrel).

A somewhat similar method of working, as shown in illustration 8, has an advantage in that the driving plug can be used for a number of different sizes of cylinders. The tail plug, however, must have a tight taper fit. An adjustable cone mandrel is worth making if you do a lot of turning on plastic cylinders.

Flat plastic stock is usually mounted by screw-fastening to a wood

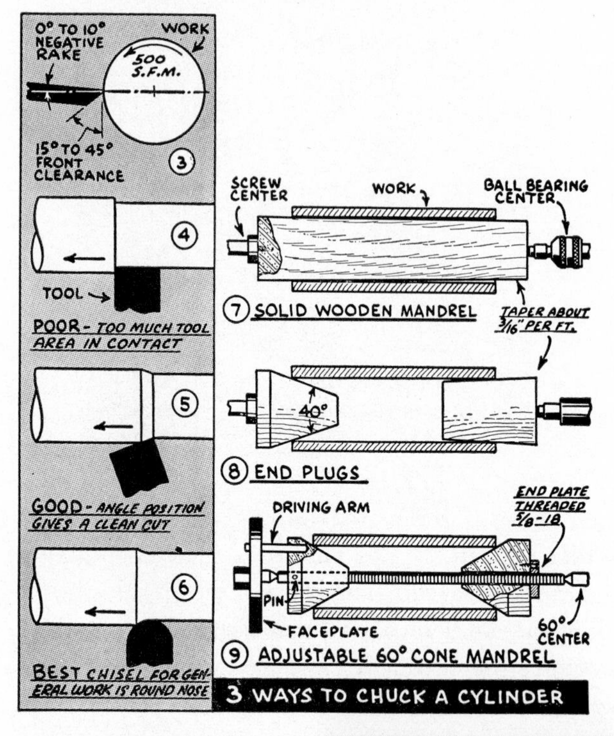

3 WAYS TO CHUCK A CYLINDER

backing block. A recessed chuck and, in general, all methods used for faceplate work in wood, can be used.

Polishing requires the successive use of various grades of sandpaper, followed by buffing compounds. Wherever possible such sanding should be carried out with wet-or-dry sandpaper, using water as a lubricant. The use of water when sanding plastics serves the dual purpose of cooling the surfaces being sanded and of preventing the clogging of the paper with plastic dust. Plastic heats up when too much pressure is applied without water, and when this happens the surface of the plastic will soften and the plastic dust will re-fuse, producing a roughened surface. For these reasons light pressure should be used in sanding operations, and water should be used as a lubricant whenever feasible. Fine steel wood can also be used for polishing. The highest polish is obtained with fine buffing compounds applied with a cloth to the revolving work.

Metal Spinning

Metal spinning is an unusual and novel branch of lathe work. Unlike wood or metal turning, the work is not cut away to form a desired shape but is formed by "spinning" the metal blank over wood or metal forms or chucks. The work is not particularly difficult, especially with soft metals such as pewter and aluminum. Any lathe with substantial headstock bearings can be used, provided that it has a speed range of from 900 to 1,400 rpm. The power unit is preferably ½ horsepower, although satisfactory light spinning can be done with less than this.

Tools and Accessories

Accessory equipment required includes a ball-bearing or live center and a special type of tool rest, consisting of a horizontal bar with a vertical fulcrum pin. Although there are many styles of ball-bearing centers, the type recommended for home workshop use is one having interchangeable centers, as shown on the next page. This is useful for a wide variety of work other than metal spinning.

Many tool shapes are used in forming the metal to shape, but the four patterns pictured will cover most operations. The flat tool is the

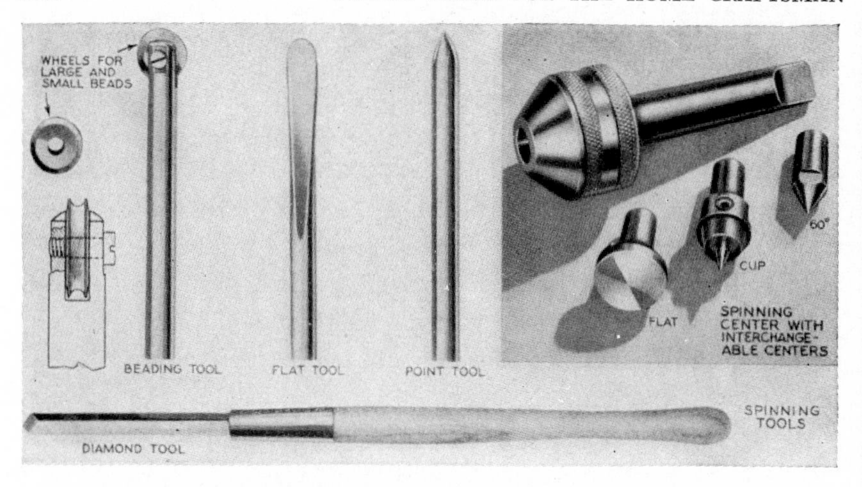

most important. It is a double-faced tool, being round on one side and flat on the other. The round side is used to break down the metal blank almost to the chuck surface, while the flat side is used for smoothing operations. The point tool is both a forming and a finishing tool, being used particularly in small work. The beading tool is used to turn the rim of the metal disk into a lip or true bead. The forming wheel rotates freely within the holder and has interchangeable wheels in different sizes to suit the dimensions of the required bead. The diamond tool is a cutting tool, used for cutting off or trimming the metal.

All spinning tools must be hardened steel and must be highly polished in order to avoid friction or marking of the work. The overall length of each spinning tool is 24 to 30 inches. Soft metals can be successfully spun with the use of oval or round tools of hickory or maple. The backstick is also made of wood and can be a length cut from a discarded broom handle and sharpened to a dull, flat point like a chisel. This is used to back up the metal during the spinning operation.

Setting up the Work

Spinning demands first, a chuck, second, a follow block, and third, the metal blank. A wood chuck must be made up to the exact shape of the proposed tray or spun project. Use a good grade of hardwood for this chuck. It is good practice to turn the chuck an inch or so longer than the proposed spinning, so that there will be some space between the finished spinning and the faceplate. The follow block, or follower, is now turned to shape, either on a separate faceplate or by simply gripping it between the chuck and the spinning center. It should be at least 1 inch thick and of a diameter from ⅛ to ¼ inch less than the base diameter of the project.

All wood chucks should be glazed with soap or beeswax after sanding and the soap or wax forced into the pores of the wood with the flat tool while the chuck is revolving.

The final operation before spinning is to center the metal blank. Where a hole in the center of the work is permissible, direct fastening is recommended. Lubricate the metal on each side with cup grease.

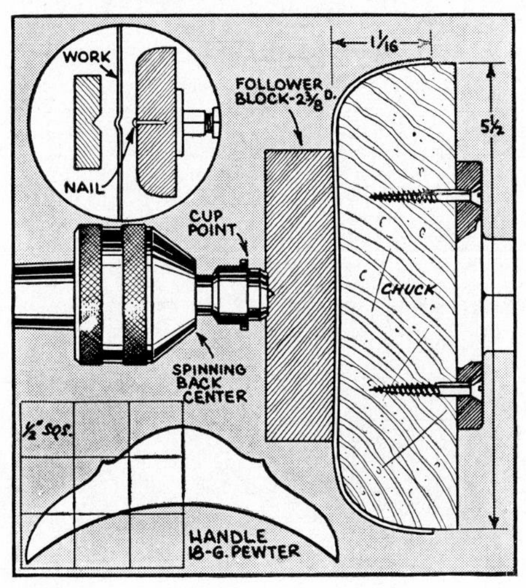

Spinning the Metal

The first operation in spinning calls for the flat tool. This is placed on the rest, to the left of the fulcrum pin. Then, with one or two sweeping strokes using the round side of the flat tool, the disk is seated against the base of the chuck. The backstick is then brought into play, holding up the metal on one side while the flat tool presses against the opposite side. The tool contacts the work well below the center. The tool action is a sweeping stroke, effected by a hunching movement of the shoulders. When the metal begins to seat against the chuck, it will have a tendency to bell out. This must be counteracted with the use of the backstick and flat tool, forcing the rim to spin to a straight funnel shape.

The two essential operations—crowding a small portion of the metal to the chuck surface and keeping the rest of the disk funnel-

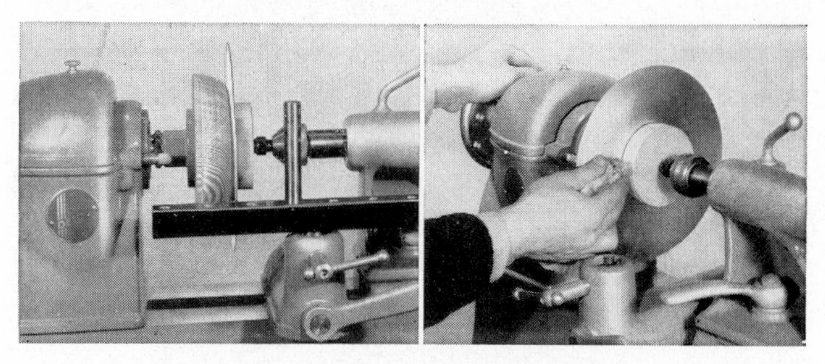

shaped—are carried out in successive operations until the entire shape is complete. The work must be kept lubricated at all times. The general stroking action should be reversed at intervals in order to prevent thinning of the metal at any one spot.

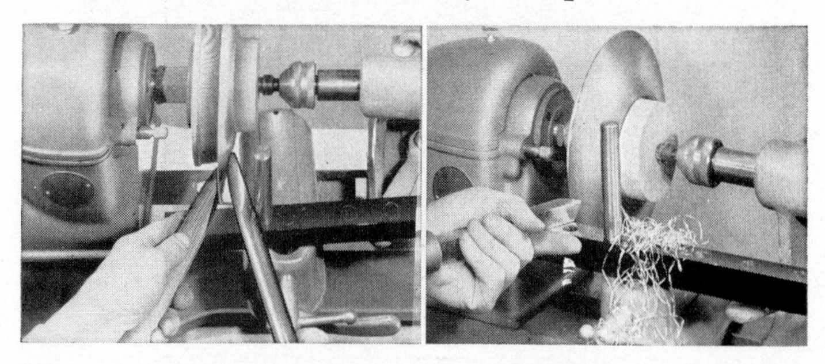

Buckling is usually caused by rushing the work. The operator should not attempt to get an immediate finished shape. Keep in mind that spinning takes time; you don't bear down and form the shape in a couple of minutes. After spinning down tight to the chuck surface, cut the disk free with the diamond tool and dress to a smooth square edge. Solder the pewter handles in place, using pewter solder and applying heat carefully with an alcohol blowpipe, and you have the completed project.

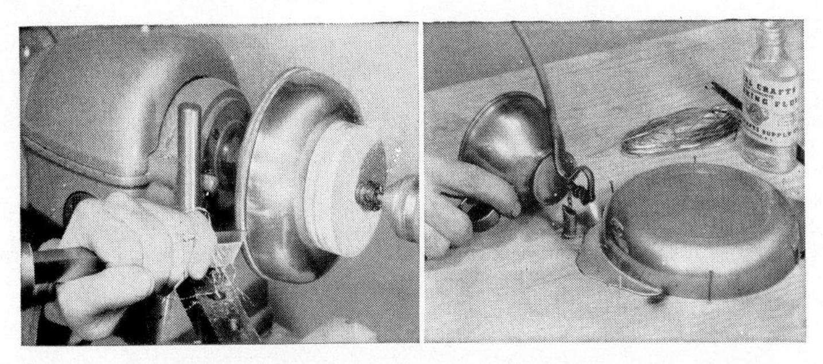

The project in the illustration was a pewter nut bowl. Pewter is a good starting choice, since it spins easily and does not require annealing.

Projects in thin metal sometimes have beaded instead of plain edges. This effect is produced with a beading tool. The edge of the metal is first trimmed square, using the diamond cutoff tool. The point of the flat tool is then used to lift a small portion of the metal from the chuck surface. Once the edge is lifted, the beading tool is used by taking the edge of the metal in the hollow portion of the wheel and swinging the tool to the right, causing the edge to turn completely over and forming the bead. A little experience is required for good work.

Shallow projects such as ash trays and plates can be worked entirely on a hollow chuck. In this case the wood chuck is turned with a hollow concave surface, which is just the reverse of the convex chuck used in spinning the nut bowl.

A wide variety of split chucks and sectional chucks can be made up for specialized spinning jobs for the more advanced craftman.

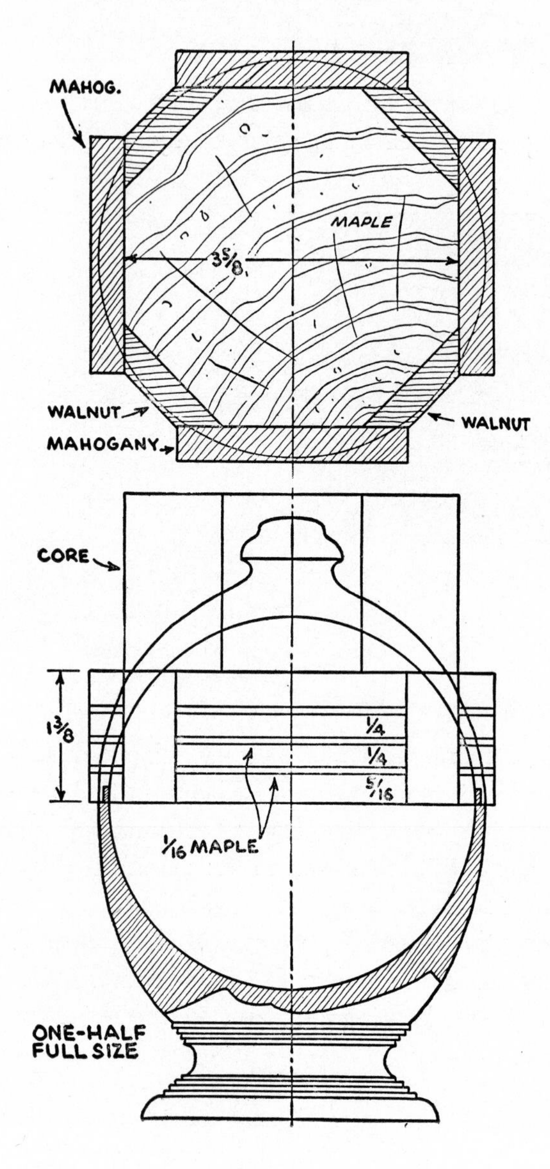

Lathe Projects

There are many complete projects in which almost all the work is done on the lathe alone. The built-up turned box is a project illustrating the post-blocked method of making turned work, previously described. See drawing opposite and the following photographs.

The turned pedestal table is a project which makes use of both spindle and faceplate turnings. The main stem and three legs are spindle turnings made by following the instructions in the section on the turning of spindles. The bridge and table top are turned on the 6-inch faceplate, both turnings being done on the outboard end of the lathe.

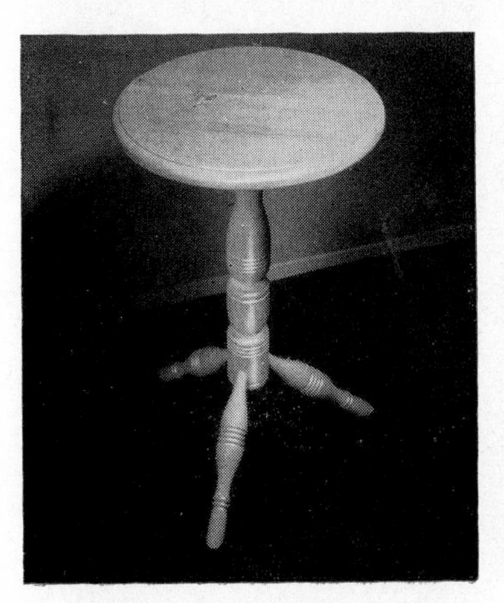

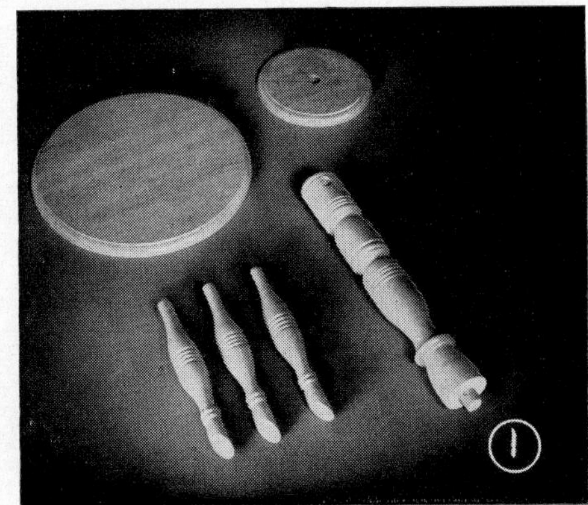

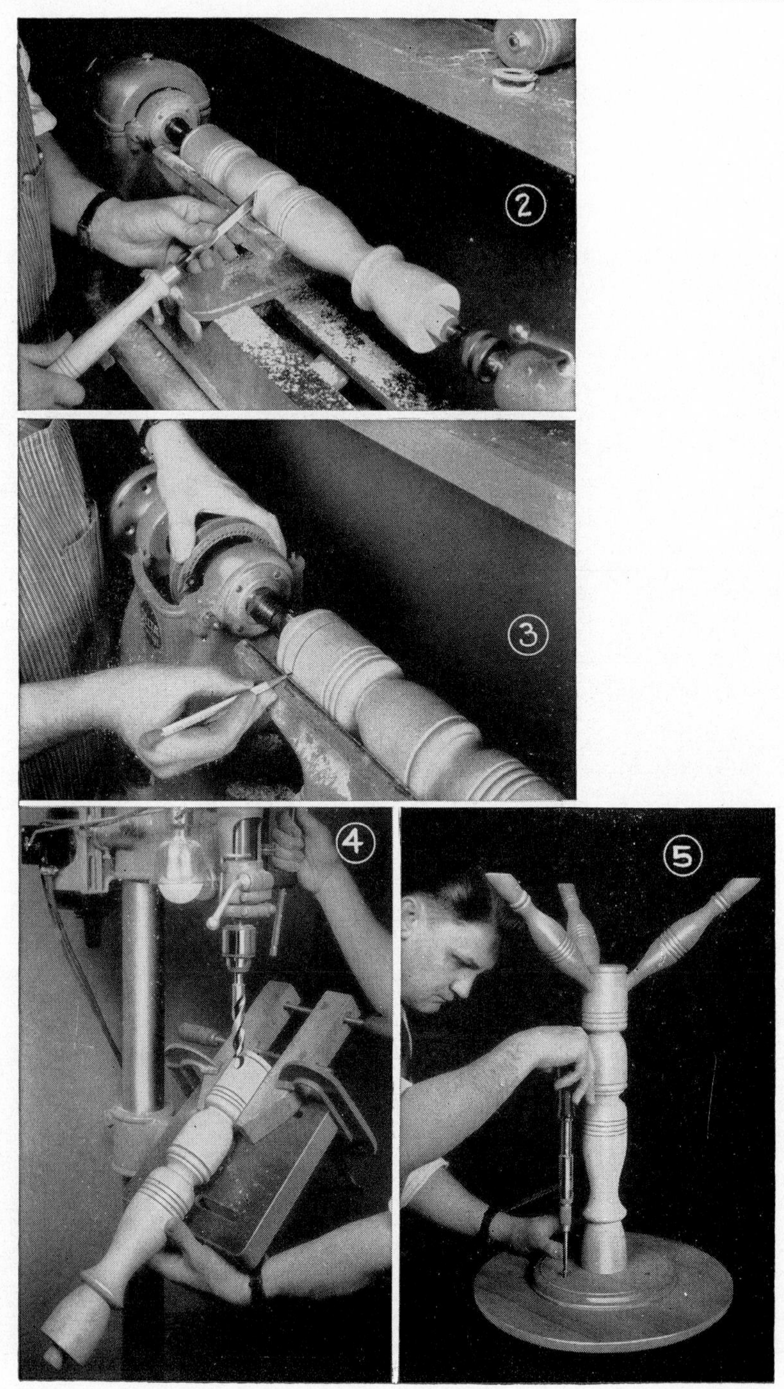
2
3
4
5

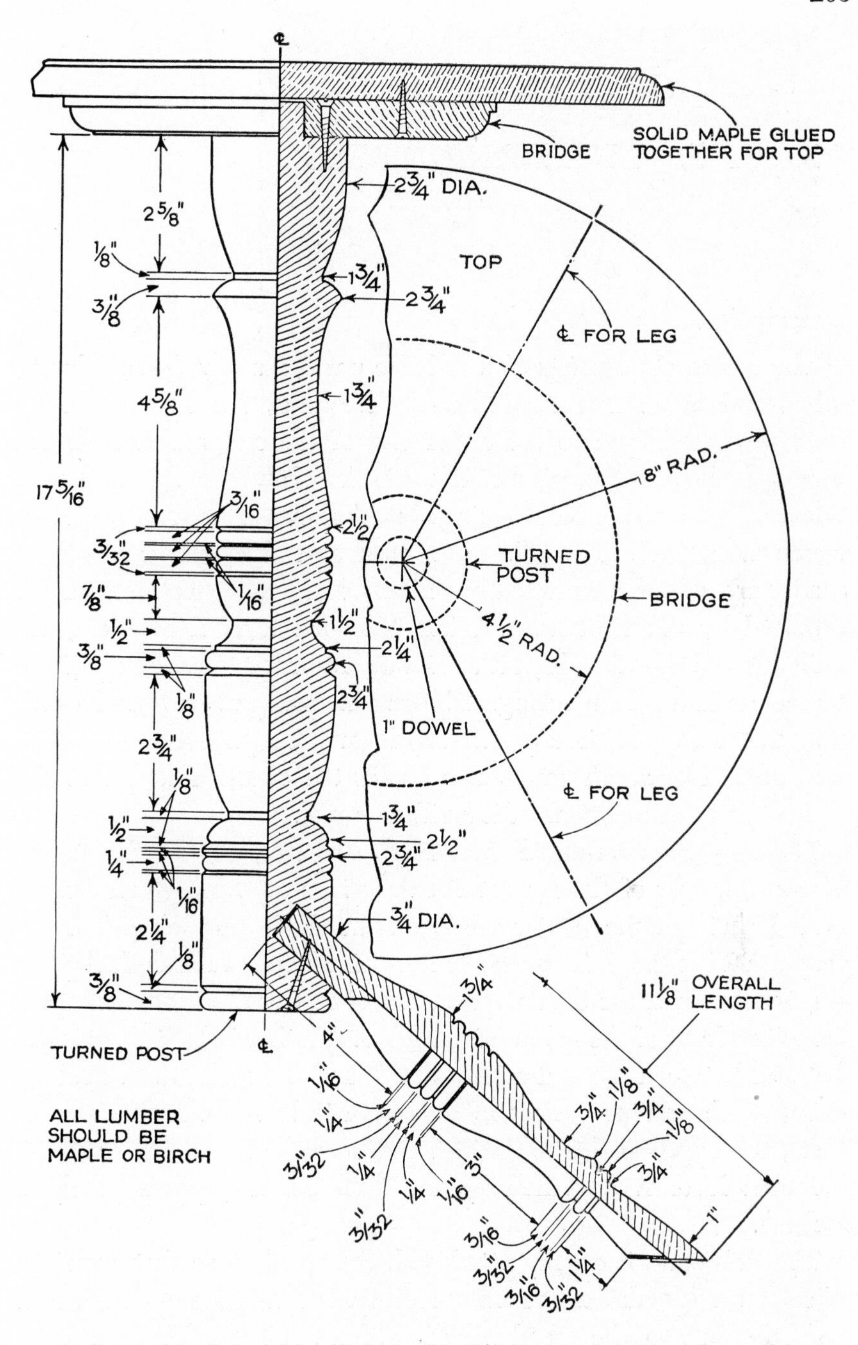
SOLID MAPLE GLUED TOGETHER FOR TOP
BRIDGE
2 3/4" DIA.
TOP
℄ FOR LEG
8" RAD.
TURNED POST
BRIDGE
4 1/2" RAD.
1" DOWEL
℄ FOR LEG
3/4" DIA.
11 1/8" OVERALL LENGTH
17 5/16"
TURNED POST
ALL LUMBER SHOULD BE MAPLE OR BIRCH

Chapter 7. THE DRILL PRESS

Description

The drill press consists of four basic parts, namely, base, column, table, and head. The term "head" designates the entire working mechanism attached to the upper end of the column. The central part of the head is the spindle. The spindle revolves in a vertical position and is housed in ball bearings at either end of a movable sleeve, which is called the "quill." The quill and the spindle which it carries are moved downward by means of a rack-and-pinion gearing, actuated by the feed lever. When the feed lever is released, the quill and the spindle which it carries are returned to normal position by means of a return spring. Adjustments are provided for locking the quill in any required position by means of a pair of depth-gauge stop nuts. The depth gauge also allows the operator to preset the depth to which he wishes the quill to travel.

The drill press is named according to its size, expressed in terms of the diameter of the largest circular piece of work which can be drilled through the center while on the drill-press table. For example, a 14-inch circle can be center-drilled on a 14-inch drill press —in other words, the distance from the center of the headstock spindle to the front of the column is 7 inches. Another index to size is the distance between the end of the spindle and the table, this of course being much greater in floor models than in bench models. In both cases, the depth of the hole which can be drilled with one stroke of the feed lever is governed by the quill travel (approximately 4 inches).

The drill press is usually fitted with cone pulleys so that a variety of selective speeds can be obtained. With a 1,725-rpm motor and four-step pulleys, the speed will range from 590 to 5,000 rpm. Since

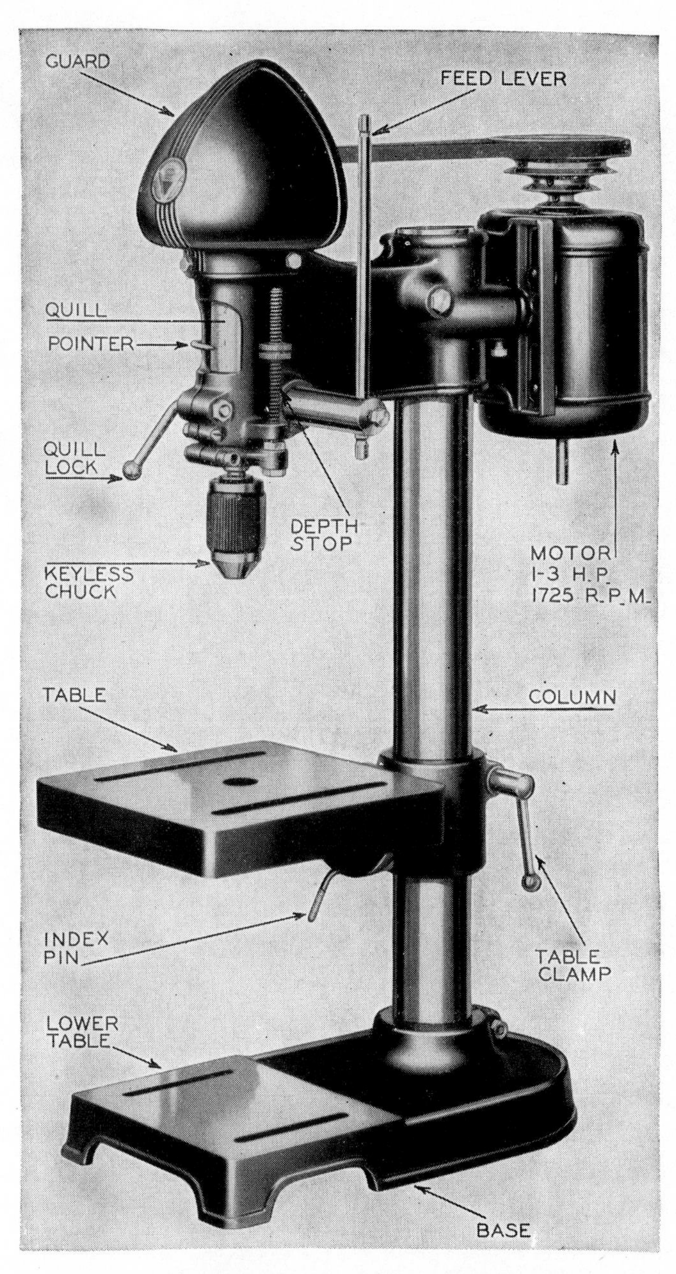

14-INCH BENCH MODEL DRILL PRESS

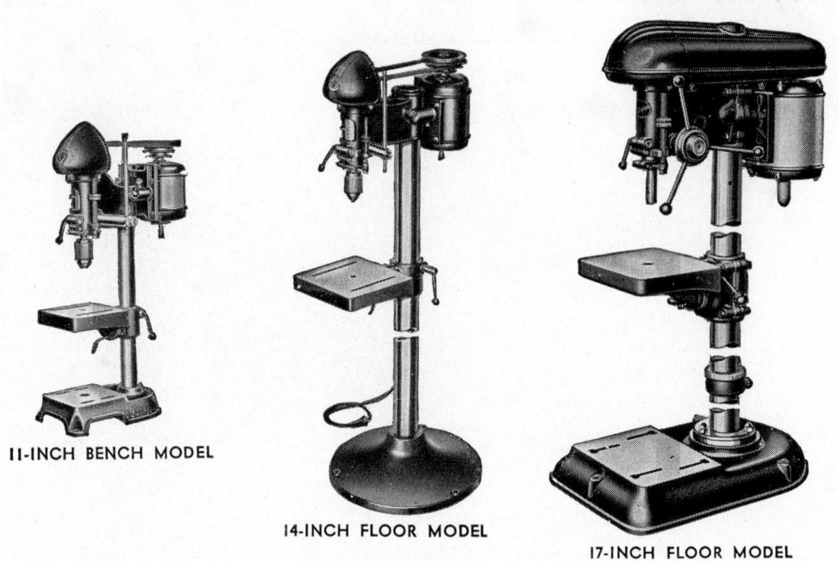

11-INCH BENCH MODEL

14-INCH FLOOR MODEL

17-INCH FLOOR MODEL

the shaft stands vertical, only a motor designed for vertical mounting should be used as a power unit. A ⅓-horsepower is sufficient, since this is approximately the power required to drill a ½-inch hole through steel.

Interchangeable spindles are supplied for most drill presses, thus adapting the machine for a wide variety of work. The standard spindle holds a ½-inch capacity gear, or keyless chuck.

Setup and Adjustment

The manner of inserting any spindle in the type of drill press shown is as follows: The quill is turned down to expose the collar which holds the upper end of the spindle. With the quill locked in this position, the spindle may be withdrawn downward through the quill. It may be necessary to tap the upper end of the spindle lightly with a wooden mallet in order to loosen it in the quill. The spindle is replaced in exactly the opposite manner, twisting the upper cone pulley back and forth as the spindle is started through the quill, so that the splines in the spindle will enter the keyways inside the quill assembly. With the spindle fully seated, the collar must be relocked to the spindle. The process of removing and replacing spindles may

B-T HACKSAW

Powerful, portable, pocket size! Saws wood, plastic, steel and sheet metal, pipe, plaster board, Celotex. Ideal for scroll work. Full ½" chip clearance. Weighs only 11 oz., folds up into pocket or tool box with blade protected. A "must" for home craftsmen, electricians, carpenters, plumbers, etc. Only **4.95**

"EDGER-N-HEDGER"

Now you can use your ¼" electric drill to trim grass, shrubs, bushes, weeds — quickly, electrically! New Edger-'n-Hedger reaches everywhere, keeps you off your hands and knees.

4-IN-1 HOLE SAW

Cuts 1", 1½", 2", 2½" holes through any ¾" stock. Used by craftsmen and tradesmen everywhere to cut holes for plumbing, conduits, pipe, outlets, drains, toys, etc. A real help when making modern furniture and fixtures in your shop. Comes complete with 4 blades, yet costs less than you would expect to pay for one — only **4.95**

Your ELECTRIC DRILL becomes a PORTABLE POWERHOUSE with these time-tested, time-saving ROTEX tools!

An electric drill is just a drill—until you team it up with these Rotex attachments. Then your drill becomes a portable powerhouse that quickly does scores of jobs that are difficult or impossible to do by hand. So start making the most of your drill; see and order these Rotex tools today—for Christmas gifts . . . for your own workshop!

ROTO SABRE SAW

A heavy duty hacksaw for any ¼" electric drill that out-performs saws selling for $25.00 up. Goes through wood, plastic, steel and sheet metal, pipe, plaster board, Celotex like hot butter! All parts of specially designed alloy steel machined to exacting standards, hardened and ground to close tolerance. Because the blade makes only one stroke for two revolutions of your ¼" drill, it is easy to operate, won't burn saw blades. Comes complete with 3 blades (one for heavy wood, one for scroll work, one for metal). Only **11.95**

"RIDGE RUNNER"

It's a 1", 2" and 3" portable drum

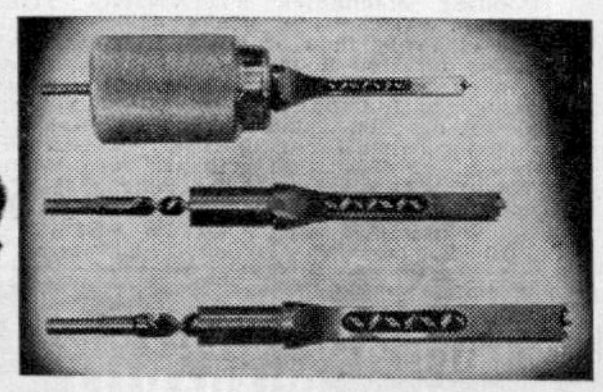

ROTO MORTISING KIT

When you need to drill "square holes" here's the powerful mortising tool that really makes the chips fly. The quick way to recess hinges and hardware; ideal for making furniture joints. Kit includes Roto Mortising Adapter cut from solid aluminum with double-shield ball bearings and 1/4", 3/8" and 1/2" chisels with corresponding bits. Fits any 1/4" electric drill or drill press. Complete, ready to chuck in your drill.. **23.90**

ROTO UTILITY KIT

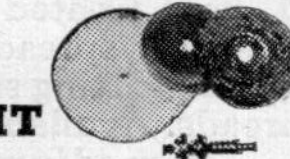

Includes 2 1/2" grindstone, 3" wire brush, 4" cloth buffing wheel and "drive shaft" that chucks into your drill. Use it on metals, to polish, buff, grind, scrape, sharpen, remove rust, paint, scale, etc. Complete, only.. **2.95**

HACKSAW-SANDER KIT

Kit includes reciprocating sander with 3"x6" surface for rough or fine finishing with grain . . . plus famous B-T Hacksaw attachment for wood or metal. Sander takes full 1/2" stroke. Perfect for polishing and rubbing out finishes with oil and pumice. Sanding sheets easy to change. Comes complete with 6 sandpaper sheets, 2 hacksaw blades and polishing kit, all for only........ **8.95**

HEDGE TRIMMER

Just chuck the Roto Hedge Trimmer in your 1/4" electric drill, and you've got a "power mower" that does all the work for you! The shuttle action of the 9" hardened high carbon steel blade clips any hedge cleanly . . . quickly . . . more evenly than you can do by hand. Also ideal for trimming grass around walls, house, trees, shrubs, etc. Blade can be turned to any angle. Light, easy to carry. No vibration. Complete, ready to chuck in your drill **12.95**

HORIZONTAL DRILL STAND

At last! a drill stand that won't shake or shimmy! It's the Roto Drill Stand — a rugged, sturdy cast stand that holds your drill firmly while you polish, buff, grind, scrape, sharpen, remove paint, scale, rust, etc............ **3.95**

If you do not own a grindstone, wire brush, cloth buffer, and arbor, order Roto Utility Kit (shown on this page) for only $2.95 extra.

Mr. B. of California writes "The lawn mower grinding business, with my Universal Grinder, **has been a gold mine** these last two years." Mr. J.L.P. of Pennsylvania says "Thank you for getting me started in this wonderful business . . . I **averaged $100.00 per week** for the month of May."

ONLY ON THE UNIVERSAL LAWN MOWER GRINDER

. . . can the inside face and edge of the stationary blade, as well as the reel blades, be ground to proper clearance

ALL IN ONE SET-UP

WITHOUT REMOVING ANY BLADE FROM THE MOWER

Users who have tried them all acclaim the UNIVERSAL far above any grinder on the market. Write today for full details of our Proved Success Plan. It's Free.

ROGERS MFG. CO., DEPT M-113, LINDSEY, OHIO

SEND THIS COUPON NOW

ROGERS MFG. CO., Dept. M-113, Lindsey, Ohio
Please send me full details about the profit possibilities of Lawn Mower Sharpening.

NAME________________

ADDRESS________________

CITY__________ STATE__________

HAVE A BIGGER — MORE EFFICIENT HOME WORKSHOP

Popular Mechanics PLANNING YOUR HOME WORKSHOP shows you how to make use of every inch of space in your workshop; detailed floor plans, wiring layouts and power tool hookups plus actual photographs of famous home workshops you can use as models. Save money by building your own shop furniture. Special Where-to-Buy It Guide. 450 Illustrations. Cloth Bound Working Diagrams. Order your copy today from **$2.5**

POPULAR MECHANICS PRESS
200 E. Ontario Street Chicago 1

MACMILLAN RING FREE *Xtra Heavy Duty* is the *ONLY motor oil to* GUARANTEE:

- to prevent Valves and Hydraulic Lifters from sticking
- to reduce Engine Ping... ***or Your Money Back!***

For further information write: R. S. MACMILLAN, PRES.
530 West 6th St., Los Angeles, Calif.

M M

ARMSTRONG

Drop Forged "C"—CLAMPS

Buy once, for life. These famous drop-forged, heat treated clamps will not creep, spring, spread or break. Screws have close fitting smooth operating threads. Available in heavy duty, medium service, extra deep throat and welding types. Recognized throughout industry as the very finest.

Write for catalog.

ARMSTRONG BROS. TOOL CO.
"The Tool Holder People"
5268 W. Armstrong Ave., Chicago 30, U.S.A.

vary slightly with drill presses produced by different manufacturers. The basic principles, however, are much the same. Be sure to check the manufacturer's own literature when making adjustments or replacing parts.

The belt tension is adjusted by moving the motor closer or farther from the spindle. A locking device is provided to locate the motor in the required position. The belt should not be too tight; there should be a small amount of slack, so that the belt can be compressed slightly with the fingers. Adjusting the belt too tight will cause excessive wear on it and also on the motor and spindle bearings. The added friction will also absorb power unnecessarily.

Drills should be inserted in the chuck and removed carefully, so that the lips are not injured by dropping the drill on the table. On no account should the drill be loosened from the chuck unless the hand is in position to prevent it from falling.

In average drilling operations, the hole in the center of the table should be directly under the drill, so that the drill, after going through the work, will enter the hole in the table. When through drilling is done, the feed handle should always be actuated without the work in place, to see that the drill enters the table opening.

The purpose of the spindle return spring is to automatically return the spindle upward to the starting position after the hole has been drilled. A coil spring enclosed in a metal case is fitted to the side of the drill-press head for this purpose. The spring is usually adjusted at the factory and requires no additional adjustment. If, however, the spindle fails to return to a normal position, or if the return is too violent, the tension should be adjusted accordingly. This is done by loosening the lock nuts which hold the case in place. They should not be completely removed but simply backed off a fraction of an inch, enough so that the case can be pulled out to clear the bosses on the head. As the case is pulled out, it must be held tightly to prevent the spring from unwinding. The case is turned clockwise to loosen the spring, counterclockwise to tighten it. The lock nuts are then retightened.

The table can be tilted by loosening the lock nut under the table. A locating pin with a series of holes is usually provided to form positive stops at both the level and the vertical positions. Where average work requires the setting of the table to various angles, it is advisable to attach a scale and adjustable pointer to the underside of the table to locate these positions.

Laying out the Work

Practically every hole that is drilled requires that first of all a layout mark be made which will locate either its approximate or its exact position. Various tools are used in making the layout, ranging from square, hammer, and punch to expensive instruments essential for very exacting work. One of the most useful of these tools for average work is the combination square. If the layout work is required on metal, a scriber or punch is substituted for the pencil used in layouts on wood. Various substances and devices are used to mark on a variety of materials. Rough cast iron, for example, may be given a coating of white chalk so that layout marks will be plainly visible. A strong solution of copper sulfate on polished steel will cause the scriber marks to stand out for the operator's benefit. A 20 per cent solution of silver nitrate is preferred by many craftsmen for copper or brass. After the scriber or pencil has been used to locate the hole position, it is necessary to indent this point farther. This is done with a center punch. There are various sizes of center punches, and the size selected will depend on the work and the accuracy which is

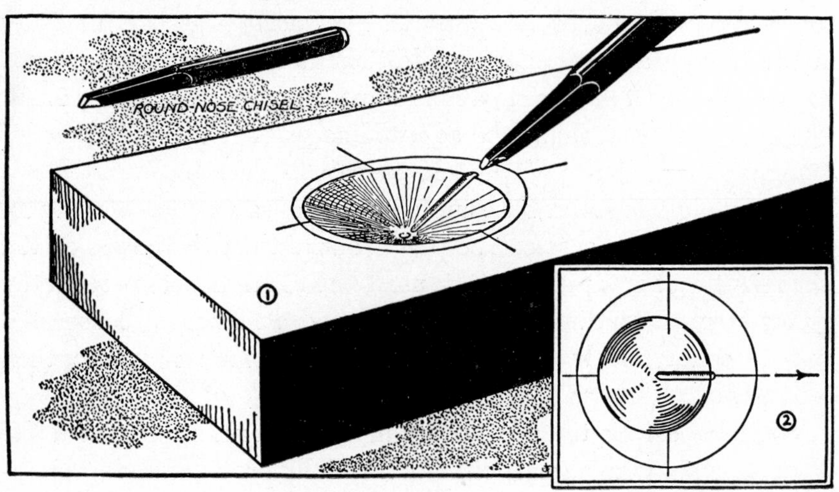

required. Center punching should be done carefully, so that the punch mark comes at the exact intersection of the layout lines. Despite care in laying out and clamping, it will sometimes be found, after the drill has cut a few revolutions into the work, that the hole is off center. The drill may be led back to the proper position by cutting from one to three or more grooves with a small round-nose chisel, the grooves being on the side toward which it is desired to draw the hole. When the drill is again started, it should drift over to the correeect position. This must be done before the drill starts to cut its full diameter.

Wood Bits

The illustration shows two common styles of wood bits. One has a screw point, the other has a brad, or diamond, point. The first has a solid center, with a single spiral running around it. The other is a

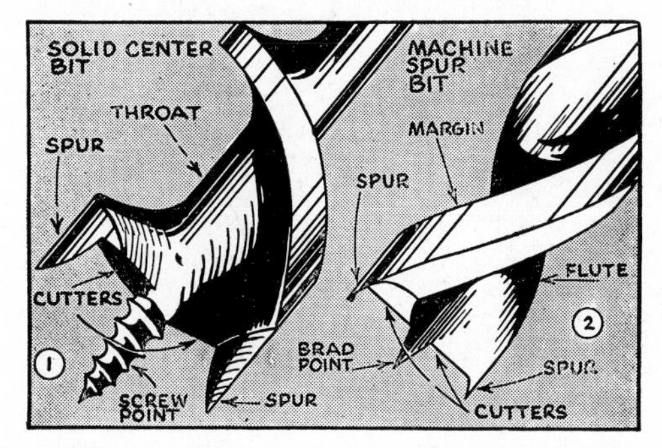

double-twist bit. The cutting edges are very similar. The opening between the spiral is called the "throat," also designated in some styles of double-twist bits by the term "flute." Both terms mean the same thing.

All cutters intended for working in wood are given the general name of "bits"; those used in metal cutting are known as "drills." A distinction is sometimes made in the cutting operation, the term "boring" applying to holes in wood, while "drilling" means a cutting operation in metal. In general practice, the term "drilling" applies to operations in either metal or wood.

The next illustration shows a hollow spiral bit. It has a screw point and one cutting edge and differs from all others in that the center is hollow to permit the passage of chips. This bit cuts very fast and is used extensively for deep holes. It does not make a smooth hole.

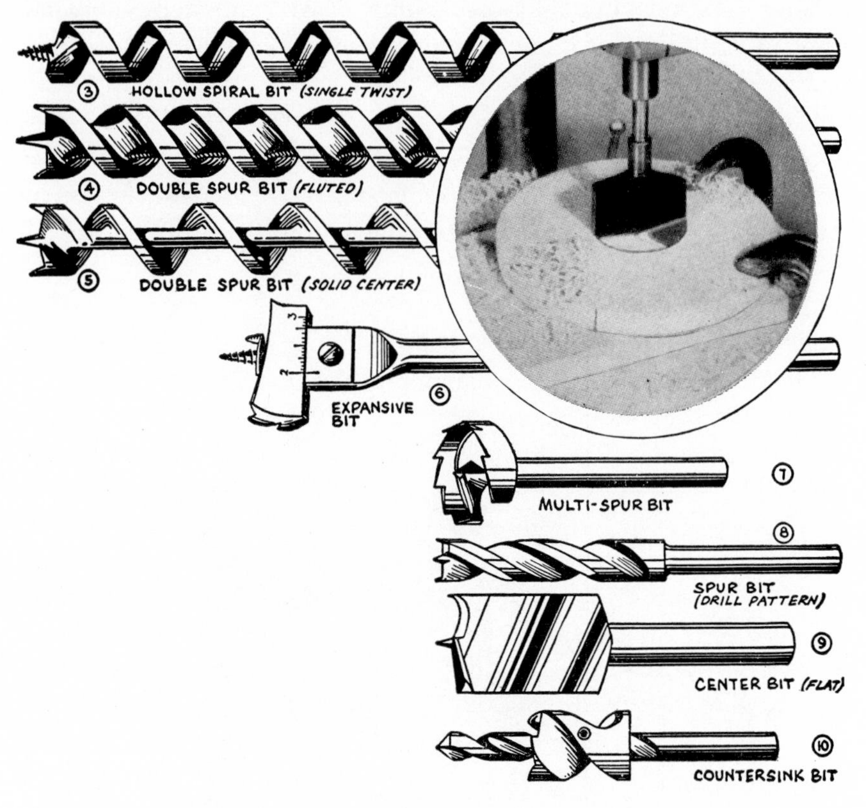

The next two shown are double-spur bits. This descriptive term is quite general and is derived from the fact that each bit has two spurs at the end. Number 4 could also be described as a double-twist fluted bit, while number 5 is a single-twist solid-center bit. Both bits could also be described by the term "extension-lip bit." It can be seen that while the solid-center bit has two cutting edges, one of these terminates directly back of the head. Both these bits cut rapidly and smoothly. Number 4 gives the cleaner hole, and number 5 is the stiffer.

Number 6 shows the common style of expansive bit. The single cutter can be moved in or out in the groove in order to cut any size hole within its capacity. This bit can be used on the drill press, but the work should be securely clamped, since the single cutter has a decided tendency to throw the work. An excellent bit for large holes is the multispur pattern. Number 8 shows a double-spur bit in a twist-drill pattern. It is one of the cleanest and fastest-cutting styles of wood bit. Number 9 shows a center bit, useful for large shallow holes. This bit is flat, with one spur and one cutting edge. Like the expansive bit, it is dangerous in action unless the work is clamped. Number 10 shows a countersink bit. This type can be obtained in various sizes and is most useful in production work, where the cutting of both hole and countersink in one operation speeds the work.

The various bits described show both screw and brad points. Both are used in drill-press work. The brad point is much more suitable for average work in the home workshop. The screw point is a necessary feature when drilling by hand, since the prime purpose of the screw point is to draw the bit into the work. This is unnecessary for a bit used on the drill press with the feed lever which it provides. Where screw-point bits are used on the drill press, the rate of feed must be the same as the lead of the screw; otherwise the bit will lift the work and prove generally unsatisfactory. Where screw-point bits are part of the shop equipment, it is advisable to partly file off the threads so that the point gives the same action as a brad point.

Conditioning Bits

The first essential in keeping wood bits in good condition is to keep them well polished. Chips are ejected easily when the flutes are clean and smooth. A rusty bit will clog and burn, because of the difficulty in ejecting chips from deep holes. Bits are easily kept clean by polishing them lightly with steel wool. A thin film of oil should be placed on bits which are not used frequently.

Wood bits are sharpened by filing. The equipment for this should include a small half-round file, an auger-bit file with safe edges, and a small triangular file. This will take care of almost any bit in the home workshop. All bits have the same general features and are sharpened in the same manner. The two points which must be sharpened are the cutting lips and the outlining spurs.

On common styles of wood bits, and also on wood bits of the twist-drill pattern, touch-up filing is done through the throat, using either the half-round file (if the throat is rounded and small) or the auger-bit file (if the throat is open). Spurs are always sharpened on the *inside,* never on the outside. An auger-bit file should be used with the uncut edges against the lip surface, as shown in illustration 2, for

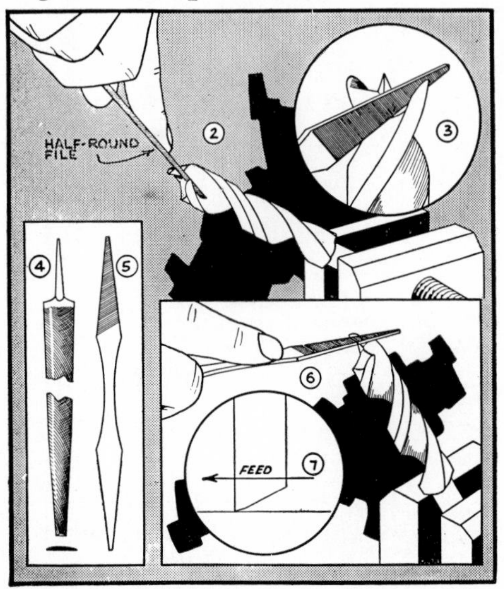

filing the spur. For more complete sharpening, when the bit is quite dull, the top of the cutting edge is filed as shown in illustration 5. It is important here that the original bevel be maintained and that the cutting surface be filed *flat* completely across. If only a small portion of the lip is filed, a condition similar to that shown in illustration 6 arises. This diagram shows a tool with a cutting edge or bevel. If, in filing, only the point of the cutting edge is filed, the rake angle of the bevel is lessened. When this happens to a drill, the chip-lifting ability of the cutting edge is destroyed. As the bit wears down, the various angles of the cutting lips, spurs, and point should be compared with a new bit of the same pattern, so that proper shape of all surfaces can be maintained.

Other Bits

Various other bits are useful in the average home workshop. Router bits in the double-flute pattern are obtainable in various sizes from $\frac{3}{16}$- to $1\frac{1}{2}$-inch diameter. Smaller sizes, from $\frac{1}{8}$ to $\frac{3}{8}$ inch, are also obtainable in a single-flute pattern. Both styles cut a flat-

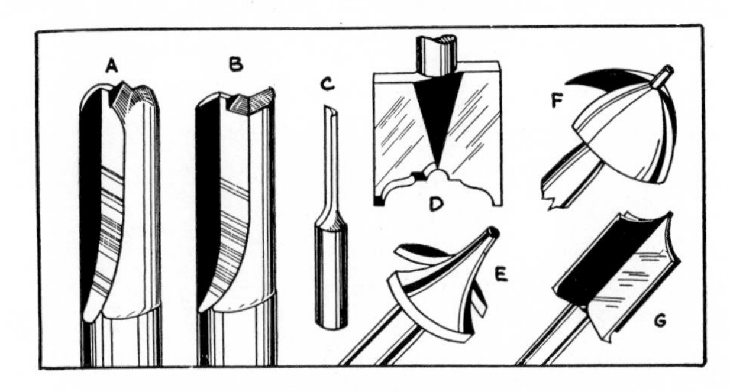

bottom hole but can be ground to cut round-bottom holes or to any other shape. Rosette cutters are available in a wide variety of different patterns. End cutters are useful for rounding over and general shaping operations on small work which will not permit the swing of a regular cutter.

Plug cutters can be obtained in sizes from $\frac{3}{8}$ to 1 inch. Cross-

grained plugs up to 1 inch thick can be cleared through the center opening, while the full length of the cutter will make dowels up to 2 inches long.

Mortising equipment consists of a hollow chisel with four cutting edges, which cuts a square hole. A bit, somewhat similar to an ordi-

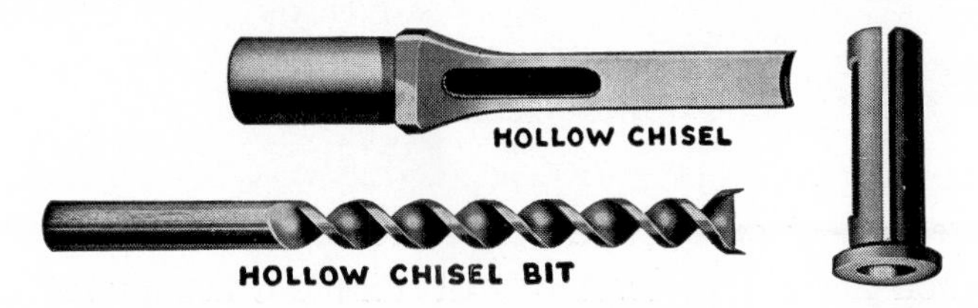

nary wood bit but without a point, works inside the chisel and removes the bulk of the wood. Bushings are usually supplied for the bits, so that any size bit can be mounted in the $\frac{1}{2}$-inch-hole spindle.

The common style of twist drill used for metal work can also be used successfully in wood. If the drills are used exclusively for woodwork, the point angle should be ground to about 40 degrees, instead of the 59-degree angle used for metalwork.

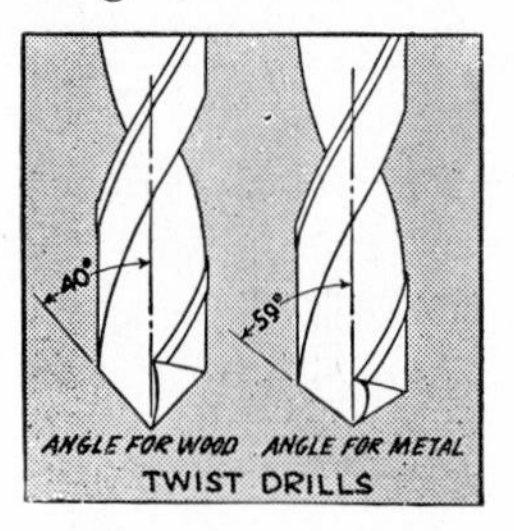

Other Accessories

Various sizes of sanding drum are used on the drill press. The smaller sizes have ½-inch shanks to fit the ½-inch-hole spindles; larger sizes have a ½-inch hole and are fitted to the spindle by means of a short length of ½-inch metal rod.

A large variety of flat and cup grinding wheels can be readily mounted on the drill press. A special spindle is usually supplied for this purpose.

Drilling in Wood

Spur bits in sizes up to about ¾ inch should be worked at a speed between 1,800 and 3,000 rpm. No specific speed for any particular size of bit can be given, since too many factors—wood, grain, depth of hole, style of bit, etc.—affect the cutting speed. In general, smaller bits can turn faster than large ones, more speed can be used on softwoods, less speed should be used for deep holes, and more speed can be used for end boring. Large bits must always be run at slow speeds. Multispur and expansive bits will burn if worked much over 600 rpm.

The first step in boring a hole is to properly lay out and mark the position of the hole. The table should be located so that the bit will pass through the table opening after the hole has been drilled. The drill is projected into the work by pulling on the feed lever. The feed should not be excessive and should be slowed down when the operator judges the drill to be almost through the work. Excessive feed at this point will tear rough splinters out of the underside of the board around the hole. Since it is hard to judge when the hole is

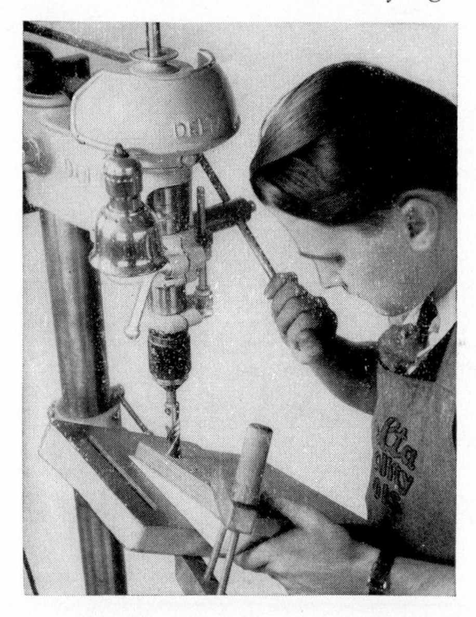

almost through, most workers prefer to use a wood base block under the work. The drill passes through the work and into the block, giving a perfectly clean edge on the underside of the hole. The spur of the bit must be sharp, since on these depends the cleaness of the hole as the bit breaks through the wood.

When a hole is to be bored at an angle, the proper slant is taken from the work with a set square. The set square is then used to set the drill table at the correct angle in relation to the drill.

Most drill presses are equipped with a depth gauge. To drill work to depth, the work is placed under the bit, and the bit is brought down until the point penetrates the work. The quill is locked in this position. The pointer is then set at some convenient mark on the scale, the quill lock is released, and the hole is drilled by adding the required depth to the previous pointer marking. The feed handle is pressed until the required depth is reached, after which the feed lever is released.

Drilling of holes in round work is usually accomplished with the use of a V block. The block can be a separate piece of wood placed on the drill table under the drill. The round work is placed in the V, forming a secure base for drilling. A fence or strip of wood clamped to the drill-press table will serve as a V block, if the drill table is tilted to 45 degrees. The angle thus formed by the drill table and

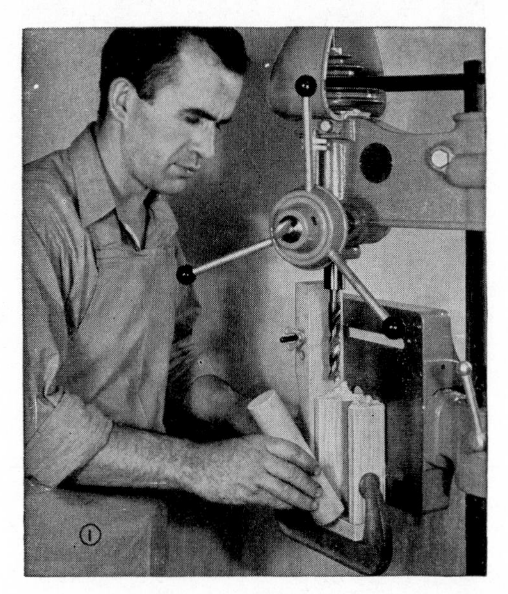

fence acts a support in drilling cylindrical work. A V block can also be used in a vertical position, as shown, for drilling into the end of cylindrical work.

The average drill press has a 4-inch stroke; the common style of machine bit also has a 4-inch twist. Thus holes which are deeper than 4 inches can be classed as deep holes. The simplest method of boring deep holes is to drill from opposite ends of the work. For this operation, the table is tilted vertical, and the work is turned end for end, thus drilling two holes which meet in the center of the block. The capacity of a 4-inch twist is thus increased to 8 inches. When the drilling is done from opposite ends, great care must be exercised in lining up the work.

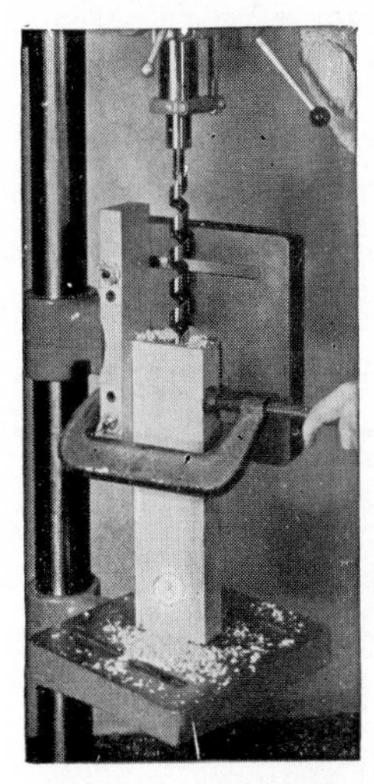

When a longer twist than 4 inches is being used, the bit may be long enough to go through the work, but the operator must contend with the 4-inch stroke of the drill press. One method of working is to first sink the drill to a depth of about 4 inches in the work, then release the feed handle, but the drill stays in the work. A base block can then be slipped under the work, allowing an additional stroke equal to the thickness of the base block.

In all deep-hole drilling, cutting should not continue after the flutes of the bit have passed below the work surface. Where it is necessary to use the bit to a greater depth than the flutes, the bits should be lifted frequently, in order to permit the hole to be cleared of chips. This rule should apply generally to all deep-hole drilling, even though the flutes of the bit may be entirely clear of and above the work.

Holes of over 1½-inch diameter can be classified as large holes. The removal of a comparatively large amount of wood in boring these holes gives a considerable twisting strain to the work; for this reason it is advisable to clamp the work securely when using any kind of bit over this diameter. This applies especially to any type of bit which has but one cutting edge.

When countersinking for boltheads, machine screws, or large wood screws, two sizes of drill bit must be used. When working with two bits in this manner, the larger hole must always be drilled first. When the smaller hole is drilled first, it is almost impossible to locate the larger drill in the center of the hole.

Dowel holes must be accurately located. Careful layout work or a mechanical jig or fixture should be used when drilling two sections of a frame assembly for a doweled joint. A convenient method for cutting short lengths of dowel is to use a plug cutter.

Drilling Metal

Metalwork should never be held on the drill-press table by means of the hand alone. It is true that for small holes this very often is enough, but the operator never knows when the lips of the drill are going to seize the work, especially when the point of the drill is about to break through the underside of the stock. When this happens, the stock is snatched from the operator's hand, often cutting the hand or otherwise injuring the workman. This also invariably results in the breaking of the drill, as the work strikes the drill-press column. All this can be avoided, and much more accurate work done, if the work is clamped securely to the drill-press table.

Various devices are used in holding and clamping the work. The simplest kind of holding device is the stop bolt. Two bolts are placed through the slots in the drill-press table, and the work placed between them in such a manner that it bears against the two bolts. With this arrangement, the work cannot be twisted out of the operator's hands.

Strap clamps are often employed to clamp the work to the table. This results in better work and sufficient safety for the operator.

Spring in the Work

One condition which must always be avoided when clamping is the springing of the work. If a light piece of steel or other material is supported at points which are too far apart, it will spring under the pressure of the drill. This will often result in a broken drill, since the work springs back and binds the drill just as it breaks through the material. Always support the work sufficiently close to the hole being drilled so that it cannot spring.

Mounting Setups

Where end drilling is done, the work does not usually possess a base of sufficient size to stand with any degree of stability, and should be clamped in place with the table vertical. See next page.

A machinist's vise or drill-press vise is very useful for holding small work for drilling. The vise is clamped to the drill-press table. The vise need not be centered in the table, since the table can usually be swung to center the work, even though the vise itself is off center. Where the vise is to be made a standard fixture, holes can be drilled in the drill-press table to center it. As in other forms of clamping, the work must be held clear of the base of the vise, so that the drill will not break through and go into the vise surface.

A lathe chuck with the backplate removed can be used in many drilling operations as a holding and clamping device for odd-shaped work.

Angle plates which can be bolted or clamped to the drill-press table are useful for holding work. Adjustable parallels, step boxes, U bolts, and many types of hold-downs are used extensively in special drilling operations.

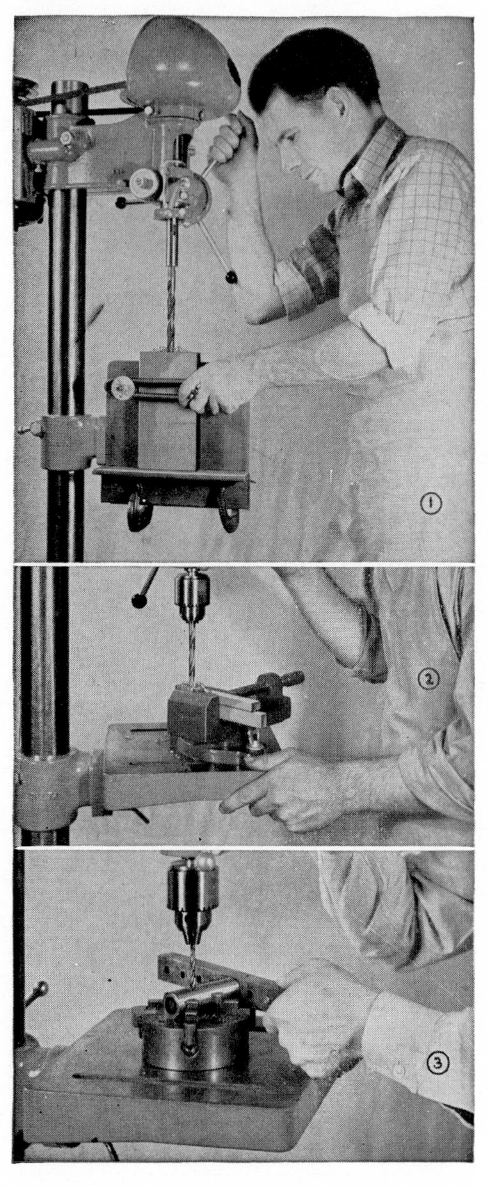

Drilling Large and Small Holes

When drilling large holes, it will be found more accurate and easier on the drill press if a lead hole, using a small drill, is drilled first. There is a right and a wrong way to drill a lead hole. The proper way is to start with the full-size drill, check and draw the hole if necessary, then, just after the drill has started to cut full size, change to the small drill and run this through the work. This ensures that the small hole will be exactly in the center of the layout circles. After the small hole is through, the larger drill is replaced and the hole drilled full size. The diameter of the small drill used, for the lead hole, should be approximately the same as the web thickness of the larger drill. The use of the small drill thus relieves the thrust against the web.

Small holes, 1/16 inch in diameter and under, are drilled at high speed. The work can be held by hand, but it must be held firmly. A magnifying glass is an aid to good work, both in starting the hole and in watching the progress of the cut.

Drilling Sheet Metal

Where sheet metal is to be cut with an ordinary twist drill, it should be backed against a wood base block or sandwiched between two blocks and clamped. In any case, a bottom support is necessary to prevent burring and crushing the metal. Large holes in sheet stock are more easily cut with a regular disk cutter made for this purpose.

Drilling and Tapping

The drill used for making a hole preparatory to tapping must be of a certain size if good work is to be done. Consult the table on the next page, and use the drill specified.

After the lead hole has been drilled, the tap can be started by mounting it in the drill press, giving it a few turns, and then pulling on the drill-press belt. After the tap is started straight and true in this manner, the work can be removed for tapping in a suitable vise, in the usual manner.

While a tap cannot be run under power when held in an ordinary chuck, it is quite simple to tap holes by power, by using a tapping attachment. The tap is held in a collet chuck at the end of the tapping attachments, various collets being supplied to take a varied range of tap sizes. The tap is advanced to the hole by means of the feed lever. After tapping to the proper depth, the tap automatically reverses rotation and thus retracts itself from the work. Reverse is usually about twice the forward speed. Attachments of this kind are essential for production work.

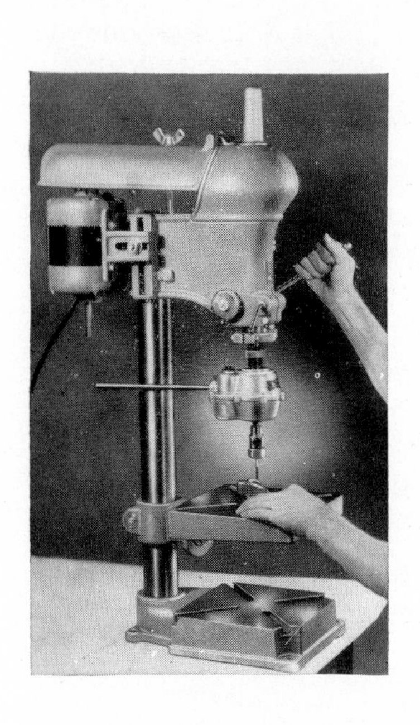

MACHINE SCREWS

Tap or Screw size	Threads per inch	Tap drill	Body drill
0	80 N.F.	3/64	51
1	64 N.C.	53	47
1	72 N.F.	53	47
2	56 N.C.	50	42
2	64 N.F.	50	42
3	48 N.C.	47	37
3	56 N.F.	45	37
4	40 N.C.	43	31
4	48 N.F.	42	31
5	40 N.C.	38	28
5	44 N.F.	37	29
6	32 N.C.	36	27
6	40 N.F.	33	27
8	32 N.C.	29	18
8	36 N.F.	29	18
10	24 N.C.	25	9
10	32 N.F.	21	9
12	24 N.C.	16	2
12	28 N.F.	14	2

Routing

Routing is done with the use of suitable router bits, usually held in the ½-inch-hole spindle. If the router bit is held in an ordinary grip or gear chuck, the lower end of the spindle must be drilled and tapped and a machine screw used to hold the chuck to the spindle. This is necessary, since the side thrust exerted in routing or similar operations has a tendency to loosen the chuck on the spindle, allowing it to spin off while the work is being done. The work must at all times be supported against a suitable fence, otherwise it will be caught by the deep flutes of the router bit and twisted out of the operator's hands. The speed of the drill press should be approximately 5,000 rpm.

The fence regularly used for mortising operations can be used successfully as a guide when routing. Shaper fences, when suitable for mounting on the drill-press table, can also be used.

The guide or fence is usually behind the router bit, and when in this position, the work should always be fed from left to right. Exceptions to this will be found when routing with a pattern. The point to be remembered is that the work should be advanced against the negative pressure formed by the cutting action of the bit.

In one method of operation, a fence is used and a mark is placed on the fence directly in line with the router bit. The curved portion

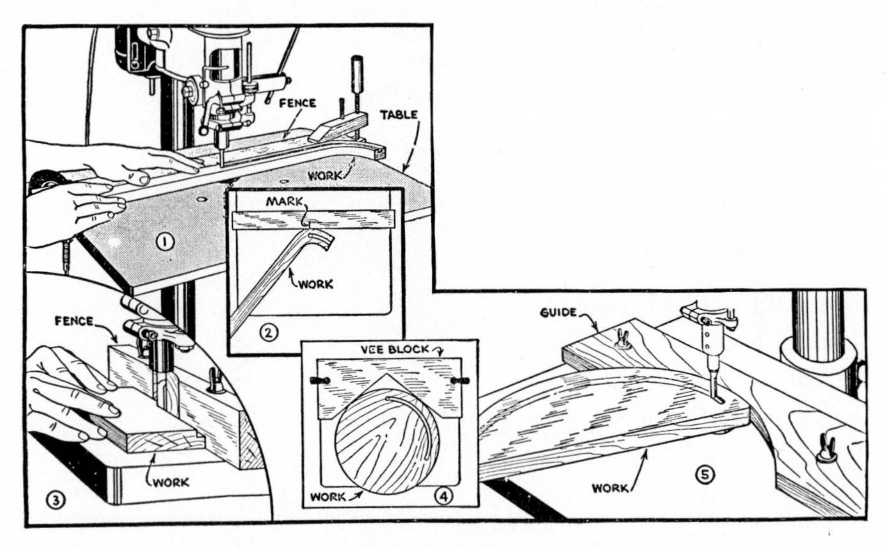

of the work must be so guided that it is in contact with the mark at all times. After the curve has been cut, the balance of the groove can be cut with the work flat against the fence.

When the work is circular, the use of a V block affords a simple, yet accurate, method of operation. A single V block can be used for a large range of circle sizes by simply clamping it at various distances from the bit. Another method of working, where the work is part of a circle, makes use of a fence cut to the same radius as the work. This method is frequently used, for the the simple reason that if the original piece of work is carefully band-sawed, the waste portion of the wood can be utilized as a guide.

Rabbeting is done against a straight fence. The fence should have a slight cutout in it, so that the bit will cut a little outside the edge of the work. The standard mortising fence is excellent for work of

this nature. In all other respects the operation is just the same as routing a groove in the center of a board, the fence being adjusted to cut a suitable width, while the depth stop is set and the quill locked to limit the depth of cut. Rabbets wider than the router bit are cut by setting the fence over for successive cuts until the required width is reached.

Small router bits are usually of the single-flute type. They are used in the same manner as the setups previously described. For some work, where the bit is not over 1/8 inch in diameter, the work can be done freehand. This is frequently useful when irregular designs are to be routed.

When the work cannot be guided against any kind of fence, a

pattern must be used. Routing with a pattern is a fast and simple method of doing production work. A full-size template or pattern of the work is required. This is usually cut from ¼-inch plywood. The next piece of equipment is a wood or metal pin. The pin must be of

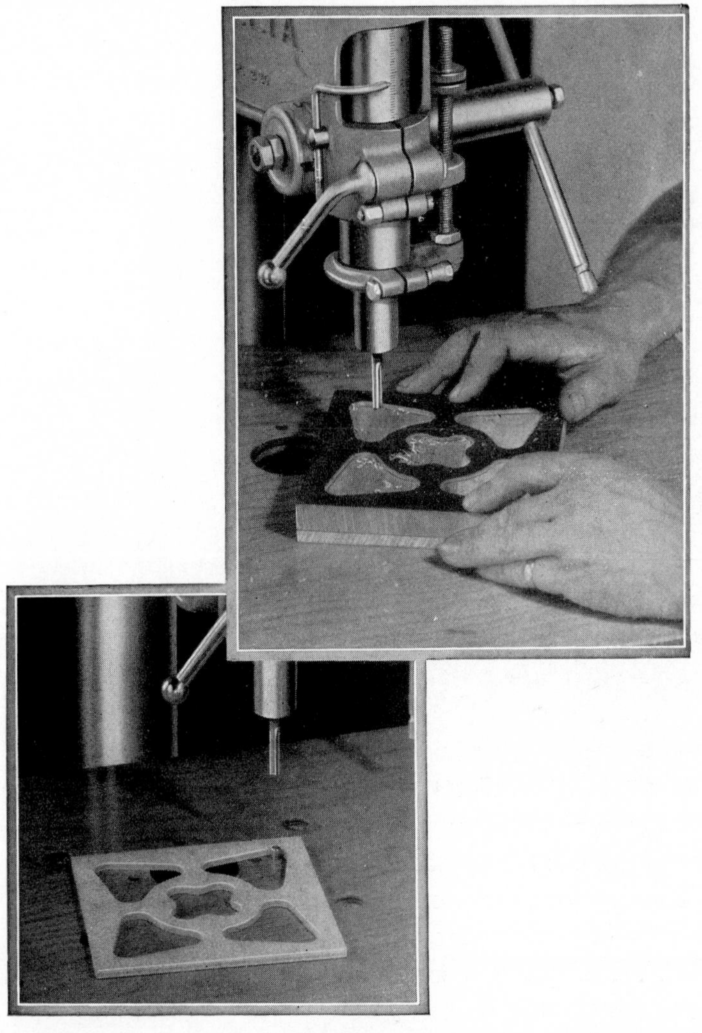

the same diameter as the router bit. It is fitted into the wood drill-press table exactly in line with the bit and projects above the table surface to a distance a trifle less than the thickness of the pattern.

For the routing operation, the pattern is fastened to the bottom of the work by means of brads or any other style of anchor. The pattern is then placed over the pin and the router bit set in motion, cutting to the required depth. As the pattern is guided against the

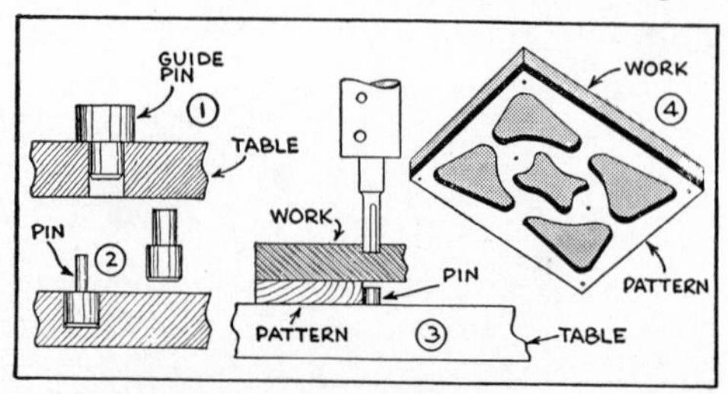

pin, the router bit will cut the same pattern in or through the work. It is sometimes a good idea to sketch the design on top of the work as a guide in keeping the pattern against the pin. After the outline has been cut, the waste wood inside the pattern can be removed by projecting the work freehand into the cutter. If the pin is off size or not in line with the router bit, the work will not be the same shape as the pattern.

Using the Drill Press as a Shaper

The vertical spindle of the modern high-speed drill press offers the basic requirements for a first-class shaper. The spindle speed of 5,000 rpm is sufficiently fast for smooth, clean work. Holes in the drill-press table are usually suitable for mounting the standard shaper fence.

The drill press may be used as a shaper in two ways, either right side up or inverted. For the inverted position, the entire head is removed from the column and replaced in an inverted position. The drill-press table is then placed above the end of the spindle, and the spindle and cutters are projected through the opening in the table. Of the two positions, the regular position is by far the most practical for the occasional shaper job, because of the simplicity of changing over from drill press to shaper.

The cutters and collars are fitted to the threaded shank of a special spindle. In place of the special spindle, an adapter spindle is available for some drill presses. The adapter should never be used in the regular drill chuck, as this brings the cutters too far below the bearings in the drill-press quill. Even with the special spindle, the extension or overhang should be kept as small as is consistent with the work to be done.

Practically all the shaper operations described in Chapter 10 can be done equally well on the drill press, except that the cut is lighter.

Mortising

The method of converting the drill press for mortising is shown in the illustration. The mortising chisel is held stationary by means of

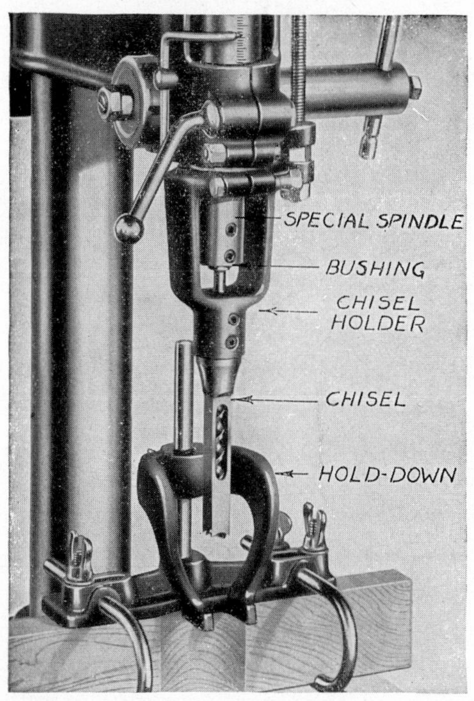

a cast chisel holder attached to the drill-press quill. The mortising bit is held in a chuck with a ½-inch hole, a bushing being slipped over the end of the bit to adapt it to the hole. A fence, which is necessary to keep the mortise straight and accurate, is fastened to the drill-press table. The fence carries a bracket on its top edge, and this bracket supports an adjustable hold-down. The bracket also carries hook rods, which are used to keep the work against the fence.

The bit is slipped through the chisel from the cutting end. The proper-sized bushing is placed on the shank of the bit, and the assembly is slipped upward through the hole in the chisel holder. Both chisel and bushing should be pushed up until they butt against their respective shoulders. The chisel is secured by tightening setscrews. The bit is then secured, after first carefully adjusting so that the spurs of the bit are about 1/16 inch away from the lower end of the chisel. This is important; there must be clearance between the

bit spurs and the lower end of the chisel; otherwise the bit will heat in operation. On the other hand, the bit should not project too far, since then the chips produced may be too large to pass through the chisel. If the bit appears to rub on the chisel, check the extension of the bit; if this is correct, loosen the chuck screws, turn the chisel a trifle inside the bushing, and retighten. Tighten the setscrews in the spindle chuck so that they bear against the flap on the bushing.

The first step in cutting a mortise is to lay out the pattern on the work. The fence is adjusted to locate the work at the required position. A square should be used in order to get the fence set exactly square with the chisel. If the chisel is not square with the fence, the mortise cuts will be staggered. The feed lever is turned to advance

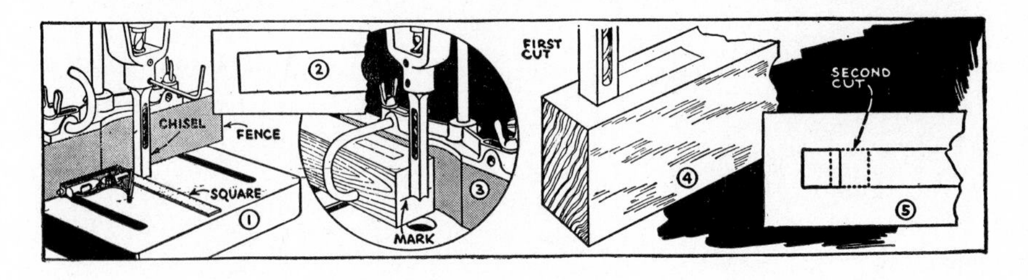

the chisel to the proper depth, and the depth stop is set to this position. The hold-down and hold-ins are now adjusted so that the work is held firmly in place but free to slide along the table.

The cut is started by bringing the chisel down at the end of the mortise. Since all four sides of the chisel are cutting, the first cut will naturally take a little more pressure than the following cuts. On hardwood, the chisel should be lifted frequently to clear the chips and permit the tool to cool. After the first cut has been made to the required depth, the work is moved sidewise a distance equal to about three-quarters of the width of the chisel, and the cut is repeated. The drill-press speed should be about 2,250 rpm.

The mortising attachment can be used to cut all kinds of square-edge openings. Where the work demands a hole wider than the

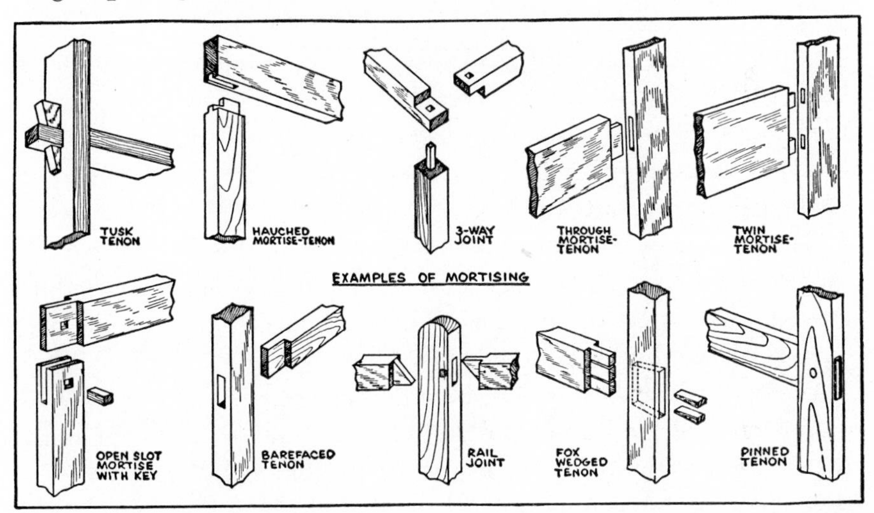

chisel, a second set of cuts is made after setting the fence over the proper distance. Various wood joints are made on the drill press with the use of the mortising attachment.

Miscellaneous Operations

A wide variety of drilling operations done on the drill press fall under this heading. Among them are the drilling of glass, of paper, plastics, etc. Various techniques are employed with a variety of drills and cutters to accomplish these operations.

Glass may be drilled with a slotted tube or a pointed triangular bit. A mixture of carborundum powder and machine oil or turpentine is fed to the bit for this operation. The speed of the drill should be about 100 feet per minute.

The most essential point in drilling paper is that the work must be tightly clamped between boards. In this way it is practically one solid piece of material. A spur bit can be used successfully. Speed should be about 1,200 rpm, and the bit must be lifted frequently to clear the rings of paper which will collect on the tip.

Most plastics are slightly abrasive, hence are hard on tools, and the chips have a tendency to cling to the drill, causing loading and overheating. Well-polished high-speed drills give good results for average home workshop use, using a speed of from 100 to 300 feet per minute.

Other operations on the drill press consist of light milling operations, such as the cutting of keyways, surfacing, and slotting. Cutting tools are available for such operations and should be used in conjunction with compound slide rests or some mechanical means of feeding the work to the cutter.

Carving and surfacing work is often done on the drill press with the use of suitable cutters and cutting heads. Sanding and grinding are done with sanding drums and grinding wheels suitably mounted on special spindles or adapters.

While the drill press cannot be used like some of the other power equipment, in building complete projects without the aid of other tools, it is extremely useful in pursuing other hobbies and in the production and assembly of work created on the other home workshop machines. Model builders and craftsmen in all fields consider the drill press one of the most important machines for both woodwork and metalwork.

Chapter 8. DISK AND BELT SANDERS

Abrasives

Natural abrasives are found ready-made in the earth and include sandstone, emery, flint, garnet, etc. Each has its own particular use. Flint is the least expensive, and this is the type of abrasive commonly associated with the word "sandpaper." Garnet is much harder and tougher than flint and is the abrasive most used by the woodworker. Emery is commonly used for sanding metals.

Artificial abrasives are a product of the electric furnace. The two main groups are made up of: first, aluminum oxide abrasives, and second, silicon carbide abrasives. Aluminum oxide is made by fusing bauxite, a highly aluminous clay, in an electric arc furnace at about 3000°F. The crystals are usually brown in color, but some types are made gray and white. They are not so hard as silicon carbide but are much tougher. Silicon carbide is made by fusing sand and coke at a high temperature. The resulting crystals are next to the diamond in hardness but are brittle, as opposed to the toughness of aluminum oxide. The color ranges from black-gray to blue-green. Both aluminum oxide and silicon carbide are sold under various trade names, such as Aloxite, Alundum, and Lionite (aluminum oxide); and Carborundum, Crystolon, and Carsilon (silicon carbide).

The grain size or grit is determined by passing the crushed ore over various silk and wire screens. Grains passed by a 12-grain screen are called No. 12, twelve grains measuring about 1 inch, if laid end to end. Scientific control methods eliminate flat and slivery grains, unless desired for some specific purpose, retaining only the ideal polyhedral-shaped grain. Sizes range from No. 6 to No. 240. Since it is difficult to make a screen of more than 240 meshes to the inch, finer grains up to No. 600 are graded by an elaborate water-flotation system.

Abrasive grains fused with a bond of flux and clay or other substance can be cast into any convenient shape, such as the familiar grinding wheel. Each grain thus becomes a miniature cutting tool. As the grains wear down and become dull, they are torn loose from the bond, exposing a new, sharp set of cutting edges. Grinding wheels are made in hundreds of different shapes.

Abrasive grains glued to sheets of cloth or paper are called

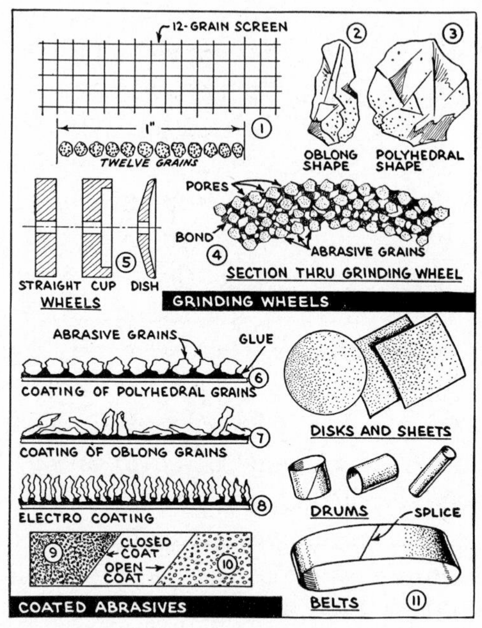

"coated" abrasives. Disks and sheets, drums, and belts are common examples of coated abrasives. The polyhedral grain shape is always used when coated abrasives are made by ordinary methods, producing a surface similar to that shown in illustration 6. It can be seen that any method of gravity coating with oblong grains would result in an unsatisfactory surface, many of the grains being almost completely embedded in the glue coating. If the oblong grains are placed on end, the result is quite different, the abrasive particles being fully exposed and capable of clean, uniform, high-speed sanding. This vertical coating of abrasive grains is done by an electrostatic method, and the greater portion of all coated abrasives used today are made in this manner.

Coated abrasives are divided into many different classes, depending on the abrasive used, the kind of backing, whether for wet or dry sanding, etc. In any of these, the normal coating is put on in a close, packed formation, hence the general descriptive term, "closed coat." The closed coat is fast-cutting and durable but has the disadvantage of clogging under certain conditions. Where the coating is spaced with a slight separation between the abrasive grains, it is described as "open coat." Open-coated abrasives are no so durable, but they are useful for finishing certain materials where the abrasive dust tends to clog the disk or belt.

Most grinders are supplied with general-purpose grinding wheels which will handle most of the work encountered in the home workshop.

Abrasive Tools

The grinder is a double-end horizontal spindle, the ends of which are threaded and fitted with flanges to take the grinding wheels. The spindle is often a continuation of the motor shaft, in which case the unit has direct drive. Other grinders employ a conventional belt drive. The size of the grinder is commonly taken from the diameter of the abrasive wheel used in connection with it. For example, a grinder taking a 7-inch wheel would be called a 7-inch grinder. Different models are further described as bench or pedestal, the latter indicating a floor model.

An essential feature of all grinders is the wheel guards, which should enclose the wheel as fully as possible in order to prevent abrasive chips or larger fragments of the wheel from being thrown at the operator. The tool rests should be adjustable for wheel wear and tilt for precision grinding. The power required to operate a 6- or 7-inch grinder is approximately ⅓ horsepower. Where the unit is direct-driven, the motor should be a 3,400-rpm type in order to give the grinding wheel an efficient surface speed. A fair standard for average grinding is 5,500 surface feet per minute.

The buffing head is mechanically similar to the grinder, except

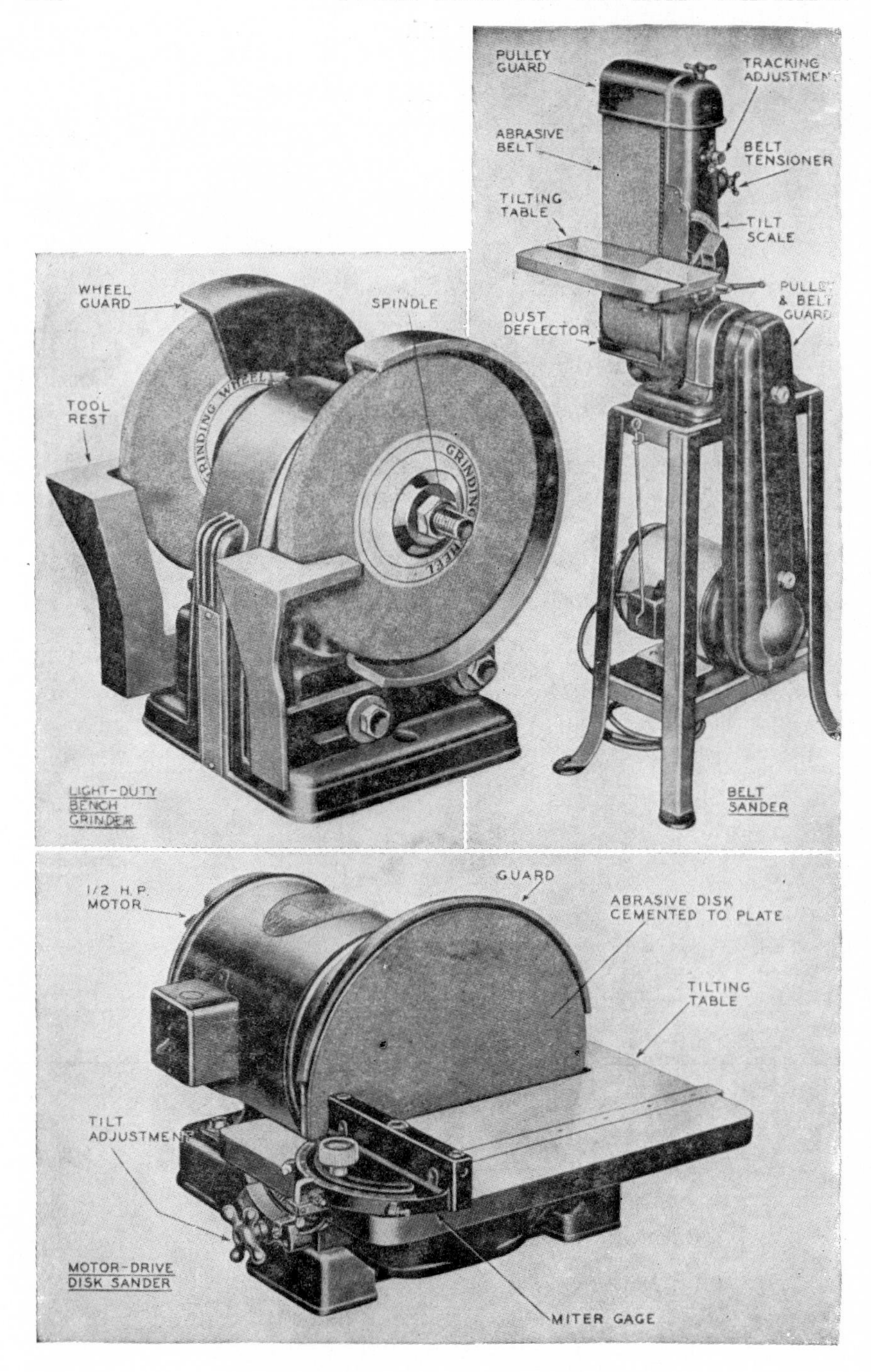
PULLEY GUARD
TRACKING ADJUSTMENT
ABRASIVE BELT
BELT TENSIONER
TILTING TABLE
TILT SCALE
PULLEY & BELT GUARD
DUST DEFLECTOR
BELT SANDER
WHEEL GUARD
SPINDLE
TOOL REST
GRINDING WHEEL
LIGHT-DUTY BENCH GRINDER
1/2 H.P. MOTOR
GUARD
ABRASIVE DISK CEMENTED TO PLATE
TILTING TABLE
TILT ADJUSTMENT
MOTOR-DRIVE DISK SANDER
MITER GAGE

that guards and rests are not required. A surface speed of about 6,500 feet per minute is suitable for average work.

The belt sander features a continuous abrasive belt working over pulleys at either end of a main sanding table. Adjustments are provided for tensioning and tracking the belt. The size of the unit is commonly designated by the width of the sanding belt which it uses. To operate the belt sander, ½ to ¾ horsepower is required. Pulleys should give the belt a surface speed of between 2,800 and 3,200 feet per minute.

The disk sander features a circular plate which operates in a vertical position. Cloth- or paper-backed disks are cemented or otherwise fastened to the surface of the plate. The diameter of the abrasive disk indicates the size of the machine, a common size being 12 inches. A disk of this diameter should run at about 1,725 rpm (standard motor speed). This will give a surface speed ranging from zero at the center of the disk to about 5,500 feet per minute at the rim.

Accessories for sanding or grinding are used on the drill press, lathe, scroll saw, and other machines. The sanding drum, used on the lathe or drill press, is the most widely used. The surface speed of such a drum should be held to a comparatively low figure; 1,200 feet per minute, as compared with an average of about 3,000 feet per minute for long belts, is an approximate comparison. An abrasive drum or belt will glaze quickly when operated at too high a speed.

Mounting Disks, Sleeves, and Belts

In order to present a true, flat abrasive surface to the work, sanding disks are mounted on an accurately machined metal plate. Glue can be used as the adhesive, in which case the plate and disk must be clamped between boards and allowed to dry overnight. Special types of disk adhesive are also used. Some types of disk adhesive melt under heat and then quickly harden. To apply such adhesive, a softwood stick is placed flat against the bare revolving disk and held firmly in place for approximately half a minute in order to heat the plate. The adhesive is then held against the revolving disk and is moved over the surface until a thin even coat is applied. The abrasive disk is then placed in position.

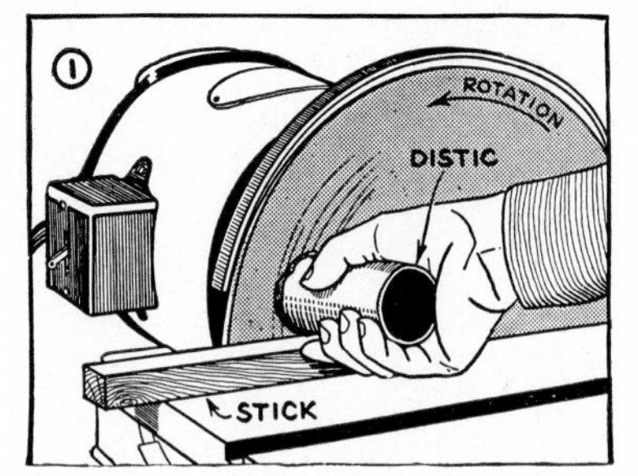

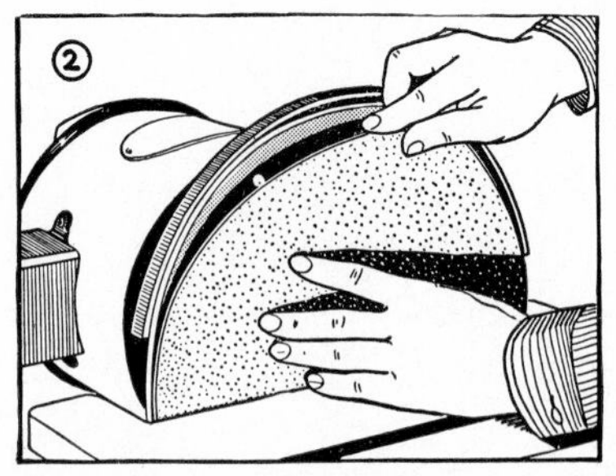

Other types of disk adhesive include the semiflexible type which never completely hardens. No heat is required for mounting disks with this material.

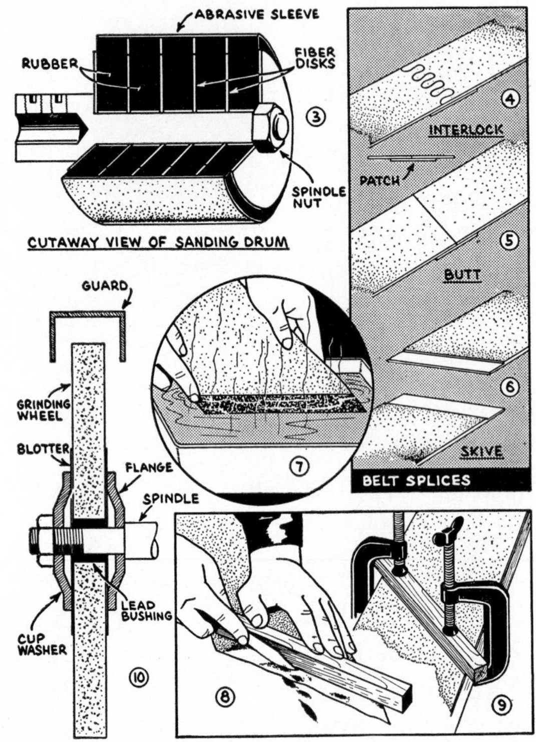

Abrasive sleeves are mounted on special drums in which alternate layers of rubber and fiber can be expanded by turning the spindle nut, thus securing the sleeve in place.

Sanding belts are usually purchased ready-made for most belt sanders. The craftsman can also make his own belts by splicing the sandpaper to form a belt of the proper length. Several varieties of belt splices are commonly used.

Good-quality grinding wheels are metal-bushed and should be a snug fit on the spindle. Disks of blotter paper should be used on either side of the wheel to serve as shock absorbers.

Operating the Disk Sander

Sanding on the disk sander is usually done freehand, the work being held flat on the table and projected into the sanding disk. A smooth, light feed should be practiced, avoiding heavy pressure. Best results on curved work can be obtained by going over the work two or three times with light cuts. Sanding is always done on the side of the wheel which is traveling down toward the table.

Circular work which is to be sanded should always be worked with the use of a pivot jig. Many of the jigs previously described under the cutting of circles in band-saw operations can also be used on the disk sander. The jigs should, of course, be adjustable, to regulate both the amount of feed and the diameter of the circle.

The sanding of corners is allied to circular work, in that the edge being worked is part of a true circle. Most work of this nature can be done freehand, sweeping the corner of the work across the face of the sanding disk two or three times until the desired round is obtained. More accurate results are possible if the pivot jig is used in the manner shown in the illustration. The sliding strip is first locked in place at the required distance from the face of the sanding disk. Guidelines are then used on the jig to locate the work in rela-

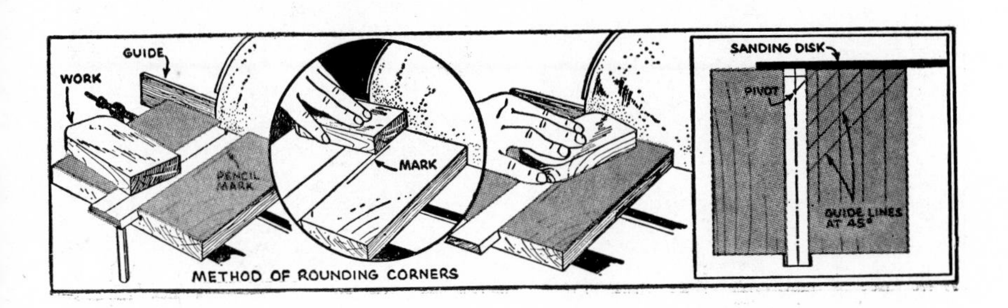

METHOD OF ROUNDING CORNERS

tion to the disk and the pivot point. Work can then be sanded on any radius within the limitations of the jig.

Accessories

Various accessories may be used on, or in connection with, the disk sander. A circular-saw miter gauge can be used to advantage in sanding square or mitered ends. The stop rod used in connection with the miter gauge makes it possible to finish work in duplicate to exact lengths.

Where the disk sander is a separate belt-driven unit, the opposite end of the shaft can be utilized to hold such accessories as the sanding drum, wire, and cloth buffing wheels.

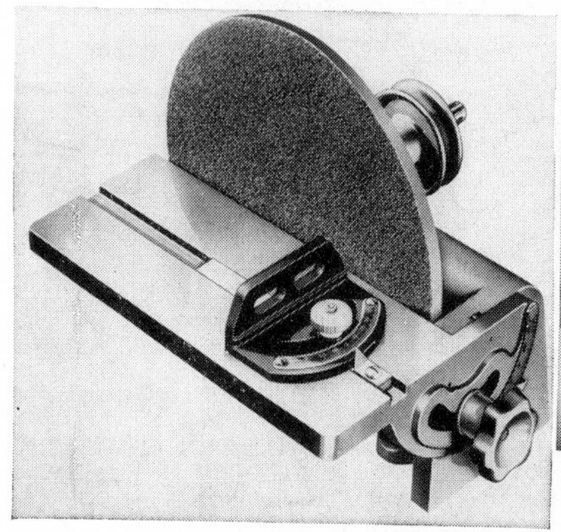

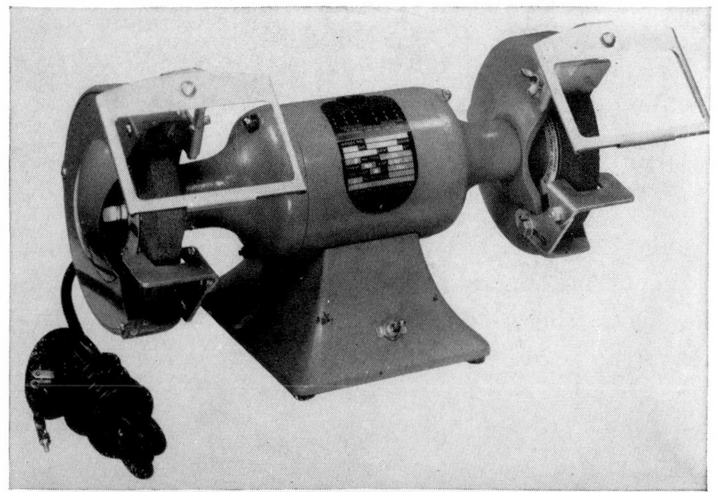

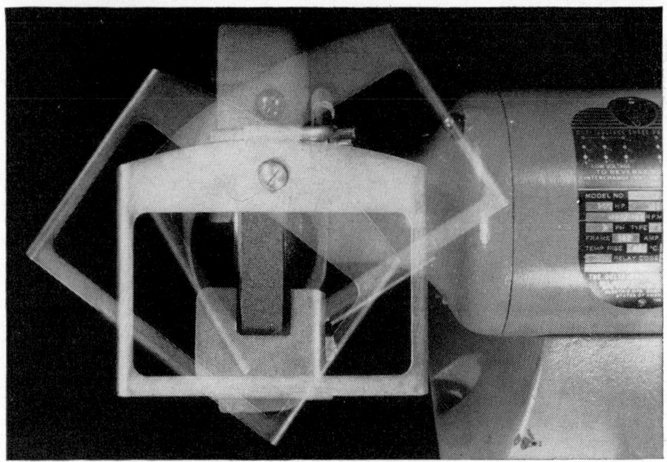

Operating the Belt Sander

The sanding table should be in a horizontal position for surfacing work on the belt sander. Work can be done freehand, that is, the piece to be surfaced is simply placed on the table, and a light but firm pressure is used to keep the work in the proper position. Excessive pressure against the belt is unnecessary and should be avoided. If the work is longer than the table, it is started at one end and gradually advanced in much the same manner as when surfacing on the jointer. Where long work is to be surfaced, it is advisable to use the sanding fence as a guide.

End sanding is best accomplished with the sanding table in a vertical position but can be done on the horizontal table by means of a guide clamped to the fence.

The use of a diagonal feed permits the surfacing of work which is considerably wider than the 6-inch capacity of the belt. The angle of the fence should be kept as small as possible in order to minimize cross-grain sanding. A fine abrasive belt should be used.

Sanding of inside curves can be done on the end drum by removing the guard. The table can be vertical, horizontal, or at an angle. The fence can be used as a guide, if it is mounted so that the end projects beyond the surface of the table.

Every kind of edge or end work can be done by using the belt sander in a vertical position in connection with the sanding table. With the table level and the work guided by the miter gauge, ends and edges can be sanded true and smooth, whether square, mitered, beveled, or compound-beveled.

Buffing and Polishing

"Polishing" is the general term applied to the complete process of removing tool marks, scratches, etc., from metals and other materials to produce a high-luster finish. The process is divided into three distinct parts. The first is roughing, which is done dry with abrasives in grit numbers from 40 to 80. Dry fining or fine wheeling, as the second operation is called, can also be done dry but is often done on a greased wheel. Grits used are from numbers 120 to 180. Finishing, often called oiling and buffing, is the final operation. It is done with fine-grain abrasives combined with lard oil, tallow, beeswax, water, etc. The exact size of grain used in all operations will depend on the original finish on the work and the desired finish on the completed product.

Buffing and polishing can be accomplished on many of the home workshop machines; however, it is most convenient to work on a regular buffing head or belt-driven grinder. If a belt-driven grinder is used, the guards and tool rests should be removed for convenient use of the buffing surfaces.

Buffs are made from disks of muslin, felt, flannel, leather, etc., and are sewed in a wide variety of patterns to produce hard or soft wheels. All polishing work should be done on the lower side of the wheel, the work being presented so that it will not be torn from the hands of the operator.

Buffing compounds are various natural abrasives, such as emery, tripoli, pumice, crocus, lime, and rouge, which are combined with a suitable wax or grease to form a mixture which can be readily applied to the revolving buff. The compound should be applied lightly and frequently to the buff, as the work progresses.

Besides the polishing of metals, buffing wheels charged with suitable compounds are used for polishing plastics, lacquered surfaces, bare wood, ivory, horn, etc. In all cases the easily obtained abrasives, such as pumice and rouge, will do good work. Benzine or lacquer thinner will remove any film of compound left on the work after buffing.

Chapter 9. THE GRINDER

General Operations

The grinder is a safe tool to operate, provided that a few simple rules are followed. Always use the guards. If guards are not provided, wear safety goggles as protection against flying fragments of abrasive. Keep the wheels round, and thereby balanced, by dressing whenever required. Do not force work against a cold wheel, but exercise light pressure until the wheel becomes warm. Always use a tool rest when the work permits. Present the work to the wheel either straight in or at a "drag" angle, reserving the "gouge" angle for sharpening and other operations demanding a minimum burr.

A level tool rest set a little below the center of the wheel is the most practical and safest position for general work. Work ground in this position, or any other position in which the work points to the center of the wheel, will be finished with a square edge. Work presented in any position other than pointing to the wheel center will be ground more or less at a bevel. Freehand grinding, without the use of a rest, should always be done on the lower quarter of the wheel.

Guides clamped to the regular rest ensure accuracy and should be used on all precision work. Exact bevel and depth of cut are controlled by means of a simple fence and tool rest.

Sharpening Tools

Two main operations are necessary in sharpening most tools. First, the edge is ground to the proper shape on the grinder; second, the edge is honed to perfect sharpness on a suitable oilstone. The grinding wheel used should be an aluminum oxide wheel, about 60 grit, and of medium hardness. The wheel should be kept properly dressed. In grinding, keep the tool cool by constantly dipping it in water—temper is being drawn when blue spots appear on the edge of the tool. High-speed steel is best ground entirely dry, using a very light feed and stopping between cuts to allow the tool to air-cool. The use of a white aluminum oxide wheel will permit a heavier feed without overheating.

Wood chisels should be hollow-ground. Project the chisel straight into the wheel to remove nicks. Next, adjust the tool rest to the required position to grind the bevel. Work the chisel directly across the face of the wheel. Worked on the face of the wheel, the bevel

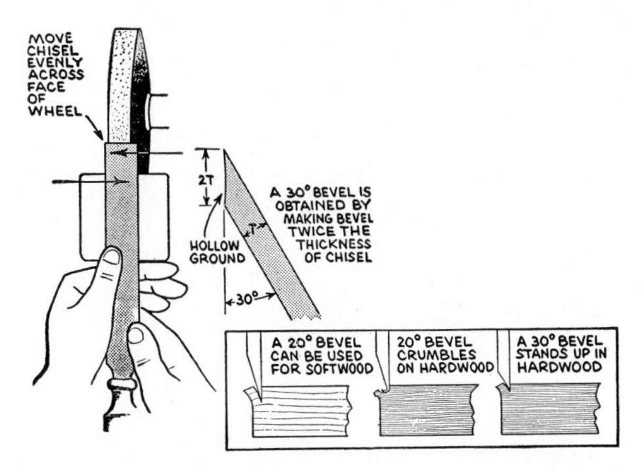

will have a slight hollow, making it easy to hone a perfect edge several times before regrinding becomes necessary. The bevel should be about 30 degrees, this being obtained by making the bevel twice the thickness of the chisel. A 20-degree bevel can be used on softwood, but the thin wedge will crumble on hardwood.

Either an aluminum oxide or a silicon carbide oilstone will give good results in honing or whetting the chisel edge after grinding. The sharpening stone should always be oiled, the purpose of this being to float the particles of metal so that they will not become embedded in the stone. Use a thin oil or kerosene. Wipe the stone after using. Honing is necessary because grinding forms a burr at the chisel edge. To remove the burr, place the chisel diagonally across the stone and stroke backward and forward, bearing down with both hands. The heel of the chisel should be a slight distance above the surface of the stone. Next, turn the chisel over and stroke the back on the stone, making certain to keep the tool perfectly level. Alternate the honing on bevel and back until the burr is completely removed.

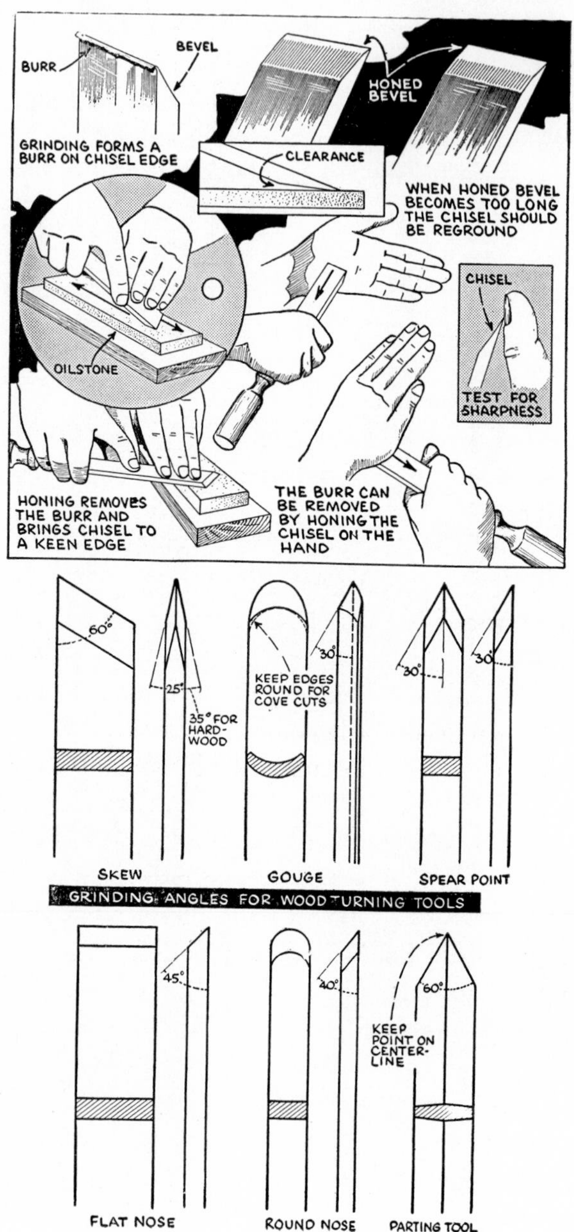

It will then be noted that honing puts a secondary bevel on the chisel. This is the correct technique for chisels, plane irons, knives, etc. This method gives a clean edge with a minimum amount of labor. When the honed bevel becomes too long through repeated whettings, the chisel should be reground.

Some wood-turning chisels are not hollow-ground. Instead, the bevels are perfectly flat and should be kept flat during honing. Any secondary bevel on a skew, for example, will prevent it from being used satisfactorily in turning, where the heel of the bevel must act as a fulcrum.

The simplest of all methods of sharpening the gouge is to use a cup wheel on the lathe, rotating the chisel inside the wheel. The curved surface of the cup wheel lessens the amount of rolling necessary and makes grinding simple. The gouge can also be ground by rolling the bevel on the face of the wheel or on the side of the wheel. In all cases the roll must be just a little less than a full half-circle.

Special sharpening stones are required for honing the gouge. The

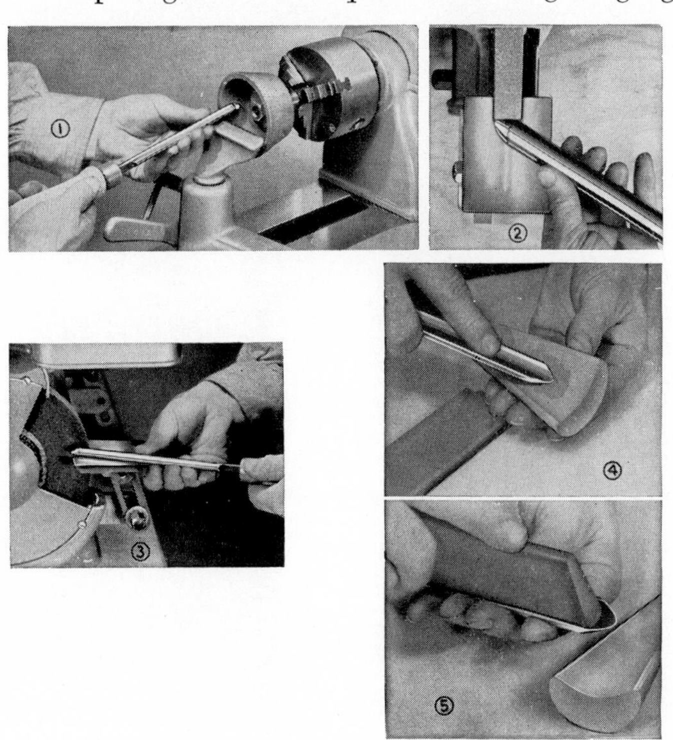

best type is hollow on one side and round on the other, especially made for honing gouges. The round edge of the stone can be conveniently used to cut the burr on the inside flat edge of the gouge, or a slip stone can be used for this purpose.

Lathe tool bits are sharpened offhand, being held in the hand to present the tool at the proper angle to the side of the grinding wheel. A light touch on the grinding wheel is all that is usually required to bring the bit to a keen edge. Maintain the original bevels, or, if working blank stock, follow the angles given in the illustration.

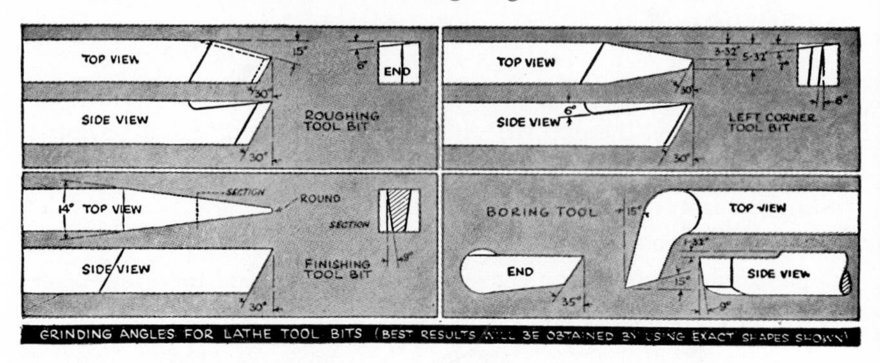

GRINDING ANGLES FOR LATHE TOOL BITS (BEST RESULTS WILL BE OBTAINED BY USING EXACT SHAPES SHOWN)

Grinding Twist Drills

The two most important considerations in twist-drill grinding are first, the point angle and second, the lip clearance. The point angle

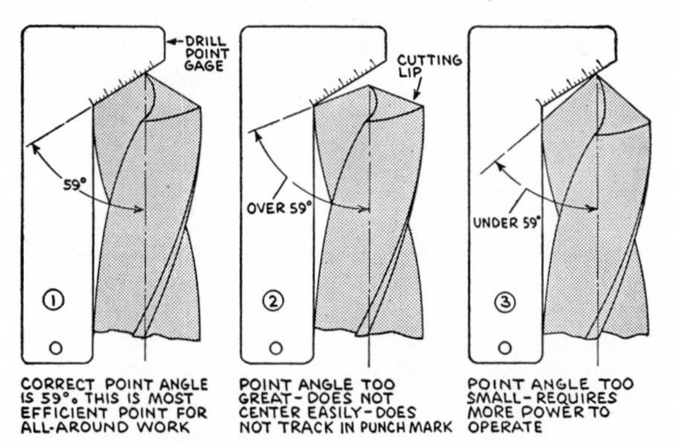

CORRECT POINT ANGLE IS 59°. THIS IS MOST EFFICIENT POINT FOR ALL-AROUND WORK

POINT ANGLE TOO GREAT - DOES NOT CENTER EASILY - DOES NOT TRACK IN PUNCH MARK

POINT ANGLE TOO SMALL - REQUIRES MORE POWER TO OPERATE

has been standardized at 59 degrees for general work, and this angle should be maintained. It is easily checked with a drill-point gauge.

Gauges in a variety of styles can be purchased, or the craftsman can make his own from sheet metal. The markings on the edge need not be accurate, since they are used only to check the length of one lip against the other. In use, the drill body is held against the edge of the gauge, in such a position that the angular edge is over the cutting lip of the drill. The gauge will then show whether or not one edge of the point is exactly 59 degrees.

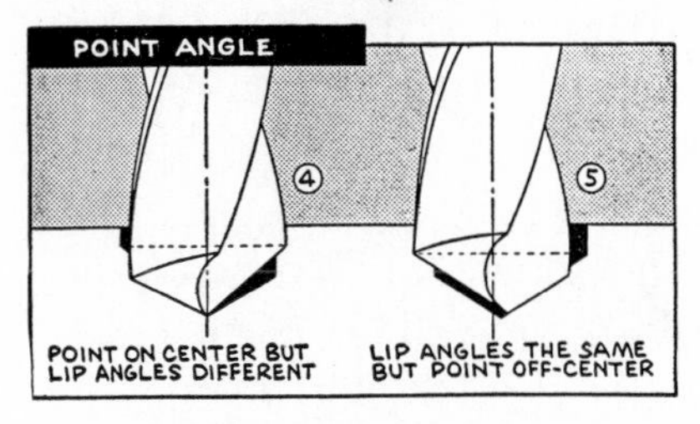

Besides being ground to the correct angle, both lips must be exactly the same length. The illustration shows what happens when the lip angles are different or the lips are of unequal length. The resulting hole will be out of round and larger than the drill.

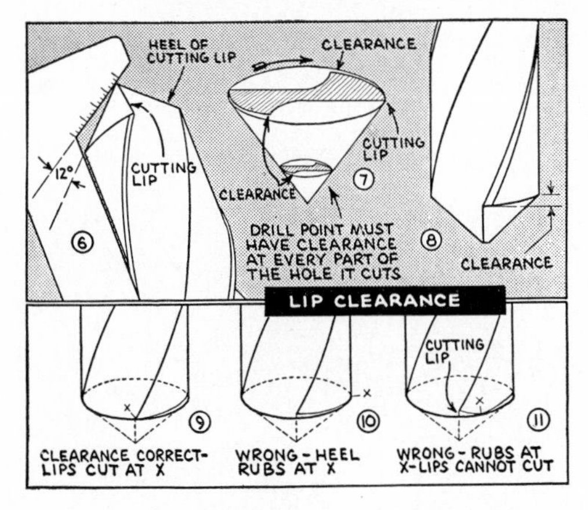

Like any other cutting tool, there must be clearance behind the cutting edge before the drill will cut. This clearance is discernible on a properly ground drill by using the drill-point gauge, placing it over the heel of the point. It will be noted that the angle here is 12 degrees less than the lip angle. This is the proper clearance for the average drill. There must be clearance behind the cutting lips at every part of the conic recess which the drill cuts. With clearance properly ground, the cutting takes place at the cutting lips, leaving every point behind the lips in the clear. If the drill rubs at the heel, the lips cannot cut.

With a fair understanding of point angle and lip clearance, the craftsman can attempt to grind a drill. Even though the theory has been mastered, it is still something of an accomplishment to grind a drill offhand and arrive at the proper point. Experienced mechanics, through long practice, go through the motions almost mechanically, grinding points which are extremely accurate, without the use of mechanical guides or other aids. The craftsman who only occassionally grinds a drill should always use some form of guide. The proper swing is best acquired by swinging a properly ground drill against the wheel, keeping the ground surface in contact with the wheel, and noting the movements required to produce this surface. This is carried out, of course, without power on the grinder.

A simple fixture which is efficient for drill grinding consists of a wood table fastened to the grinder tool rest. On the table, lay out guidelines for both the 59-degree point angle and the 12-degree clearance angle. Then, with the body of the drill parallel with the 59-degree guideline and the cutting lip flush against the side of the grinding wheel, start the grind. With a quarter-turn of the drill end

against the grinding wheel, bring the surface of the drill end down to the heel of the lip. At the same time, and with the same motion, pivot the body of the drill over to the 12-degree guideline. This combination of twist and pivot against the side of the grinding wheel should result in a smooth grind from the cutting lip to the heel. Each lip is treated in turn, checking with the drill gauge to see that both are exactly the same length. One or two light twists on each lip will usually bring the drill to a sharp point.

Various mechanical drill grinders, both self-powered and for attachment to a standard grinder, can be purchased. Where a considerable amount of drill grinding must be done, it is usually a saving of both time and money to use one of these purchased units.

As the point of a drill is ground down and resharpened, the web becomes thicker. This means that more power must be used to force it through the work. To partly eliminate this heavy end thrust, the

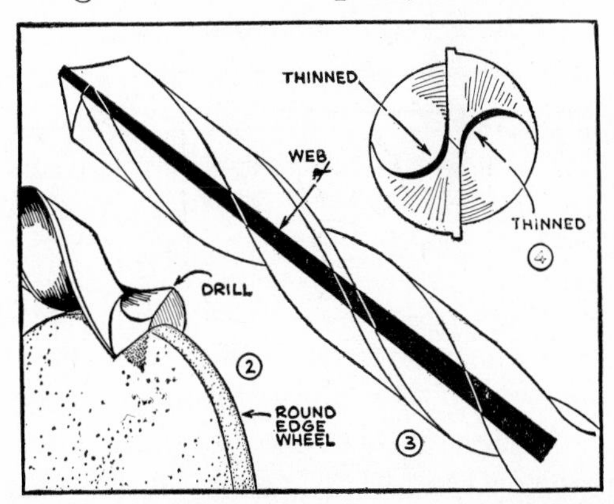

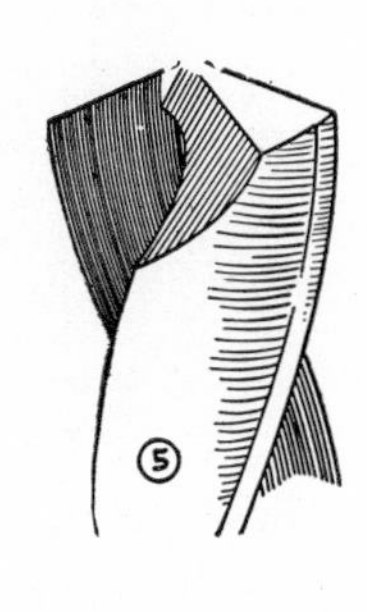

web of the drill should be thinned. This operation is usually done on a round-face grinding wheel, the drill being held so that the wheel cuts in the flutes. The web can be thinned to about one-half its original thickness, provided that the metal is removed from the immediate point only. Where the shop owner does not possess a suitable round-edge wheel, the web can be thinned on an ordinary square-faced wheel. In this form of web thinning, most of the grinding is done on the back of the lips, the grind being carried up to the center of the point on each side.

For drilling brass and copper, it will be found to the craftsman's advantage to modify the cutting edges of the drill. The effect to be obtained is exaggerated in the illustration (next page), which shows how the cutting edge of the lip is ground off. This makes the edge scrape rather than cut and reduces the tendency of the drill to "grab" in brass and other soft metals. This form of grinding can be done on a fine-grit wheel. Very little metal is ground off, just a few thousandths of an inch; for this reason it is often better to flatten the cutting edge with a small sharpening stone.

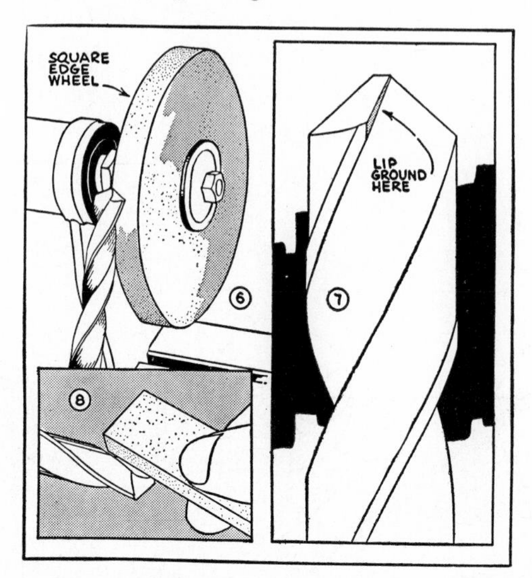

Specially ground drills for certain work are helpful. For example, fiber takes a drill with a point angle of 30 degrees, while manganese steel requires a 75-degree point angle.

Spcial jigs and fixtures are used for a wide variety of grinding and sharpening jobs. Some of these jobs require special dressed or formed wheels, while others require only a special jig or fixture for holding and feeding the work to the grinder.

Chapter 10. THE SHAPER

Description

The shaper is a vertical spindle, different from the drill press in that it has been designed and built to withstand side thrust. The spindle is generally hollow, so that auxiliary spindles can be fitted

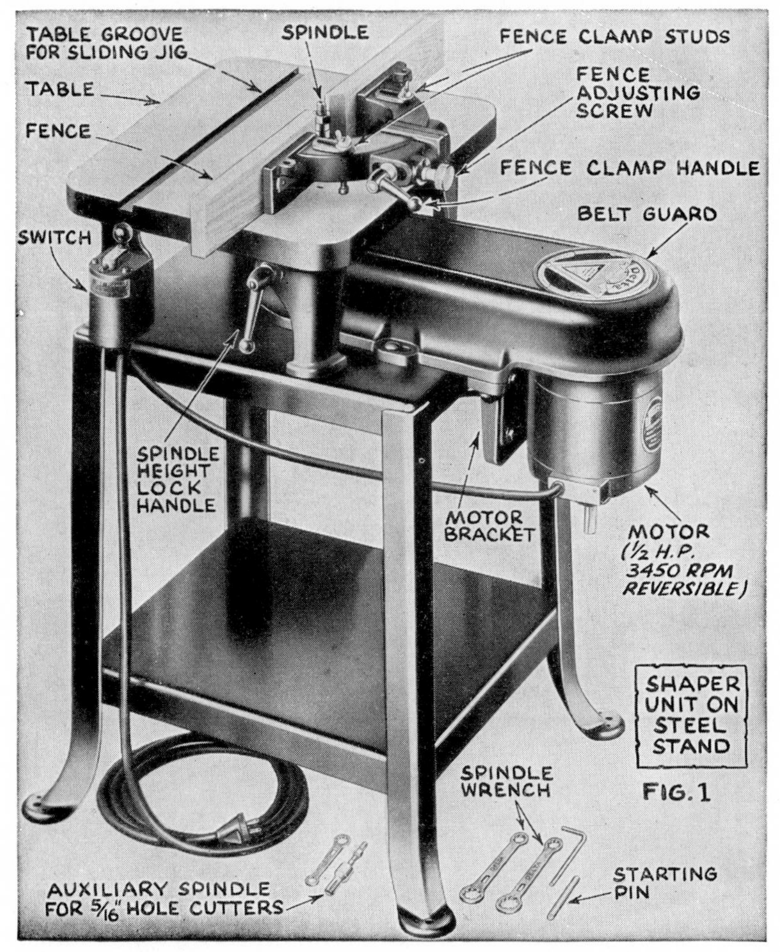

FIG. 1

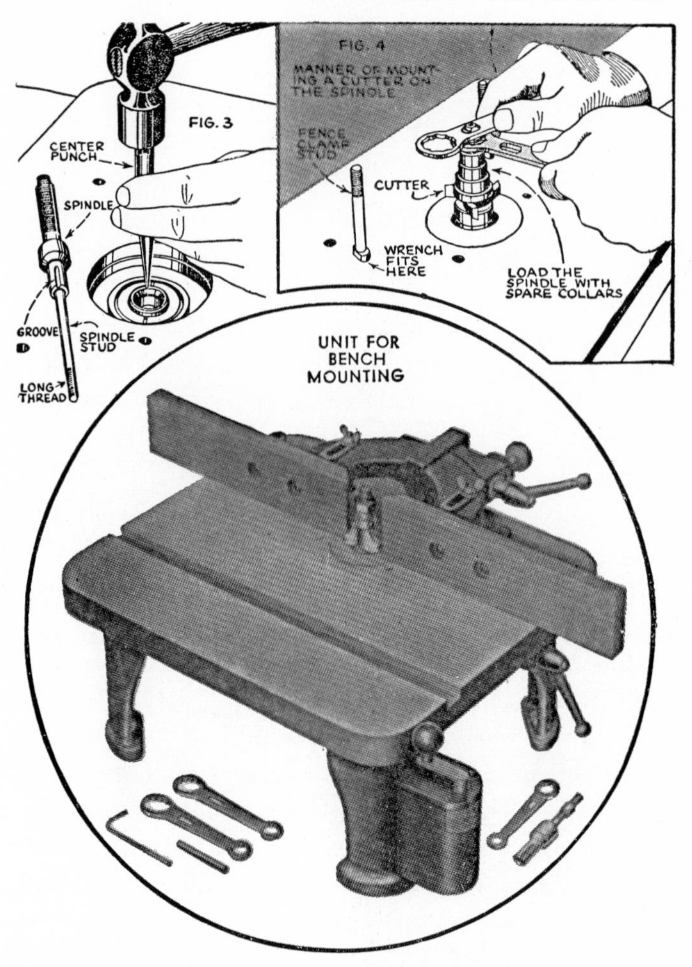

to it, much in the same manner as drills are fitted to a drill chuck. Adjustment is provided so that the spindle may be raised or lowered and so that it may also be locked at any desired height above the table.

A medium-sized shaper using ½-inch-hole cutters works well with a ½-horsepower motor. When large knives mounted between slotted collars are used, ¾ to 1 horsepower will give best results. The motor must be a 3,450 rpm type, in order to give the shaper spindle the required speed. Pulleys are generally in about a 3 to 1 ratio, so that the actual spindle speed runs slightly over or under 10,000 rpm. The motor should be reversible, since an opposite direction of rotation may often be required. Most shapers employ a reversing switch fitted to the side of the shaper stand and wired to the motor.

There are four auxiliary spindles: the stub spindle for cope cutters, the 5⁄16-inch-diameter spindle for cutters having this size hole, the ½-inch-diameter spindle for ½-inch-hole cutters, and the ¾-inch spindle for ¾-inch-hole cutters. The latter can be used only on the heavy-duty cabinet-model shaper. Each spindle is fitted with a tie rod, threaded at both ends. One end of the rod is fitted to the spindle, while the opposite end is capped with a tapered nut after passing through the hollow main spindle. The shank of each spindle is fitted with a keyway. This engages a ball or key inside the main spindle to prevent it from turning. A light punch mark on the rim of the main spindle is an aid in locating the auxiliary spindle.

Once in place, the spindle can be fitted with the necessary collars and cutters.

The fence is usually fitted to the table by means of two studs and wing nuts. Either half of the fence can be adjusted independently. For most work, the two halves of the fence should be in line. A punch mark across the two parts is a useful index in resetting. The wood facings of the fence are adjustable, so that the opening can be made large or small, depending on the size of the cutter. The opening should never be any more than is necessary to clear the cutter being used.

A ring guard should always be used when shaping curved work

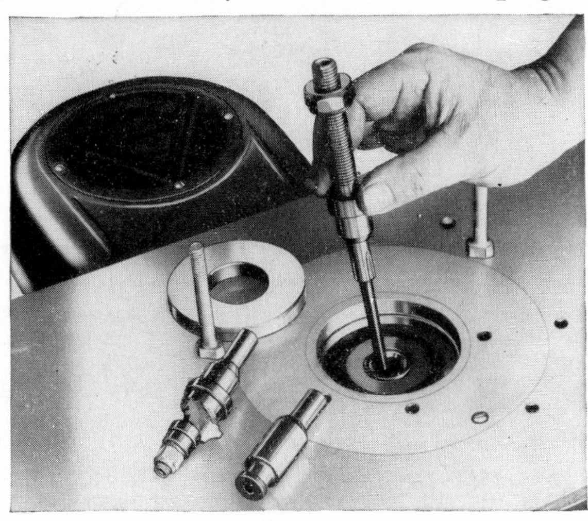

directly against collars. Besides offering protection, the guide provides a hold-down, pressing the work down on the table surface.

The sliding jig is an essential part of any shaper. Its purpose is to clamp the work securely, so that it can be advanced to the cutter. It is used chiefly in returning moldings across the ends of narrow strips.

Shaper Cutters and Collars

A wide variety of knives, saws, collars, etc., are used in shaper operations. Standard three-lip cutters for the ½-inch spindle are available in a wide variety of shapes and are undoubtedly the safest and most practical type of knife for average work in the home workshop. Similar cutters with a $\frac{5}{16}$-inch hole can also be used by substituting an auxiliary spindle of the proper diameter. A second type of commonly used cutter is the open-face knife clamped between two

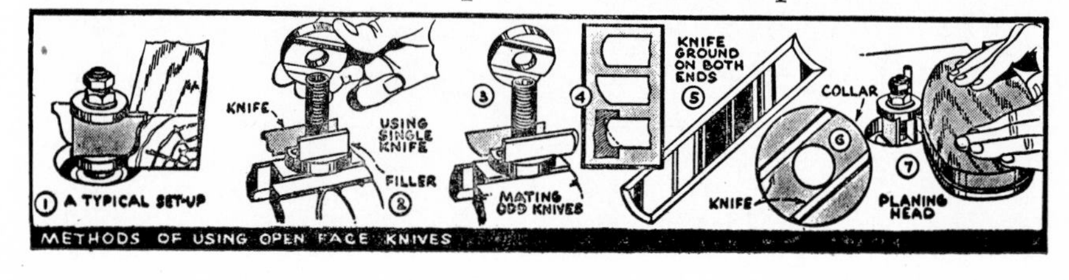

METHODS OF USING OPEN FACE KNIVES

slotted collars. Blank knives can easily be ground to any required shape.

Special cutterheads, small saws, sanding drums, wing cutters, and panel-raising cutters can be fitted to and used on the shaper.

Standard shaper collars, from ⅛ to ½ inch thick, of various diameters permit control over the depth of cut. Stationary collars, which fit into the table opening, and ball-bearing collars (these are simply ball races which fit over the spindle) are often used instead of standard collars to eliminate scoring, especially in production work.

Open-face knives are perfectly safe to use, but only when they are properly mounted. Knives must be of exactly the same width, otherwise one will be held tightly, while the other is left to fly out when the machine is set in motion. *Knives of unequal width should never be used together between slotted collars.* Knife projection should be measured, setting both knives to project exactly equally.

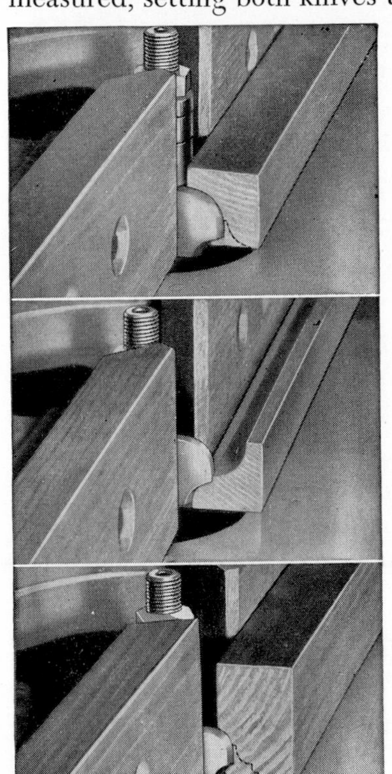

Knives are sometimes made to cut a required molding in one pass of the work. More often, however, two or three passes are required, using standard shapes, to complete the desired molding.

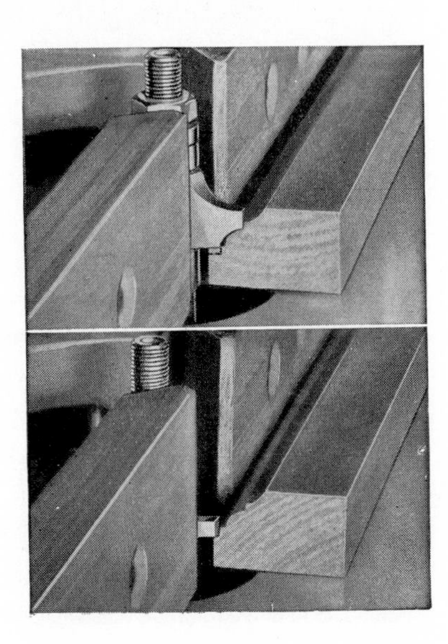

Operations

There are four main methods used in shaper operations: first, shaping with guides; second, shaping against collars; third, shaping with an outlined pattern; and fourth, shaping with forms. Each of these methods is widely used, and each is adapted for a particular type of work. In the following description of each method, the same cut is used for each; but this, of course, would not apply to actual work.

In shaping with guides, the guides are fastened to the shaper table and form a support for the work as it is advanced to the cutter. The most common type of guide is the standard fence. In addition to this,

there are a number of other straight, concave, and convex fences (for curved work) and special fences for odd shapes. Shaping with a guide is the safest and most satisfactory method of working. This method should always be used when the work permits.

Work which cannot be shaped against a guide is usually shaped against a collar. In this method of working, the rim of the collar

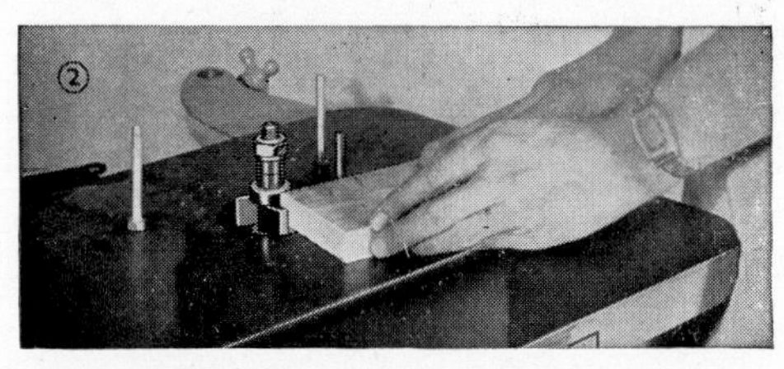

rides against the work and limits the depth of cut. This is one of the most useful methods used in shaping, the only drawback being that the revolving collar will slightly score or burn the work. When the work is properly handled, this scoring is usually light.

Shaping with an outline pattern is similar to shaping against a collar, except that the pattern, and not the work, rides against the collar.

Scoring is thus eliminated, and the same pattern can be used for any number of duplicate pieces. This feature makes the method prefer-

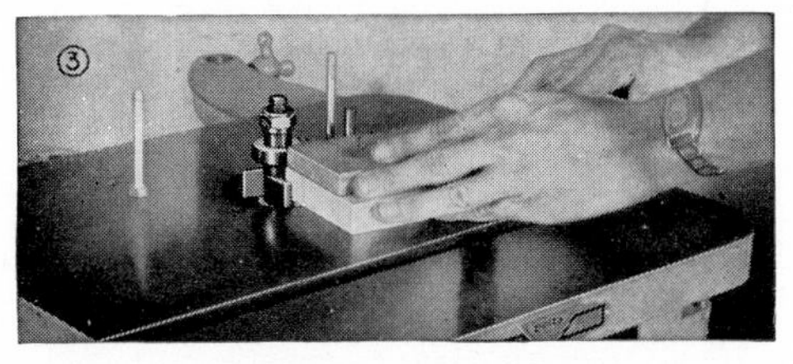

able for shaping jobs when light pieces must be produced in quantity.

In shaping with forms, the form is any device in which the work

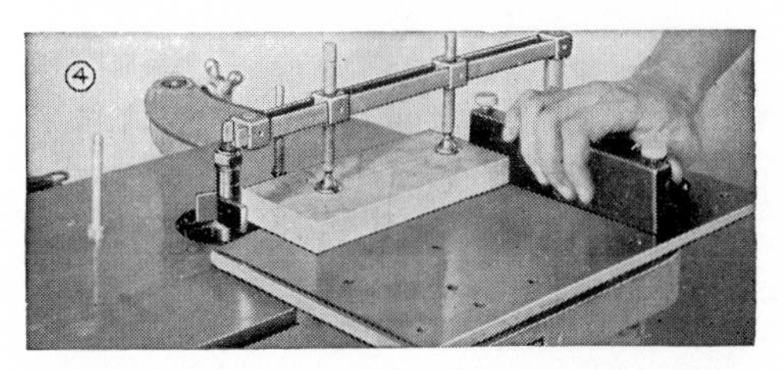

is held so that is can be advanced to the cutter. The most common form is the sliding jig.

Setup and Feed

In making any molded edge, the pattern is usually marked on the end of the work. The proper cutter is then mounted on the spindle, after which the spindle is raised or lowered to the proper height. The fence is then located to give the correct depth of cut. Where collars are used, the collar is checked against the work in a similar manner.

The recommended spindle speed for small cutters is 10,000 rpm. The shaper is fitted with a reversing switch, so that the cutter can rotate in either direction. Whatever the direction, the work must be advanced *into* and *against* the cutter. Feeding from the right side of the machine, the rotation of the cutter is counterclockwise. When the work is fed from the left side, the cutter rotates in a clockwise direction.

When returning moldings or cutting all edges of a piece of work, the first cut must be made on end grain, each edge being taken in turn, so that the final cut is with the grain.

Hold-downs

Any device which holds the work against the fence or shaper table is known as a "hold-down." There are many different styles of hold-downs—wheels, weighted arms, spring tensioners, etc.—all of which serve the same general purpose of keeping the work in close

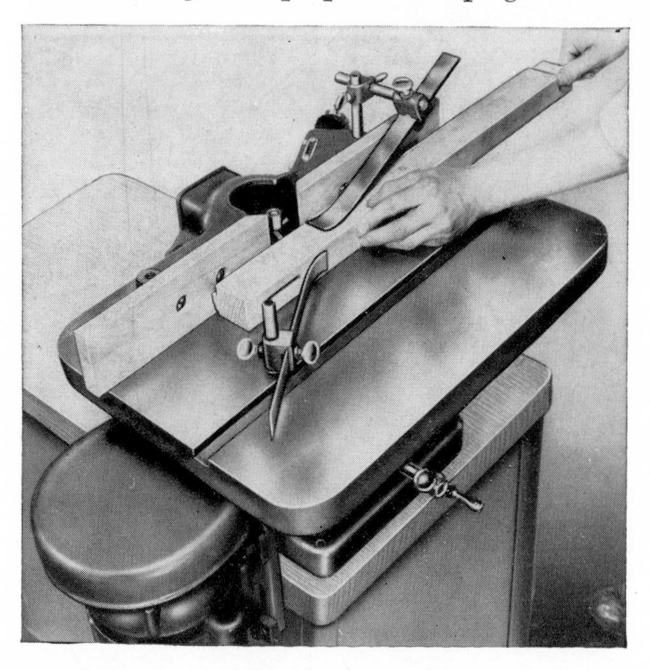

contact with the table or fence. Any hold-down is more effective when it supports the work at a point slightly behind the point of cutting. Suitable mountings on the standard shaper fence permit the hold-downs to be used at either end to correspond with the direction of feed. Another common type of hold-down or jig for narrow moldings, commonly called "strip moldings," is so constructed that the work is at all times supported against the impact of the cutter. The wood spring holds the work *in,* while the top piece of the jig holds it *down.*

Some form of hold-down should be used whenever possible.

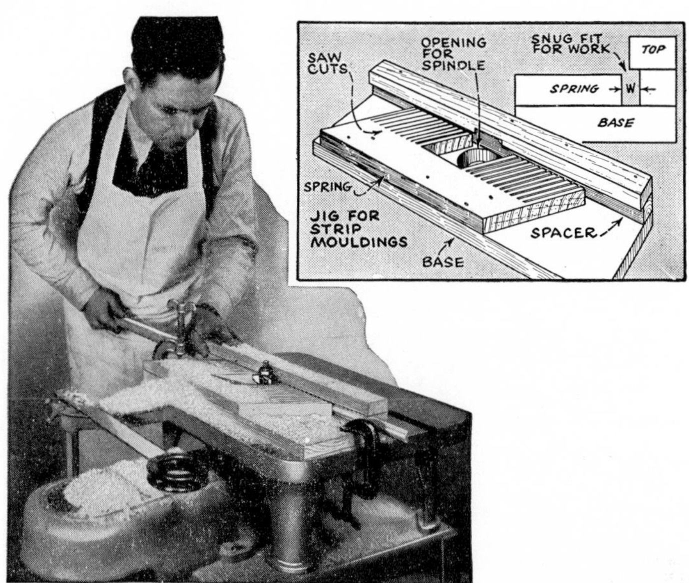

Shaping with Collars

Certain conditions must always prevail when work is shaped directly against collars. First, collars must be smooth and true, free from all gum and other substances. They should be inspected frequently during long runs, since some woods will deposit a layer of hard pitch on the rim of the collar as thick as $1/16$ inch in the space of a very few hours. The gum is easily removed with a stiff brush and benzine or gasoline. Second, the edge of the work to be shaped must be smoothed to net size. Any irregularity in the surface which rides against the collar will be duplicated on the cut molding. Third, a portion of the edge of the work must remain untouched by the cutters as a bearing surface for the collar. Fourth, the work must be fairly heavy in proportion to the cut being made. Never under any circumstances should a small piece of work be shaped against collars. These four rules as to smooth work, clean collars, riding edge, and body of the work are important for good work and for safety in operation.

The collar must be used above, below, or between the cutters. The advantage in having the cutter uppermost lies mainly in the fact that the progress of the cut can thus be observed at all times. The collar-between-cutters method is frequently used where both edges of the work are to be molded.

Practically all shapers are fitted with a starting pin. This pin must be used as a support when starting the cut. If the work is advanced to the cutter without this side support, it may be kicked back. The work must be advanced into the cutter on a line tangent to the outer edge of the collar. After the cut has been started, the work is swung free of the starting pin and rides only against the collar.

Shaping is usually done with one continuous cut, the work being manipulated to turn corners.

Shaping with Patterns

Shaping with the use of patterns offers two outstanding advantages: first, it permit the working of the entire edge of irregularly curved objects, an operation which is impossible in any other manner; second, it provides one of the cleanest and most efficient methods of doing production work.

The average pattern is made from wood, the usual stock being ¾ or ⅞ inch thick. Production patterns are often made from fiber to withstand the continual riding against the guide collar. The shape of the pattern is the *exact* outline of the work which must be molded. The edges must be smooth and clean.

The work which is to be shaped is roughly sawed to about 1/16 to ⅛ inch oversize. It is fastened to the pattern by means of anchor points. The simplest anchor point is a brad or nail.

A typical example of work done with an outline pattern is shown on the facing page. This particular example can also be described as "outline planing." Certain shapes can be planed directly from square-sawed stock, removing all the excess stock with the shaper cutter. In this, however, excessively deep cuts are to be avoided.

Where symmetrical moldings are being cut, a double pattern with the work sandwiched between is sometimes useful. The advantage is that the work can be turned over at any time in order to favor the grain.

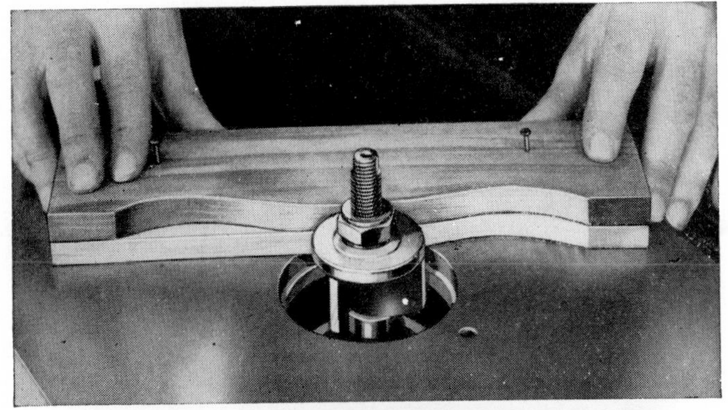

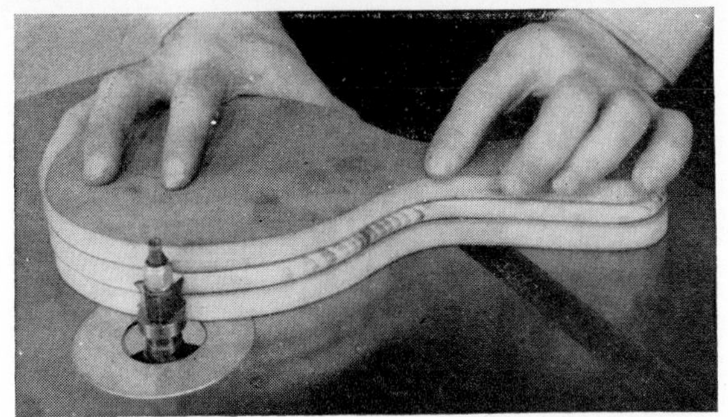

Forms and Jigs

A form is any device or jig in or upon which the work is securely fastened by means of clamps, screws, or wedges, so that it can be advanced to the cutter. In this classification are included the sliding jig and the tenoning jig, but the term is more truly applied to special forms which *must* be used to support odd-shaped work. Since the construction of the latter type of form requires both money and time in making, it is used only when the work cannot be shaped by other methods. This condition does not apply to the various all-purpose forms, such as the sliding and tenoning jigs, the fluting jig, etc. Indeed, in this case the jig offers the simplest and least expensive method of working.

The tenoning jig, made especially for making tenons on the circular saw, can be used to good advantage in various shaper operations, especially where narrow stock must be face-shaped.

The sliding jig is a standard shaper accessory and is indispensable for various kinds of work, especially for returning a molding on narrow stock. It is useful for making joints, either straight or at any specified angle. The sliding jig is to the shaper what the miter gauge is to the circular saw. Its application to a hundred and one different jobs will readily become apparent under actual working conditions. It should always be used when working the ends of narrow stock. Listed as a miscellaneous shaper operation, it is even useful in accurately sanding small work on the shaper. In this operation, a sanding drum is used in place of the conventional shaper cutters.

The fluting jig is a form familiar to most workers. It is essentially a small lathe in which the work is held for shaper operations. The fluting jig is mostly used for fluting, hence its name. The next photo shows the jig being used to make flutes in a table leg. The collars ride against a form fastened to the bottom of the jig. The auxiliary fence shown is used only to hold the stopblocks which limit the length of

the cut. Stops are sometimes worked directly on the jig itself, the pattern curving out to limit the cut.

Panel Raising

Raised panels are fastened in both casework and furniture construction. The essential feature of the work is that a heavy panel is reduced in thickness in all edges to fit a corresponding groove in the frame for which it is intended. Several methods and various types of cutters are used. The method shown on the next page features a small saw with a beveled edge fitted to the shaper spindle. The work is tilted a slight amount by clamping a strip of the required thickness next to the shaper fence. This strip, together with the edge of the shaper table, form an angle of from 3 to 5 degrees. The work rides the strip and the edge of the shaper table to get the angle required, while the edge rides the fence to keep the cut straight. The cut may or may not be made in one pass, depending on how much wood is to be removed. Generally speaking, one or two roughing cuts followed by a light finishing cut will produce better work.

Raising panels with a two-wing panel cutter is much simpler, since the required tilt is incorporated in the construction of the knife, and the work is carried flat on the shaper table.

Application of Shaper Cutters

The application of the shaper cutters in cabinet and interior-door construction is shown opposite. Typical setups are shown for making square-stuck doors, bead-and-ogee sticking, and applied moldings.

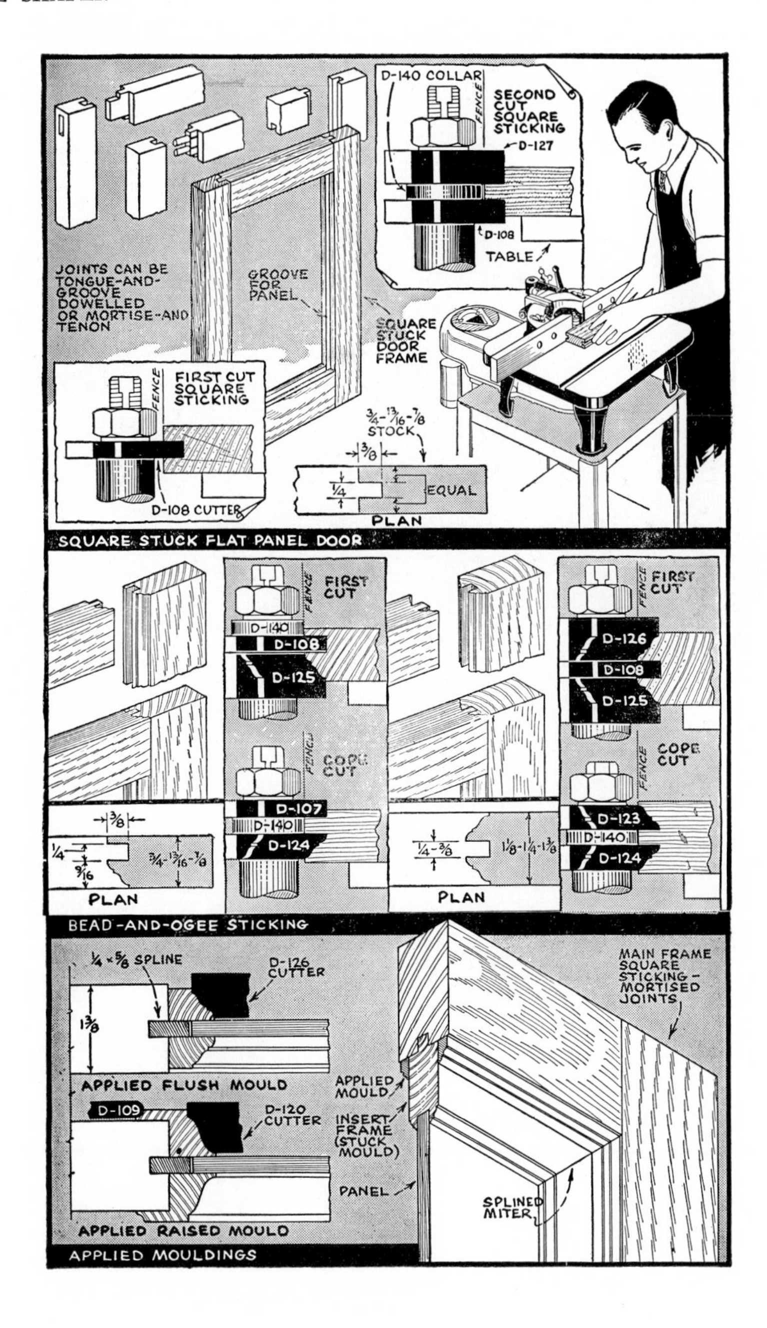
D-140 COLLAR
FENCE
SECOND CUT SQUARE STICKING
D-127
D-108
TABLE
JOINTS CAN BE TONGUE-AND-GROOVE DOWELLED OR MORTISE-AND TENON
GROOVE FOR PANEL
SQUARE STUCK DOOR FRAME
FIRST CUT SQUARE STICKING
D-108 CUTTER
3/4-13/16-7/8 STOCK
3/8
1/4
EQUAL
PLAN
SQUARE STUCK FLAT PANEL DOOR
FIRST CUT
D-140
D-108
D-125
COPE CUT
D-107
D-140
D-124
3/8
1/4
9/16
3/4-13/16-7/8
PLAN
FIRST CUT
D-126
D-108
D-125
COPE CUT
D-123
D-140
D-124
1/4-3/8
1 1/8-1 1/4-1 3/8
PLAN
BEAD-AND-OGEE STICKING
1/4 × 5/8 SPLINE
D-126 CUTTER
1 3/8
APPLIED FLUSH MOULD
D-109
D-120 CUTTER
APPLIED RAISED MOULD
APPLIED MOULD
INSERT FRAME (STUCK MOULD)
PANEL
MAIN FRAME SQUARE STICKING - MORTISED JOINTS
SPLINED MITER
APPLIED MOULDINGS

Casework

Casework includes such jobs as china cabinets, kitchen cupboards, etc.

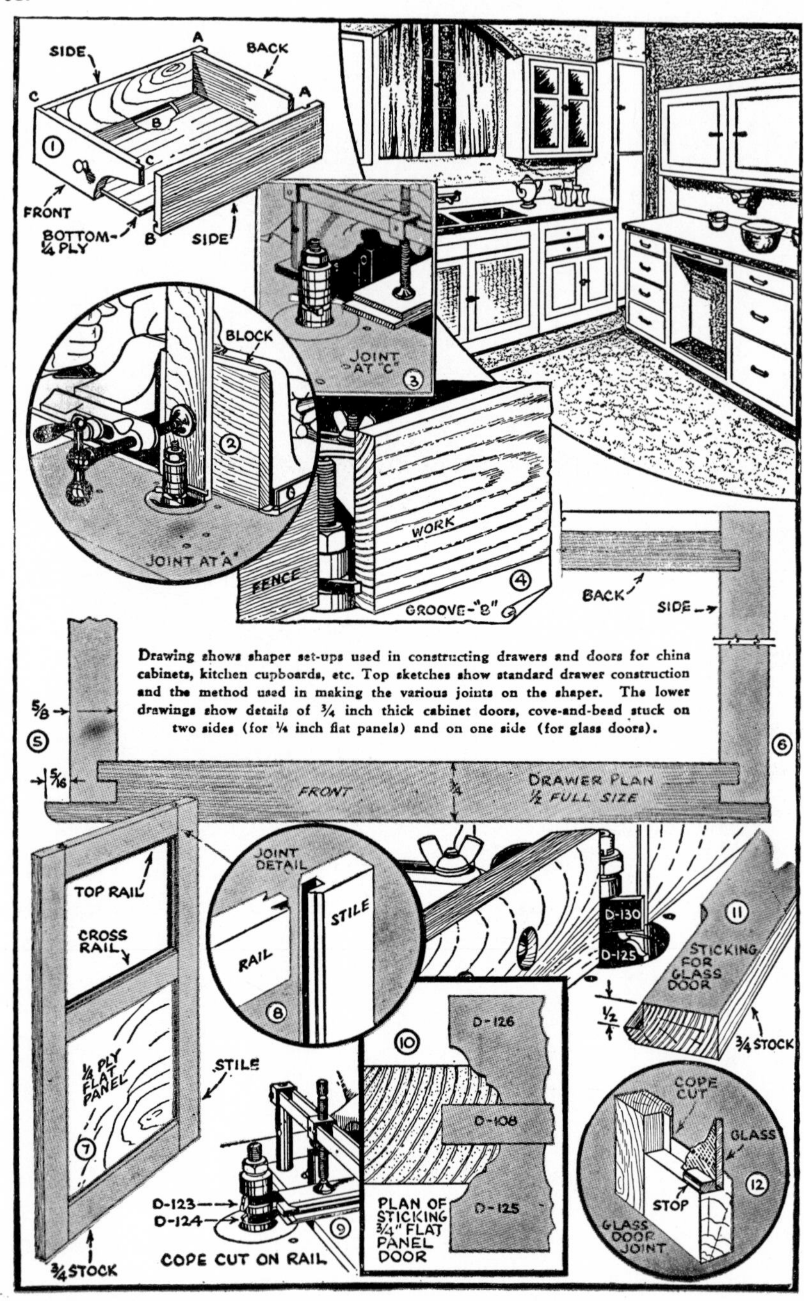

Drawing shows shaper set-ups used in constructing drawers and doors for china cabinets, kitchen cupboards, etc. Top sketches show standard drawer construction and the method used in making the various joints on the shaper. The lower drawings show details of ¾ inch thick cabinet doors, cove-and-bead stuck on two sides (for ¼ inch flat panels) and on one side (for glass doors).

Paneled Frames

Paneled frames are constructed according to the methods and set-ups previously described in shaper operations. The illustration shows several methods of making the corner joint on these frames.

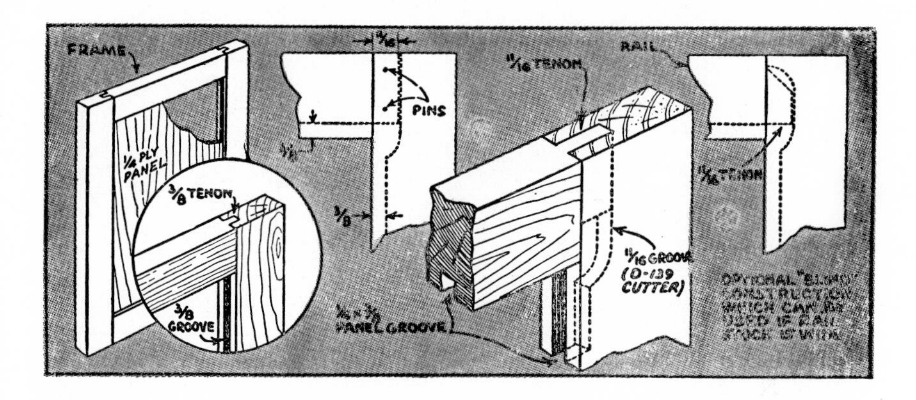

Project Material

The shaper is not a power machine with which complete projects may be made. It is important, however, in adding decorative moldings to projects completed on other shop equipment.

Rules of Safety in Operating Power Tools

In the various chapters on operating power tools, cautions and safety measures have been pointed out. The following is a summary covering the most important of these rules.

1. Avoid loose clothing, sleeves, ties, etc., when operating power machines.
2. Disconnect current when making adjustments on power machinery.
3. Whenever possible, turn the blade, cutter, etc., by hand, to see that it does not strike the tool rest or fence, etc., before applying power.
4. When machining small work, use a clamp or holding device for the work.
5. Before using, make sure that all blades, cutters, etc., are firmly locked in position on the power equipment.

6. Always use guards when the power tools are so equipped—they are for your safety.
7. Check the direction of feed before operation, so that your hands do not have to pass too close to a revolving cutter or blade.
8. Never reach into a revolving cutter or blade to remove scraps or shavings; shut off the machine and wait until the blade stops.
9. Do not overload or force-feed your work—you are inviting kick-back.
10. Study the operation of each machine carefully. Remember that while safety features can be built into power tools, they cannot be built into the operator.

INDEX